# A STORYTELLER'S
# CHILDHOOD

# A STORYTELLER'S CHILDHOOD

*by*

## PATRICIA LYNCH

W · W · NORTON & COMPANY · INC ·

NEW YORK

Library of Congress Catalog Card No. 62-10985

PRINTED IN THE UNITED STATES OF AMERICA

TO THE GOOD DAYS

# CONTENTS

1. THE OLD HOUSE ON FAIR HILL     1
2. MRS. HENNESSY     9
3. MY FIRST JOURNEY     16
4. TINKERS     23
5. HOME WITH THE HENNESSYS     27
6. THE CABIN BY THE THORN BUSH     33
7. THE SHORT CUT     44
8. O'CALLAGHANS     52
9. TO THE FAIR     63
10. LOST     69
11. NEWS FROM CORK     82
12. GOING BACK     90
13. AUNT HANNAH AND COUSIN KATE     98
14. GOING AWAY     112
15. EMIGRANTS     118
16. END OF THE JOURNEY     131
17. THE CADOGANS     138
18. THE CORNER     144

# Contents

19. THE CROUCHMANS     152

20. THE HOUSE IN THE WOOD YARD     164

21. THE SHINING CORRIDOR     173

22. ST. PATRICK'S DAY     185

23. TROUBLE COMES TO THE DRISCOLLS     196

24. GOLD-MINES AND THE BLACK BOX     201

25. LIKE THREE TINKERS     209

26. GOOSE GREEN     222

27. WE GO TO THE CIRCUS     234

28. CHRISTMAS STOCKING     254

29. LOST ON THE MARSHES     263

30. SISTER FRANCIS     270

31. THE SEWING CLASS     283

32. MRS. CAPTAIN     293

33. AUNT HANNAH AND UNCLE MICHAEL     305

34. ON THE BOG     316

35. THE ROAD TO EGYPT     328

# 1. THE OLD HOUSE ON FAIR HILL

WE lived in a tall stone house on the north side of the river Lee in Cork. The steep road climbs from the huddle of quays and bridges where apple women sit by their baskets and dilish sellers hold up strands of dark, dry seaweed; up, up from the hucksters' shops and away beyond Fair Green.

Before that we had a big house on Sundays Well with a high grey wall round the garden and a green gate opening into it. We left for Fair Hill when I wasn't yet three, but my mother liked walking past our Sundays Well home and promising me we'd live there again—some day.

The house on Fair Hill was dark and narrow, built where the ground dropped suddenly, so that it leaned forward and seemed to be bowing in greeting to the city below. The kitchen at the back was like a cave, opening on the yard, and six wide steps at the side led down from the road. These steps were so broken and uneven that the fish woman, who was dark and thin and quarrelsome, the fat, clean egg woman, and Peadar Keeley, the turf man, had to feel their way carefully as they clambered round with their loads. So many slates had fallen from the roof it was a wonder any remained. The wind from the sea blew straight up from Cobh, and on stormy nights every window rattled, every board creaked, and I shivered under the bedclothes in the attic where I slept with my mother, wondering would the house be blown down the river and out across the great harbour to the ocean.

When the wind didn't blow and the sun shone the yard was a grand place. Dinny Foley, from over the way, went with me to the kindergarten at the convent down the hill. When we weren't in school, or exploring, or helping Mrs. Foley, who was the washerwoman for Fair Hill, and it wasn't raining, or time to go to bed, we played in the yard.

The ruined coach-house with only two walls standing was filled with logs. Beside it the stable, which hadn't sheltered a horse for years, cluttered with boxes and trunks, hid behind the turf pile. My grandfather would not allow coal to be burned in the house. He loved the smell of turf and logs. So did I. The pump, with a puddle before it, was over in the far corner.

The kitchen door stood wide open even in winter, for Aunt Kattie was always darting to bring in a couple of sods or a bucket of water and she couldn't be bothered opening and shutting a door. Aunt Kattie liked looking out as she stood at the table beating a cake, scrubbing potatoes, or talking about when she'd have enough money saved to buy a ticket for America. She put every penny she could save in the middle part of the tea-caddy. It was black, inlaid with gold-coloured wood, and when the lid was raised there were three compartments, each with a glass top. Instead of tea, sugar, and coffee, Aunt Kattie kept letters in one, her savings in another, and bills in the third.

'When I have the money for the ticket I'll be saving for me travelling cloak,' she told me. 'A black cloak, Tricia, lined with crimson, and a hood to pull over me head.'

She was like a bright eager bird, with her sparkling eyes and the loose sleeves of her flowered dress flapping as if they were wings.

'If only I could be watching out on the road to America, 'twould give me patience,' she declared. 'I'd turn the house round if I had me way. Run, Tricia, and see who's passing!'

Out I would run, up the broken steps and back in a hurry. 'Aunt Kattie! Sheep! Thousands of them! All running down the hill and the little lambs are crying.'

Or: 'All the black bullocks in the world, Aunt Kattie! They're lovely! Do take a peep at them!'

But Aunt Kattie shared my mother's terror of any animal larger than a cat or a dog.

'Mind now and keep the gate shut tight and don't be letting mad bulls in on us!' she'd warn me. 'Will you see what human creatures are going by? We aren't living in the jungles of Africa yet!'

Sometimes there'd be a farmer and his wife in their best clothes driving down to the grand shops on Patrick Street, or the Grand Parade, or North Main Street. But Aunt Kattie wasn't interested, not even when a tinker tribe went by. Canvas-covered carts with babies hanging over the front and back: tousled women, hidden in ragged shawls, carrying armfuls of shining tins: wild, barefoot boys and girls with blank, staring eyes and tangled hair running alongside: thin, watchful men in tattered clothes, leading horses—even these wouldn't bring Aunt Kattie out to the gate. She only wanted to know if there were lads or girls on sidecars, and wagons piled with bags and parcels, making for the boat that would take them to England or the train to Cobh where they would be carried off to America.

Aunt Hannah was the one who went marketing on the quays. She never bought in a shop for she loved haggling and arguing at the stalls. Strangers thought her good-natured, because she had a rosy face and was always laughing. But her laugh was malicious, she made mischief, and she liked frightening me.

My mother, the third sister, made lace, yards and yards, fine as the spiders' webs on the bushes in autumn and with the loveliest patterns worked into it. She didn't stay in the kitchen with Aunt Kattie and Aunt Hannah but sat on the big chest in the hall. On wet days I sat beside her, watching the tiny steel crochet hook as it caught the fine *guipure* thread and flashed in and out like a fish. She said long pieces of poetry to me, for she knew the whole of Scott's *Lady of the Lake*, Moore's *Melodies*, most of Longfellow's poems, as well as Byron and Burns. She never tired of Burns's poems, especially the one about the field mouse and *A Man's a Man*. She remembered queer old ballads and sang them softly so that only she and I could hear. The chest was covered with black leather, fastened by big brass nails and bound with strips of metal. It had belonged to Uncle Henry, who was lost at sea on his first voyage. The ship and every one in it disappeared during a storm off the Algerian coast, but the chest was so heavy it had been left behind, and when my father began wandering, grandfather gave him the chest, because he was a cousin of the family. He took it with him as far as Liverpool, then he found it too heavy and sent it back. Every time my father went away he took less and less luggage, until he carried only a toothbrush and a comb, a razor, and a coffee-pot. My mother told me of the chest and its travels when she could think of no more poetry or ballads, and I made up my mind that, one day, I would pack all my belongings in it and go off to see the world.

Sitting in the hall we could hear all that happened in the kitchen. Two deep steps led down to it and, as there was no door, every sound and smell travelled up through the house.

No one, except my grandfather, entered by the front door. Fish woman, egg woman, turf man, friends and neighbours, stumbled by the broken steps to the yard and the kitchen, sat on the settle, and drank tea. I don't believe grandfather had ever set foot in the kitchen, but he kept his door open and he had very sharp ears, so maybe he heard more than we imagined. His room, beside the front door, was the best in the house. He had the next best to sleep in and the little one at the back for his books. There were books on every shelf in his bedroom, on top of the great press, in the corners, and under the bed. He poked them there at night before he fell asleep. The room grandfather worked in looked as if the walls were made of books. They were piled on the floor and on chairs, and presently they lined the landing, the big stairs, and even the steep winding stairs to the attic, so that we had to squeeze between. He always came home with a bundle of books under his arm; not bright shining books with pictures on the cover, but old, dusty books which looked as if no one had opened them for years. When there was no more room on the stairs the books invaded the attic and, on wet days, I hunted through them for pictures. Even those which had pictures were no better than the others, for the black lines were dim on the dingy yellow pages.

Grandfather wore a long black coat, with a cape, buttoned all the way down, and a top hat tilted to one side. His shaggy eyebrows made him appear stern, but his grey eyes were gentle. He kept his hand in his pocket ready to pull out pennies for the beggars. He boasted he had never passed a beggar or a bookshop in his life. He seldom smiled, but when a beggar said: 'I knew ye'd put yer hand in yer pocket for a neighbour in distress, Mr. Lynch,' or 'God reward ye for that kind help, sir!' he looked very pleased. He taught Greek and Latin to lads going up to the university and Irish to those who wanted the old language. If they were poor, grandfather wouldn't take any money at all, and they were mostly poor. In his spare time he was writing a poetic history of Ireland in Irish that was to make him famous. Then we'd all be rich and the family's debts would be more than paid.

My aunts and uncles were proud of their learned father, but my mother was proudest of them all. When my brother, Patrick Henry, did well at school, she would tell him that one day he might be as clever as grandfather. She couldn't give Patrick Henry any praise he'd like better, but I wanted to be the same as my father, to travel in boats and trains, not to spend my life shut up in a room, with dusty books around me.

And the three of us were waiting for the letter that would start us on our wanderings.

When my brother came in from school he always asked first was there a letter in the post? He didn't mean the letters which came to grandfather about books or students, or Uncle Tim's letters from Dublin where he was for ever writing about positions in shipping firms, or the little thin printed slips for Uncle Liam about horses and races, or even the long important business envelopes with Uncle Cathal's name on them. Patrick Henry meant the square, foreign letters with strange stamps, the ones addressed in my father's sprawling writing. There was money inside —not gold or silver but pieces of paper which were every bit as good as real money. The two of them, my mother and Patrick Henry, read the letters together, lingering over each word, and I listened. The money was to send him to college, to buy her silk dresses and diamond earrings, to get me a French doll with real hair and eyes which opened and shut, and to keep in the bank.

I never had the French doll, I didn't want her. I had the rag doll my mother made when I first went to school, to be company for me. I was very young, only two and a half, and the doll was dressed in my old clothes. Patrick Henry painted the face and Aunt Kattie sewed on hair made from ravelled twine. For the rag doll's sake I hated

**wax** dolls with flaxen hair, blue eyes, and red, smiling lips. She was supposed to be a Red Indian baby, so we called her 'Papoose' and, at school, that soon became Poosie.

Patrick Henry never went to college. All he learned he was taught by the Christian Brothers, and he knew a wonderful amount. My mother did have the diamond earrings, but only when my father sent them to her in a tiny green box, lined with white satin. She didn't wear the earrings, but sometimes she opened the box and showed me.

'They'll be yours, one day,' she said.

At last the letter came which was to take us away from Fair Hill. From breakfast to supper time my mother was running up to the attic and down to the black chest. My brother, in the room he shared with Uncle Liam, was wondering which of his books he could bear to leave behind. Aunt Kattie helped me tie my belongings in a little red shawl and, when the black chest was full, I climbed on top, the bundle beside me, the rag doll, Poosie, on the other side, my picture book under my arm. My feet, in strap shoes and thick hand-made socks, stuck straight out before me. My mother, coming down the stairs, this time with empty hands, saw me there. She gazed at me sorrowfully with her big grey eyes.

'I hadn't the heart to tell you,' she said. 'You're too young to be travelling to the other side of the world and we not knowing what's to become of us.'

I stared back without understanding.

'I'm all packed up,' I explained. 'I've said good-bye to Dinny Foley. He's going to Merica, so he doesn't mind.'

She just stood looking at me. I understood.

'You're going without me?' I asked, beginning to cry. 'And me nearly six!'

'I must!' she said. 'I must!'

I let go of my bundle. The picture book slipped to the floor. Only Poosie remained with me.

'I want to come! I want to come!' I sobbed, hugging the rag doll for comfort.

Then Aunt Kattie, standing at the foot of the steps, called to us:

'Mrs. Hennessy's here!'

## 2. MRS. HENNESSY

'MRS. HENNESSY!' cried my mother. 'Mrs. Hennessy!'

She ran along the hall, with me holding to her dress, and stood smiling down at someone in the kitchen.

I had been hearing of Mrs. Hennessy all my life, but I had never seen her. Our house was her resting-place when she came to Cork, but nowadays she came seldom, and always I had been at school, or wandering with Dinny Foley, who was so sensible no one minded where he went. Maybe I had seen her, but I had forgotten.

Mrs. Hennessy travelled with Peadar Keeley in his turf cart. They had so far to come they couldn't stay long and she could never tell when she'd be coming. But my mother talked to me for days after of Mrs. Hennessy and her stories. She was a shanachie, one of the real old story-tellers. Her father had the gift before her. She knew more about Finn MacCool and the Red Branch Knights, Oisin and the Three Sorrows of Story-Telling than could be found in the books. The people who lived in Ireland before the days of history were as well known to Mrs. Hennessy as the neighbours in her village. Only she wouldn't tell her stories in every house. The moment she came in at the door Aunt Kattie filled up the brown teapot from the big kettle on the range and called out:

9

'Mrs. Hennessy 's here!'

And there she was, thin and frail, her face very white, her eyes looking beyond the room and the people in it, her thin lips smiling. She sat very straight in the comfortable sugan chair, flinging back the hood of the pleated black cloak that all the older women of West Cork wore, and turning up the skirt of her dress to prevent the fire scorching it.

As the old storyteller sipped her tea, my mother sat on the creepie beside her, ready to hand sugar or milk and keep her plate filled with well-buttered, hot potato cake. Uncle Liam, who hated moving quickly, came sliding down the banisters. Fat little Mrs. Foley, wiping her wet, wrinkled hands on her sack apron, squeezed on to the settle between the turf man and the Reillys from next door. Two young men, who were on their way to a Latin lesson with my grandfather, came round by the side when they saw Mrs. Hennessy step from the turf cart. They all had a great opinion of Mrs. Hennessy. The steps up to the hall were crowded. Dinny Foley and I rolled a log across the yard and perched by the open door.

We had scarcely settled ourselves when I heard my brother come whistling up Fair Hill. He could whistle every tune he heard and imitate the birds so that you wouldn't know was there a blackbird or a thrush on the wall or just Patrick Henry. I jumped up to run out and tell him 'Mrs. Hennessy 's here' when I realized there was something different in his whistling. He liked merry tunes—dances and songs with fun in them. But now he was whistling the saddest one of all, *The Valley lay smiling before me*, and, instead of racing, he was dragging his feet as though he carried one of Peadar Keeley's sacks of turf.

He came to the corner of the house and stopped. I looked at Dinny. He was listening too; his bright eyes were round with wonder, his chubby red face was anxious. Patrick Henry finished the sad melody and came on down the stone steps. He leaned against the wall and, looking up, I saw his dark Spanish face and large, brilliant eyes gazing sadly at me.

'An' why wouldn't de lad feel desprit sad?' demanded Mrs. Hennessy suddenly. 'Isn't he lavin' his own home an' goin' to foreign parts an' dear knows if he'll ever again set eyes on de little sister! Hasn't he de right to be sad?'

She finished her cup of tea and set it down on the hearth without turning round.

'If we were going to America you wouldn't say that, Mrs. Hennessy,' declared my mother, her voice trembling.

'I would not,' agreed Mrs. Hennessy. 'But den, Nora allanna, dere's nothin' betwixt us an' Ameriky barrin' de salt ocean. An' dey do say dere's more Irish in Ameriky dan troughout de length an' breadth of Ireland. More-over if ye were makin' for Ameriky ye'd take the child.'

I liked her sing-song voice and the way she said 'de' for 'the' and 'troughout' for 'throughout.' But I was un-happy, so I began to cry: so did my mother. Patrick Henry stared gravely at the old storyteller. Aunt Kattie picked up Mrs. Hennessy's cup and refilled it.

'Aren't we to have a story?' she asked. 'It might well be the last time Nora and the boy will hear you, Mrs. Hennessy. Don't let them go without something to remember.'

Mrs. Hennessy drank the tea slowly and we all watched her.

'We'll get this business righted first,' she answered. ''Tis for that I'm here. The child must come to me if her own are goin' from her.'

My mother sat silent. I kept very still, not knowing what to think.

'Ye're terrible kind, ma'am,' said Aunt Kattie. 'But this is Tricia's rightful home, Mrs. Hennessy.'

My mother wiped away her tears.

'You mean you'd take her, Mrs. Hennessy!' she exclaimed. 'Patricia! Do you hear? Mrs. Hennessy will take you to ftay with her!'

Her grey eyes were dancing as she turned to me. My brother was smiling. Uncle Liam, the two ftudents, the neighbours, all looked at me as if something wonderful was happening. Even Aunt Hannah hadn't a jeer.

But I wasn't consoled.

'I want to go with you,' I told my mother. 'I'm all packed up.'

'The poor scrap!' sighed Mrs. Foley, shaking her head at me. 'God help her!'

'Can I come an' visit Tricia, Mrs. Hennessy?' asked Dinny. 'She'd be loft widout me!'

'Whift, lad! Mind yer manners!' snapped his mother. 'Don't be bould, Dinny lad!'

Mrs. Hennessy smiled at the fire.

'Peadar Keeley will bring him any time his mother can spare him. An' now I'll tell ye the true ftory of how Oisin, son of Finn, the son of Cuhal, was tempted away to Tir na nOg by Niam of the Golden Hair an' left his own country for three hundred years. When he came back, God help him, 'twas too late. An' now I'll tell ye what did happen.'

I didn't hear a great deal. I was too unhappy and frightened. Yet I was proud. There had never been such a fuss made about me. I wondered what kind of a house Mrs. Hennessy lived in. Surely a caftle like Blackrock Caftle, only bigger. I wondered if her ftairs were lined with books and if I'd see the ftars through a little window in the roof when I lay in bed at night.

I knew the ftory was coming to an end, for my mother had brought out her crochet hook and a new ball of thread. Aunt Kattie was handing cups of tea. Only Mrs. Hennessy herself ate or drank while she was speaking. My Aunt

Hannah, leaning against the dresser, her arms folded, leaned forward.

'Mrs. Hennessy! Ye won't mind me asking, but do ye really believe that old chat?'

Her black eyes were malicious, though she was smiling. Every one stared in horror. Mrs. Hennessy raised her strange eyes.

'Ye shouldn't ax such questions, Hannah,' she replied. 'I know ye're only a make-game, but others might think ye just ignorant.'

She sipped her tea calmly. Aunt Hannah's face grew red. She was angry, for Mrs. Foley, the Reillys, and the students were laughing. I could see my mother was sorry. But I was glad. Aunt Hannah was always tormenting. When I was very small she told me *something* with long hairy arms and no head lay hidden in the press on the landing, and if the door was open the tiniest crack after dark, one of the arms would come out searching and snatching. Before that I liked playing on the stairs even when the light was gone. But after, I hated going to bed. She made fun of my rag doll and she hid Patrick Henry's books to make him late at school. She mocked Peadar Keeley, who wouldn't take a sup of tea until his donkey had a lump of stale brown bread and her nosebag was fixed.

'Ye may get half Fair Hill to listen to yer tales,' she declared. 'But there's one who'll never step the length of the hall to listen.'

Mrs. Hennessy nodded in agreement.

'Mr. Tighe Lynch has too much learning in his head to be considerin' anythin' else,' she said. 'Don't we all know well how he's writin' a history of Ireland an' it in potry? Yet 'tis a woeful pity he doesn't know the truest history an' the best is in the old stories!'

Aunt Hannah flung back her head.

'I give up!' she declared. 'What's the use of talking!'

Mrs. Hennessy drew her hood over her white hair and stood up.

'If the child's ready we'll be movin',' she said.

I looked from one friendly face to another. My mother was smiling as if all her troubles had said good-bye, my brother was pursing his lips as if he were whistling, but I was desperate. They weren't going from me, I was going from them.

'No!' I shouted. 'No!'

Dinny Foley clutched my hand.

'I'm comin' too!' he announced. 'Her's frighted!'

Mrs. Hennessy held out her hand to me.

'Ye'll see the place where yer own mother was a child,' she coaxed. 'Ye'll meet me own husband, the happiest man in the whole of Munster. An' Francis Joseph—he'll play ye every tune of this world an' the other. An' I know well ye've a great likin' for stories, pet. Come with me, Patricia!'

I put my hand in hers. I wasn't ready. My bundle was ready, but I wasn't. She led me out of the kitchen and Peadar Keeley lifted me into the cart. My mother hugged me then, and Patrick Henry kissed me. Uncle Liam brought out my bundle, my picture book, and the rag doll. He held her upside down and Dinny snatched her away indignantly; but I didn't mind. Peadar Keeley took off the donkey's nosebag and I sat looking down at the patient little grey creature with its long ears drooping, and tried not to cry.

'I'm comin' too!' declared Dinny, scrambling up beside me.

His mother pulled him back.

'Is it disgracin' me ye are, Dinny Foley?' she asked sternly.

'Be a good girl,' said my mother. 'You should be very grateful to Mrs. Hennessy.'

My hair was over my eyes as I peered at her mournfully, when the front door was flung open and my grandfather, his long coat unbuttoned, books under each arm, stood there, looking down on me.

'Safe journey, happy ending, Patricia Nora,' he said, raising his top hat and bowing.

No one else called me Patricia Nora. I was so proud I would have set off for America. I waved my hand without being told.

'Home, Moddy, ye little robber, ye. Home!' ordered Peadar Keeley, his hand on the donkey's neck.

He walked on; the donkey kept with him. I discovered Mrs. Hennessy beside me and looked back.

'Ye'd think 'twas the Empress of China going on a voyage!' called a jeering voice. There was a mist between me and Aunt Hannah, between me and the old house on Fair Hill.

'Did ye never go travellin' before?' asked Mrs. Hennessy. 'There's nothin' to aquil it, nothin' at all—bar comin' home agin.'

## 3. MY FIRST JOURNEY

'WE 'll walk now,' said Mrs. Hennessy. ''Tis time Moddy took it aisy.'

I had been staring over my shoulder. Our house had vanished and a strange huddle of roofs and chimneys took its place. Shandon bells were ringing and pigeons flashed into the sunshine as if tossed by the bells. Suddenly, through a gap, I could see along the river bank. The rushing tide swirling against its white walls, a tiny castle stood there like a forgotten toy. The turrets gleamed and the waves sweeping by the arch were blue as the sky.

'Will you look!' I cried, pointing. 'Will you look!'

Moddy stopped and turned her head inquiringly. Peadar Keeley, leaning on the cart, grinned up at me. His face was brown as his turf sods and his clothes had the good reek in them. He was never cross, never in a hurry, yet he was a great man for work. Aunt Kattie said so.

'Did ye never see Blackrock Castle before, child?' asked Mrs. Hennessy. 'Ah, 'tis the dote of a castle!'

One day Dinny and I had been in the yard building a house with sods of turf. Trying to find ones that were smooth and square we clambered to the top of the stack and lay there in the sunshine, watching the world below.

16

The stack was high, for Peadar had been bringing in loads for weeks, and we had never been able to see so far before. There were boats on the river—row boats, fishing boats with rounded sails filled with wind as they swung to the centre of the river. A crowded passenger steamer trailed a grey banner of smoke and the thin sweet music of a fiddle came up to us. As I watched there was the little white castle, standing out from the shore, as if it wanted to go down the river with the steamer. I was so excited I called to Aunt Kattie to come and look. I made such a noise that every one in the house came running. My grandfather, setting off for the city, strode down the stone steps at one bound. He carried a book in his hand and one under his arm. Aunt Kattie had a rolling-pin, and flour was sprinkled over her hair, her face, her frock. My mother was making a long strip of lace and it fluttered in the wind as she rushed to rescue me, for she thought I was hurt or in trouble. Aunt Hannah, last of all, came with her head tilted sideways, ready to jeer. The uncles were out, or they would have been there too, and my brother was at school. I gazed down from the height of the turf pile a little alarmed at the fuss I had caused.

My mother shook her head.

'Is it Blackrock Castle the commotion's about?' she asked, laughing up at me. 'Sure, it's been there all the time!'

My grandfather held his book under his chin.

'How wonderful to see Blackrock Castle for the first time!' he sighed.

Aunt Kattie grumbled.

'Such nonsense! Letting on something's happened and me rolling out me dough!'

'Blackrock Castle—how are ye?' jeered Aunt Hannah. 'An old boathouse! That's what it is. Not big enough to keep goats in!'

'What's the news? What's the news?' demanded Mrs.

Foley, hurrying into the yard with a bundle of washing in her arms.

'News indeed! That young one's discovered Blackrock Caſtle,' Aunt Hannah told her. And flinging her apron over her head she rocked with laughter.

'That a daughter of mine should wear an apron like a servant!' exclaimed grandfather, marching back to Fair Hill.

'Never mind that make-game,' my mother consoled me as I slid from the top of the turf pile to the bottom and landed on the heap of soft turf mould at her feet. 'She's never excited about anything but teasing and tormenting.'

Now I wondered would Mrs. Hennessy and Peadar Keeley jeer or be aſtonished, yet somehow I was sure they wouldn't.

'There's not another city in the world like Cork!' declared Mrs. Hennessy. 'Did ye know 'tis an island, a city, yet an island, mind ye! An' not only is the river all round it, 'tis under it too. One day ye'll see the houses an' shops floating off to sea like a fleet of ships.'

'Sure a city can't behave that way, Mrs. Hennessy, ma'am,' objeſted Peadar Keeley. 'Cork's safe enough.'

Mrs. Hennessy looked at him severely.

'"Tis a prophecy, Peadar,' she said. 'Ye'll not be settin' yerself up agin' a prophecy, surely!'

'Will ye look, ma'am,' implored Peadar. 'The size of it! There it all is, lyin' before ye.'

Mrs. Hennessy frowned. Her thin lips were so closely pressed they made scarcely a line in her face.

'Jump down, pet. We should be on our way. 'Tis a long journey before us and poor Moddy has done her day's work.'

I could see she was angry with Peadar and I wondered at his boldness. Besides, if Blackrock Caſtle could go sailing out to sea, why shouldn't Cork itself follow? Street by ſtreet, house by house, slipping away, leaving the hills

empty and the river lonely? As I watched, a shiver went
through the houses. Suppose my own home went out to
sea while I was away with Mrs. Hennessy! I stared at her
with frightened eyes.

'Ye 've scared the child, ma'am,' said Peadar, not sorry,
I 'm sure, to prove her in the wrong.

Mrs. Hennessy turned from Peadar to me.

'Sure now, Patricia, ye 're not feared of a prophecy? It
won't happen in our time, not for years an' years!'

'And Fair Hill will be there when we come back?' I asked.

She laughed. Peadar laughed and I laughed too, though
I wasn't at all sure what we were laughing at.

'"Twill last our time, I promise ye,' she consoled me.

I jumped down then and walked with Peadar, the donkey
between us. Moddy was a friendly donkey and made little
noises at us. Once she rubbed her head against me and
I could scarcely breathe for delight. Mrs. Hennessy
walked at the side of the road, on the grass edge. A great
flock of sheep came towards us. They filled the road
from side to side, baa-ing as they trotted along. Peadar
and Moddy stood still, so did I. The sheep moved round us
and I stroked each one as it went by. Mrs. Hennessy
stepped up on the low stone wall which bordered the road
and scolded the man driving the sheep. He was a tall,
thin man dressed in tatters, his red hair standing up straight
through the top of his hat.

'There should be room for dacent folk on the road!' she
told him. 'I 've travelled this way year in an' year out
an' never before have I been druv into climbin' the wall to
save meself from a pack of sheep!'

The man carried a long stick. He leaned on it and
listened. His dog, a lovely brown and white collie, sat
beside him, panting, its pink tongue flickering.

'Ye 're dead right, ma'am,' agreed the man, when Mrs.
Hennessy stopped talking. He nodded until I feared his

head would fall off. ''Tis too big a flock to expect one man wid a young dog to drive in any comfort. I started out from Goatsferry up along wid only ten. I collected fifteen more from Micky Sweeney, the far side of Berehaven, five more from—wait a bit till I find me tally.'

He pulled a dirty piece of paper from his jacket pocket and held it out.

'Don't trouble, me poor man,' said Mrs. Hennessy. 'I was vexed. But, sure, I had no right to be. The road's clear now an', if ye don't stir yerself, yer sheep will be in Cork on their lone.'

The man looked round. The sheep, pushing and scrambling, were going out of sight, round a bend in the road.

Suddenly Mrs. Hennessy stepped from the wall. She was so light she seemed to float down.

'Micky Sweeney! Ye come from Micky Sweeney?' she cried. 'An' did Micky Sweeney give ye nothin' to lave at Mrs. Hennessy's as ye passed by?'

The man dropped his stick in the dust, clapped his hands, and stepped back.

'Are ye indade Mrs. Hennessy? Tell me truly, ma'am, are ye the wumman that has all the stories of Ireland in her head?' he asked quickly.

Mrs. Hennessy smiled.

'Not all the stories. But the most of them. An', if I'm spared, I'll know the rest, please God!'

The man nodded.

'I've often heard tell of Mrs. Hennessy. An' now I've seen her, face to face. Isn't it the world's pity, ma'am, ye're always away from home when I'm after comin' to ye wid a message from Micky Sweeney. But one day I'll hear a story from yer own lips. An' Micky Sweeney bade me say—there's six ounces of the Orange Peekow Tips this time.'

'The dacent man!' sighed Mrs. Hennessy. 'But the sheep, lad! The sheep!'

The man gave the dog a slap.

'Off wid ye!' he ordered. 'D' ye want them sheep to be arrivin' in Mallow when 'tis Cork they should be aimin' at?'

The dog leaped and ran, crouching so that the dust rose in a cloud after him. The herd chuckled.

'D' ye mind that dog now? He could bring sheep from the mountains of Kerry into Cork city widout a soul to guide him! Safe home, ma'am.'

He took off his hat with a flourish. Then, putting his hands on his knees, he thrust his face towards me.

'Ye lucky little divil, ye! Ye lucky little divil—to be kapin' company wid a shanachie!'

Catching his stick, he rushed after the dog, stirring the dust which was beginning to settle.

'A ragin' lunatic!' declared Peadar. 'Come along outer that, Moddy! Pull yerself together, girleen!'

'Six ounces of Orange Tips!' said Mrs. Hennessy, clasping her hands. 'Ah, Micky Sweeney 's the dacent man!'

A cart carrying two calves and with a cow walking behind came along. The driver saluted Mrs. Hennessy.

'Isn't it a terrible pity, Mrs. Hennessy, ma'am, we 're goin' the opposite ways,' he said. 'I 'm not at all pleased to see ye stravagin' the roads alongside an old ass cart. 'Tis ridin' up out of the dirt an' roughness ye should be. Aren't ye ashamed, Peadar Keeley? Or have ye no shame in ye?'

He drove by, flourishing his whip. Peadar glared after him.

'Mebbe ye 'd as well step back into the cart, ma'am,' he said. 'Sure ye weigh nothin' at all an' the child is no more than a stone of praties.'

Mrs. Hennessy looked at Moddy. Moddy waggled her ears and hee-hawed softly.

'Sure the baste 's tellin' ye to mount, ma'am. Come up, girleen.'

I wanted to be good to the donkey, but I wanted to ride So, when Peadar swung me to the seat, I sat still, hoping Mrs. Hennessy would agree. She hesitated until we heard an uproar on the road.

'Tinkers!' said Mrs. Hennessy.

'Up wid ye, ma'am,' urged Peadar. ''Twouldn't do for them to see ye trailin' yer skirts.'

She stepped up and sat beside me without making the cart swerve an inch. I wouldn't have been surprised it she had stepped higher, into the air, and drifted away over the fields. I was proud to be with a woman so well known. I wished my mother could see us. The noise and the tinkers who made it were coming nearer. We passed a clump of trees, the road twisted, and there they were, taking up the whole roadway.

# 4. TINKERS

I HAD seen that tilt cart before! And the long, dark man who lounged on the seat, puffing a blackened clay pipe and staring at us with glittering mocking eyes—I had seen him too.

Dinny and I, on a March Monday morning, instead of going downhill to the convent school, had climbed and climbed until we were tired. We sat on the edge of the Fair Green and ate the bread and butter we should have kept until playtime. We didn't know what to do. It was grand to be sitting on the grass when the other children were chanting 'The cat sat on the mat,' or 'One and one make two; two and two make four.' But the wind was piercing and dust whirled along the road in dancing pyramids turned upside down. Our faces were dirty and our mouths dry. And what would happen when we went back home? It was the first time we had mitched. I watched Dinny's fat, cheerful face grow serious. Suddenly he dug his fists into his eyes and roared. I roared too. I longed for the high-backed benches in the classroom, the counting-frame with its coloured beads, the monstrous blackboard

and Sister Alphonse, her robes smeared with chalk, her big
white hands beating time, singing louder than all the
children together.

Another sound rose above our weeping—hard, unkind
laughter. I looked up at a tall, dark man standing in the
roadway. His clothes were tattered and a yellow handkerchief was twisted about his head. He stood with his hands
on his hips, swinging backwards and forwards, showing
his sharp teeth in a mocking grin. Behind the man was
a battered cart, drawn by a bony white horse. The cart
had a torn, dirty-white cover and a row of babies' faces
peered at us from the back. A young woman with an
armful of sticks leaned against the shaft and an old woman,
hidden in a black shawl, held her hand over her eyes as
she looked at us. Other tinkers were hurrying along the
road, each one loaded. I was so terrified I shut my eyes.

'Two little mitchers,' chuckled the man with the yellow
handkerchief. 'An' I 'm wonderin' what the dacent, very
respectable people of Cork will do when they catch 'em.'

Dinny clutched my hand and we both howled louder.

'I suppose yez set out to jine the tinkers,' went on the
dark man. 'Sure we 've more childer than we know what to
do wid. Ye can't sell 'em at a fair. Ye can't ate 'em for
yer dinner. Still an' all, I 'm terrible soft-hearted an' we 'll
squeeze in two more. Jump in there under the sate an',
when the polis come sarchin', don't let the ghost of a
sound out of yez.'

I opened my eyes to see was he pretending. But he stood
there frowning and all his tribe looked so serious.

Dinny jumped up, pulling me with him. Away we ran.
The tinkers' laughter followed us. I thought I could hear
the dark man's feet pounding the road. Dinny still held
my hand. He could run much faster, but he kept beside
me. You could always trust Dinny. When we dared look
back the tinkers had drawn their cart against a clump of

bushes and the white horse was grazing. A fire of sticks
blazed and not one of the tattered group bothered to gaze
in our direction.

We didn't venture near the school. We went in to Mrs.
Foley and told our adventure. She was hanging wet
clothes on the line at the back of her tumbledown little
house. But she sat on her upturned bucket and listened
with great sympathy.

'Ye poor scraps. Ye must have been demented. Don't
I know 'tis great fun goin' mitchin'. But, mark me words
—school 's the safe place. The tinkers 'll never come next
or nigh ye while yez are in the school wid Sister Alphonse!'

'We weren't axactly mitchin',' explained Dinny.

'Ah, well, yez 're only young once,' sighed Mrs. Foley.
'Come in till I blow up the fire an' heat a sup of tay.
'Twill comfort yez.'

We drank the hot stewed tea. She found us two clay
pipes and we blew soap bubbles with her washing water.
When school time was over I went home across the road.
Mrs. Foley never told on us and Dinny and I kept our
mitching a secret. But I dreamed night after night that the
terrible tinker had put me into his cart with the tins and
the babies. And here he was, sitting up in his cart, smoking
steadily, his followers straggling over the roadway, leaving
no room for our donkey to pass.

Peadar Keeley whistled and tried to draw Moddy to the
side. But Moddy liked the centre of the road and kept on
until her nose butted the white horse's. Mrs. Hennessy
sat up straight and folded her arms. She gazed at the dark
tinker so calmly that he took his pipe from his mouth and
held up his hand in greeting. Then he saw me. He flung
back his head and laughed.

'Mitchin' again!' he cried. ''Pon me word, ye 're a
little strap!'

'I 'm not mitching!' I declared, very brave now I had

grown-up friends to protect me. 'I'm going visiting with Mrs. Hennessy.'

The tinker stared at the storyteller. He stood up in the cart and bowed.

'The road's yours, ma'am,' he said grandly. 'I'd no notion 'twas yerself, Mrs. Hennessy.'

With a tug of the reins he swung the white horse so that the restless, crowding tinkers had to scatter.

'Thank ye kindly, sir,' said Mrs. Hennessy.

Moddy stuck one ear forward and trotted on, looking as pleased and proud as a donkey can look, while the tinkers made way for us.

'If that don't bate all!' exclaimed Peadar Keeley. 'Don't tell me! Didn't I always say 'tis better to have a gift than a crock of gold? If I'd only been a storyteller, or mebbe a fiddler instead of a turf carrier!'

Half asleep, leaning against Mrs. Hennessy; warm, yet feeling the sweet night air, I saw the stone walls black against the white road. The bushes were black too, and seemed to leap and clutch as we went by. I had never seen such strange bushes, but I had never been out so late before.

'I'm not a bit afraid,' I thought proudly.

Indeed I had no reason to be afraid, with Mrs. Hennessy holding me close and Peadar and Moddy just ahead, their little shadows trotting along with them. Peadar was still talking when I fell asleep. I slept while we passed through Macroom and crossed the river by the little stone bridge.

## 5. HOME WITH THE HENNESSYS

MODDY woke me. We were bumping across a cobbled yard in the moonlight. Another donkey watched from an open shed, hee-hawing nearly as loud as Moddy.

'They 're friends, God help them!' explained Mrs. Hennessy, as Peadar lifted me out, slung me over his shoulder, and marched towards a half-door. The glow of a fire and the white light of a lamp streamed over it, the sound of voices and a fine, hot smell.

Peadar set me down on the threshold of a crowded room. A huge turf fire was piled on an open hearth. Over it hung a steaming black kettle. A big woman was taking a piece of bacon from a pot oven surrounded with hot ash. She laid it gently on a dish of pale green cabbage.

'That 's beautiful!' I said.

'Bedad, the child 's right!' agreed the big woman. 'But where in the wide world did ye spring from?'

Mrs. Hennessy came up behind me.

'She 's wid me, Mrs. Flanagan. Tighe Lynch of Fair Hill is her grandfather.'

27

'She's welcome!' declared Mrs. Flanagan. 'But no more than yerself, Mrs. Hennessy.'

''Tis a cup in our han's an' no more,' said Mrs. Hennessy. 'We've a good piece of the road to cover yet an' himself'll be waitin' up for me.'

'Ye'll sit down to a plate of bacon an' cabbage or ye're no friend of mine!' retorted Mrs. Flanagan. 'Don't I know well that yerself an' Peadar Keeley get no rest in Cork? An' sure, the poor donkey needs a bite an' sup. Let yer eyes take a glimpse of that bacon. 'Tis the best bit I've cooked this month. An' will ye look at the child. She'll not stir a step widout her share.'

We squeezed in on a bench against the wall. Peadar Keeley had a seat by the fire next to an old woman. She had the biggest brown rosary I had ever seen and the beads were slipping through her fingers all the time Peadar was talking to her.

I had a saucer piled with slices of pink bacon, so thin and tender my spoon cut through to the cabbage beneath. Then I had a baked potato cut in two with a lump of butter and a pinch of salt poked in each half. I thought of my mother and Patrick Henry. If only they were sitting on the bench beside me!

Although the top of the door was looped back, the air was comfortably warm. A man whose clothes smelled of fresh-cut turf sat opposite me. His long-handled slane for cutting the sods leaned against the back of his chair. His hands and face were deep brown and his rough hair was like the twigs in a bit of loose turf.

'An' who might ye be?' he asked, smiling at me.

'I'm Tricia Lynch,' I told him. 'Tricia Nora.'

'Pleased to meet ye, Tricia Nora,' he said. 'I've a little gerrul of me own an' a young lad too. If ye lived over in our part ye'd all be friends. I'm sure of that.'

'Do you cut turf?' I asked.

'I do indade. I'm a turf-cutter. 'Twould be a gran' trade only for the coal. Coal's good enough for the town. 'Tis only foolish in the country.'

Peadar Keeley came over to the table for another potato. 'How're ye, Peadar?' asked the turf-cutter.

'Gran'! How's yerself?' replied Peadar.

He put his elbows on the table and they talked about turf-cutting and carrying, so that I was forgotten. I laid my head on the table. It was hard and I was uncomfortable. But that couldn't keep me awake. At home on Fair Hill I was always having bad dreams. The thing with long hairy arms that lived in the press on the landing, Aunt Hannah, a big boy with very large feet who had chased Dinny and me down the coal quay, the tinkers—all the fears of the day were more terrible at night. Yet now, in Mrs. Flanagan's eating-house, my head on a hard table instead of a soft, clean pillow, I dreamed I sat on the green rug my mother had packed in the black leather chest. It had grown so big it stretched as far as I could see. Beside me was a golden bird-cage, and I felt so happy I wanted to stay there for ever. Someone I couldn't see lifted me up, but I held on to the golden bird-cage.

'Wrap the bit of blanket round the child, for 'tis turning cold,' said Mrs. Hennessy's voice. I blinked enough to discover I was back in the cart with Mrs. Hennessy and Peadar Keeley was leading Moddy through the gate to the road.

'The bird-cage,' I whispered. 'I want me goldy bird-cage.'

'In the mornin', pet. Ye shall have everythin' ye can wish.'

The moon was gone and we rode through a grey mist which hid the road and the walls and made Peadar with a sack over his shoulders and his donkey with another sack to keep her snug, dim and far away. The mist turned

silver, then golden.   A wind blew down the road and sent
grey filmy tatters flying before us.   The clouds were
changing from gold to pink and there was the sun beaming
at us from over a craggy hill.

'Aren't ye the lucky one?' asked Peadar, peering at me
over his shoulder.   I nodded.   I didn't want to talk.
'Ah, well,' said Peadar.   'A nod's as good as a wink to
a blind horse an' a still tongue never yet broke a man's
jaw.'

'Whist, Peadar!   Whist!' said Mrs. Hennessy.

'Whist it is,' agreed Peadar, and he strode along whistling.

My eyes were shut, but I couldn't have been asleep, for
I heard Mrs. Hennessy say: 'Here's home.   God be praised.'

I scrambled down, determined not to be carried this
time.   Here was another half-door, and, as Peadar held the
gate open, music came out to us, so gay and lovely I
wanted to stand and listen.   But Mrs. Hennessy pulled
me on.

'''Tis Francis Joseph, me own brother, back home again.
He promised he'd be here,' she whispered.   'He's the
best fiddler in the whole of Munster and he's been away
for dear knows how long.   Go softly.   We'll give them
a start.'

We stole on tiptoe towards the half-door, but the music
roused Moddy, who was standing wearily in the middle of
the road, her head hanging, her long ears trailing in the
dust.   She flung up her head and 'hee-hawed' as if she were
singing to the music.

'Is that Peadar Keeley outside?' called a voice.   'I'd
know his donkey's singin' a mile away.'

A man looked out at us.   He was like Mrs. Hennessy,
only brown where she was pale and his white curly hair
stood on end.

'Is it yerself?' he cried.   'Come along in, Brigid.   The
kettle's boiling and himself's nearly settin' off to meet ye.'

He swung the door open, caught Mrs. Hennessy's hand in his, and drew her inside. An old man was sitting by the fire, his hands on his knees, his face turned to the door.

'Are ye well, James? Are ye well?' asked Mrs. Hennessy, bending over him.

'Brigid! I missed ye!' he said.

I knew now why Mrs. Hennessy wouldn't spend the night in Cork. I had heard as much about Mr. Hennessy as I had about Mrs. Hennessy. He was blind, but he looked at her as if he could see every line in her face.

'And the child,' he said. 'Will she not let an old man bid her welcome?'

I went to him at once. He ran his fingers over my face and I didn't mind, for I knew it was his way of looking at me.

'She's not like Tighe Lynch,' he sighed. 'She has a touch of Nora. But she's her father's daughter, that's sure.'

'I'd best be on me way,' said Peadar from the doorway. 'Poor Moddy's ready to lie in the roadway wid the tiredness. I'll be seein' ye.'

'Safe home, Peadar!' they called back.

Mrs. Hennessy took off her cloak and Francis Joseph hung it on a hook behind the door.

'Now yours,' he said.

I pointed to the fiddle he had laid on a bench.

'You made the music?' I asked.

'I did indeed, an' I'll play more. Ye couldn't stop me when I get goin'. Now give me the coat an' the cap.'

I fell asleep while Mrs. Hennessy was taking off my frock. For a while I heard voices, and when I woke once more I was lying in the settle bed, with a bright patchwork counterpane over it. My rag doll lay beside me next the wall. On the other side a monster of a tabby cat was stretched, his green eyes watching me, while he purred and kneaded with his thick paws. The door was wide open and the room was filled with sunshine. Just outside, the blind man was seated on a creepie, twisting twigs to make a creel. A brown hen and a brood of chickens pecked about his feet and on the flat stone at the door a white duck was softly quacking.

## 6. THE CABIN BY THE THORN BUSH

'So ye 're wakin'?'

Mrs. Hennessy was standing at the table by the window, cutting a flat soda cake in thick slices and spreading them with deep yellow butter. She smiled over at me, went to the fire, pulled out the kettle on a chain, and filled the brown teapot.

'We can all do wid a cup a tay,' she said. 'Rale Orange Peekow, child. Ye 'd not drink that in many houses these days.'

I lay watching her. Fair Hill seemed a long way. I wondered if my mother and Patrick Henry were on a train and if they had forgotten me. Mrs. Hennessy put down the teapot and came over.

'Sure, ye 're not frettin', Patricia?' she asked anxiously.

'I like being here,' I assured her. 'But I wish——'

Mrs. Hennessy sat on the bed beside me. The cat wriggled to her lap and blinked up at her happily.

'I understand, pet. There 's alwys been the three of ye an' ye 're lonesome widout the others. Mebbe they 're lonesome too. Ye wouldn't have been so strange if ye

33

were in the old house. But when I heard yer da had sent word, an' yer mammy an' yer brother were off wid them, I thought of the way Hannah torments ye an' I knew ye 'd be better here. Listen now—when yer mammy was a girleen like yerself I had her here to mind. Ah, she was a lovely child—wid big sad grey eyes, an' skin like milk, an' long brown hair smooth as silk.'

'It 's that long now she can sit on it,' I told Mrs. Hennessy proudly. Then I added: 'Was she sad then—when she was a little girl like me?'

Mrs. Hennessy nodded.

'Ever an' always. She was discontinted wid the way things do be. There was them that said she 'd been taken away, ye understand?'

I shook my head. I didn't understand at all.

Mrs. Hennessy whispered.

'The Good People took her for a day an' a night. But she wanted her father. That 's yer grandad. Ye know the grah she has for him. So they let her come back. An', God help her, she can never forget what she had to give up to be wid him.'

'Tell me about the Good People,' I demanded.

'Later on, Patricia. Haven't we all the time there is. An' ye should know yer own people. Yer da now, he was different. Always laughin' an' coaxin' an' wild as the wind.'

'You knew him? You knew me daddy?' I asked in amazement.

'I did indade. Ah, he was the lad. Ye have a bit of a look of him—yer eyes mebbe. Deed then, there was nothin' sad about him. He thought the world a gorgeous place an' he couldn't see enough of it. Kape quiet now wid Midgie an' I 'll give ye yer breakfast in bed like a lady, though 'tis long past dinner time.'

I had never had breakfast in bed before. I sat up and

looked through the doorway at all that was happening outside.   A path bordered with glistening chunks of white rock led to the queerest gate in the strangest fence imaginable.   Instead of wooden stakes or iron railings I saw black twisted horns stuck in the ground with bright green periwinkle creepers twining in and out and the gay blue flowers wide open.   At each side, on the grass, washing was laid out to bleach and all around were flowers.   I knew daisies and buttercups and the tall Easter lilies, but these flowers were all strange to me.   The gate of twisted horns was open.   Hens were scuttling in, while a brown cock with a tail of bronze and green stood proudly crowing on the topmost horn.

Mrs. Hennessy picked up a tin bowl from the table and, standing on the step, scattered handfuls of grain along the path.   I nearly tumbled on the floor trying to see the hens and chickens.   Midgie, the cat, was so disturbed he climbed over me and curled up on the rag doll.   Then Mrs. Hennessy came in and piled sods on the hearth.   Instead of blowing the fire with a bellows, she turned a wheel at the side and little flames ran up the brown sods until they glowed.   She brought over a red tray with black dragons along the edge.   The cup and saucer and the plate as well had golden dragons with outspread wings and claws.   They were the loveliest delph I had ever set eyes on.

''Twas yer own da brought me them from foreign parts,' Mrs. Hennessy told me as I drank the rich brown tea and bit into the soda bread which she had piled with blackberry jam.   ''Tisn't every little gerrul I'd let have her breakfast off them, let me tell ye.'

I didn't know what to say, so I just smiled and she smiled back.   Midgie ate the crusty corners of the soda bread for me and licked out my cup, then, leaping to the ground, went off to sit with Mr. Hennessy.

Mrs. Hennessy cleaned out the tin bowl and I washed in

it with soft rain water from a barrel at the corner of the cabin. She combed my hair with the new green comb Mrs. Foley had given me. I put on the red and white check frock, my new Sunday one, myself. Then I looked round for my shoes and socks.

'Wouldn't ye like to go barefoot?' asked Mrs. Hennessy. 'Sure, there's no sinse wearin' out good wool an' shoe leather an' ye in the country.'

In the summer Dinny Foley went barefoot and I always envied him. I liked the feel of the earthen floor on my bare soles and, without waiting to be told, ran through the doorway on to the grass.

'Good morning. How are ye, Mr. Hennessy?' I called as I passed the blind man.

'Good mornin' to ye, allanna! Isn't it gran' an' free to be runnin' over the grass on bare feet?'

I stood and stared at him.

'Then you can see me, Mr. Hennessy?' I asked.

He laughed and shook his head.

'Not wid me eyes, child. But there's more than one way of seein'. But tell me what you see.'

I looked about me, determined not to miss anything.

'There's the fence of horns,' I told him. 'All black and twisty. That's a strange fence, Mr. Hennessy.'

He nodded.

'Queer enough. Though 'tisn't horns, child, but bog oak. Branches of trees that were growin' in Ireland hundreds an' thousands of years ago. 'Twas Peadar Keeley dug them out an' he cuttin' turf. He brought them here when we came to live in this house. He's a good kind friend, is Peadar Keeley.'

I gazed at the fence and wished we had one like it round the yard in Fair Hill.

'Then there's the turf pile, Mr. Hennessy,' I went on. 'It's like ours at home, only tidier. We're the only ones with a turf pile. And there 's hens and chickens and ducks and a lovely cock. What 's his name, Mr. Hennessy?'

'Mickeen is the name that 's on him. Mickeen! Mickeen!'

The cock heard his name, fluttered to the ground and stalked across the grass, jumped to the blind man's knee and perched there, crowing softly.

'An' what else is there, Tricia?'

'Up on a bush, one with big white flowers, only they 're little ones growing close together, just by the water barrel, there 's a bird all black, only his beak, and that 's gold.'

'The blackbird,' said Mr. Hennessy. 'He was singin' away to ye this mornin', only ye were too sound asleep to hear a note. Himself an' Mrs. Blackbird have a nest in the elderberry an' a whole family of young ones. Ah, he 's the sweetest singer in the whole countryside, if he is a robber.'

I looked again and a demure brown bird was peeping out at me from the elderberry. And then I heard music, not from a bird, but a fiddle, coming down the boreen. There had I been staring at fences and birds and never bothering about the boreen at all. I looked now at the rutted, stony path which went down the hill to the big wide road where I had been riding in the moonlight. I went to the gate and saw how the boreen climbed the other way until it vanished in a fold of the dark hills. The music came nearer and, at the point where the boreen vanished, a fiddler appeared striding towards me.

'Francis Joseph!' I cried, and ran to meet him. But the stones hurt my feet and I went slowly, keeping to the ruts soft and cool with mud. Francis Joseph waved his bow.

''Tis aisy seen ye 're only a towny!' he shouted.

His eyes were friendly and I didn't mind his teasing. But I wouldn't be called a towny.

'I 'm not a towny!' I declared. 'Only the stones are terrible sharp.'

He put his fiddle under his arm and, as he came up, swung me to his shoulder.

'If ye weren't a towny ye 'd hop an' skip on them same stones an' never know they were there.  Have ye arned yer dinner yet?'

I shook my head.  'Do I have to?'

'Do ye have to?  Would ye ate widout arnin'?'

He cocked his head sideways so that I could see his laughing eyes.

'What can I do?' I asked anxiously.

Dinny's mother often let me beat up hot suds and carry out the little basket piled with collars and handkerchiefs for her to peg on the line.  She even let me sweep the floor and carry in sods of turf.  Aunt Kattie was different.  She did everything so well she hated help.

'What can ye do?' repeated Francis Joseph.  'What 's most important of all?  What can't we do widout?'

'Turf?' I suggested.

'Important enough,' agreed Francis Joseph.  'But 'tis ready stacked beside the fire.  I did it meself.  Think again.'

I thought of going to the shop for tea, bread, butter, jam. But the tea came from Micky Sweeney, Mrs. Hennessy baked her own bread, the butter came from O'Callaghan's farm and the jam too.

'I never can guess riddles,' I said.

'Ye never thought of water,' Francis Joseph told me. 'Yet water comes first.'

I laughed.  He must be joking.

'There 's a great barrel of water outside the window,' I cried triumphantly.  'And you never thought of that!'

'Now I know ye 're a towny for sure!' declared Francis Joseph.  'Rain water is for clanin' an' washin', not for

makin' tay. When I 'm home 'tis one of me jobs to carry
the water, an' ye can help.'

'Indeed I will,' I promised.

But I was ashamed. I waited for him to tell me where
we went for the water. But he didn't say a word and
I had to know.

'Do we carry water from the river?' I asked, as we came
to the gate.

'No, girleen. We have a grand spring juſt over the wall.
A wishing spring. Good water an' three wishes. 'Tisn't
many have that, let me tell ye.'

He set me down and went into the house to put away
his fiddle. I swung on the gate and watched Mr. Hennessy
twiſting willow twigs to make a creel.

'I wonder now would Francis Joseph fix up a swing for
ye on the apple-tree,' said the blind man. 'Swingin' on a
gate is great, but there 's nothin' can aquil a rale, long
swing.'

'Is there an apple-tree?' I asked. 'A real apple-tree
with apples on it?'

He laughed. 'There is indade. Ye haven't seen the half
of all there is at the Hennessys. Round at the back,
girleen! Round at the back!'

Beyond the cabin the ground rose in a huddle of rocks
and tangled bushes. The level patch around the cabin was
planted with potatoes—twelve rows of them, a long bed of
parsnips, and short rows of carrots and beetroot. I didn't
know what they were then. Mrs. Hennessy told me afterwards. They were bordered with a row of raspberries, and
gooseberry bushes grew alongside the rhubarb. A big
tree ſtood in the middle and I walked by the raspberry
canes longing for a soft red apple, or one of the pink and
yellow Americans the women sold on the bridges in Cork.
I could see apples, dozens and dozens of them, high above
my head, but they were all small and green. I ſtood on

tiptoe and reached up. The lowest branch was still beyond me. I found a flat rock and tried to drag it over to the tree, so that I could stand on it, but I only scraped my fingers. Then I saw Francis Joseph watching me.

'Now what in the wide world are ye up to, Tricia Lynch?' he asked.

'I'm after an apple,' I told him. 'They're too high up, but you're big.'

'Ye little robber!' chuckled Francis Joseph. 'Temptin' me to stale apples, are ye?'

'"Tisn't stealing!' I cried indignantly. 'Not when they're growin' on a tree.'

Mrs. Hennessy came out with a knife in her hand.

'I'm wonderin' would a cauliflower be tastier than cabbage,' she said. 'Mebbe I'd as well stick to cabbage. After all, what can ye cook wid pig's cheek only cabbage?'

'Ye'd better give the young one an apple,' Francis Joseph told her. 'She's after the green ones.'

I looked at Mrs. Hennessy anxiously. Would she think it stealing to want an apple from a tree?

She laughed. 'Show the child where the apples are, an' don't be tormentin' her.'

She went on to where all kinds of greens stood in neat, stiff rows, while I followed Francis Joseph to a big shed beside the fence. It was nearly as big as the cabin and had a red roof. The door stood open and a lovely smell of apples, onions, and herbs came out. Inside the light was dim but I could see ropes of onions hanging from the rafters, bunches of herbs swung in the breeze, and tall creels with lids were ranged against the walls. Francis Joseph lifted the lid of the nearest.

'There y'are, me lady. Some say a russet's the best aitin', but I know a winesap can't be bet. Help yerself.'

The creel was filled with big red apples. I picked the one in the middle. Francis Joseph took another and we bit them at once. The skin was crisp and thin and the juice spurted as my teeth met.

'Now for the wishin' spring!' said Francis Joseph.

I carried one bucket—at least I put my hand on the handle, but the fiddler really carried two. We went out through the gate, across the boreen, and climbed the wall. A path of stones lay before us. Tall, rustling bushes, bound with brambles, rose at each side and met overhead, even over Francis Joseph's head, and we walked in a dim green light. I heard the splashing of water and a bird sang a little tune very softly. I stood still, trying to learn the tune, and Francis Joseph walked on, swinging the empty buckets, right out of sight. The bushes whispered, the bird sang, and the noisy water was talking too, only I could not understand.

'Tricia! Are ye comin', or are ye lost?' I heard.

I hurried on, stumbling over the stones, and suddenly I was out in the sunshine where a spring of golden water gushed from a cleft in the high grey rock. It dropped into a sandy pool, walled with stones, to keep out leaves and twigs.

'Listen now to what I 'm tellin' ye,' said Francis Joseph, sitting on a rock and stretching his long legs before him.

I listened.

'Ye see that dark hole, up there behind the fallin' water?'

I looked and nodded.

'That's a doorway into Tir na nOg. Remember now. And under that flat stone lives the trout of wisdom. He 's been there for years an' years. Dear knows how many years he has been there. If ye see him, an' ye will, three times runnin', an' ye wish what ye want more than any-thin' else in the world, mebbe ye 'll get it. Mind now!'

He took a crust from his pocket, broke it in three and tossed one piece into the pool. A slender silver shadow darted from under the flat stone, seized the bread, and flashed back.

'Oh!' I said.

Francis Joseph tossed in the second piece. I wished it had been bigger. I feared the trout wouldn't come again for such crumbs. But out shot the silver streak and vanished once more. I waited, clenching my fists in excitement, and out dashed the trout. I could see it properly this time, its fins, its tail, its speckles.

'Did ye wish?' asked Francis Joseph.

I shook my head. Hadn't I seen the trout? What more could I want. Francis Joseph frowned.

'I showed ye the entrance to Tir na nOg. I told ye to wish three times an' all ye did was to wish ye 'd see the trout ye were bound to see. Oh, Tricia Lynch, I thought better of ye!'

I tried to console him.

'We 'll bring another bit of bread and we 'll do it all over again.'

Francis Joseph sighed.

'Ye 've had yer wishes, Tricia. Ye can never have them again. An' 'pon me soul, I don't believe ye know what Tir na nOg means.'

I shook my head. I didn't know.

''Tis the Land of Youth. D' ye understand?'

I didn't. So I sat on the rock beside Francis Joseph and he told me of the Land of Youth.

It was pleasant sitting there in the sun, with the water tumbling and foaming, hidden birds singing all around, butterflies riding on sunbeams, bees, very active and serious, booming from flower to flower. Francis Joseph's voice was tangled up with all the other sounds. I was happy and wanted him to keep on talking.

'And then there 's O'Callaghans,' said Francis Joseph. 'I don't know any place I 'd sooner live than there, barrin' our own, of course.'

'Which is the way there?' I asked.

'There 's the road—that goes along be the village. Ye 'll be seein' it. Ah, the village shop 's the place, Judy Leahy keeps it. But the short cut to O'Callaghans—'twas that ye were askin' for? Well, child, we 're on the way there. Ye go on from here till ye come to the three birches. Ye 'll know them the minit ye set eyes on them. Sure the birch is the daintiest of all the trees. Turn to the left an' folly the stream till ye come to the plank bridge. Over ye go, careful now, up the boreen to the ruins. Round 'em, cross Cassidy's two fields an', on the far side of the bank as ye top it, be the scarecrow in a green coat wid a gun on his shoulder, starin' ye in the face is the farrum, O'Callaghans!'

'Are ye there, Francis Joseph?' came a call from the boreen. 'Herself 's waitin' on the water.'

Francis Joseph jumped up.

'That 's Bridie O'Callaghan after us. We 'll be murdered!' he exclaimed.

He filled the buckets and ran down the dim path without spilling a drop. I ran too. I had heard of Bridie. She was Mrs. Hennessy's niece and I wanted to see her.

## 7. THE SHORT CUT

BRIDIE O'CALLAGHAN sat on the low stone wall whistling and tapping with her feet. She could whistle even better than my brother and I liked her the moment she glanced back and I saw her merry eyes and freckled face.

'There's luck for ye, Tricia,' said Francis Joseph. 'A girl wid fairy spots to be lookin' at ye over her left shoulder.'

'How are ye, Tricia Lynch?' asked Bridie. 'Are they makin' ye work? No! Don't tell me! Francis Joseph showed ye the door to Tir na nOg an' the wishin' trout, an' all ye could wish for was sour apples an' black pudden. Never mind, ye can always go until ye're turned seven. Sit up here with me under the fairy thorn an' I'll teach ye to whistle *Shule Agragh.*'

'If ye do that, her mother'll come down an' murder ye!' Francis Joseph warned her.

'Take in the water, like a good man!' ordered Bridie. 'I'll be along and make an apple cake the minit me an' Tricia have had our chat.'

Francis Joseph laughed, shook his fist at her, picked up the buckets, and ran across the boreen, through the gate, up to the cabin.

44

'Don't be lookin' at me like that, Tricia,' said Bridie, 'or I 'll think ye 've been hearin' tales about me.'

'I know all about you!' I declared. 'You 're dancing mad, and you 'd walk ten miles out and ten miles home again to a ceilidhe; and you want to go to America and you 're the best cook in all West Cork.'

I was breathless. But I sat up proudly and swung my legs the way Bridie did.

She slipped from the wall and bowed.

'The best cook in West Cork, indeed! 'Tis the best dancer in the whole of Cork I am—watch me!'

Pulling me with her she raced into the garden and began dancing on the grass. Mr. Hennessy was stooping over a rosebush. He straightened up, clapped his hands slowly, then quicker and quicker, and Bridie's feet in their buckled shoes kept time with him. Francis Joseph came to the door with his fiddle, but he did not play. He stood there and Mrs. Hennessy, a big iron spoon in her hand, came out from the room. I tiptoed close to them.

I had never seen any one dance like Bridie. Even when she stamped there was no mark on the grass. She held her hands stiffly at her sides, her head was flung back, and her eyes were strange, almost like Mr. Hennessy's. Faster and faster the blind man's hands beat together and faster tapped Bridie's feet up and down the little patch of grass. Suddenly she stopped and stared at us, blinking as if she had been asleep.

'There 's a queer, strange music in your hands, Mr. Hennessy,' she said. 'I thought I danced best of all for Francis Joseph, but you have him bet.'

'And a girl who can dance like you can, Bridie O'Callaghan, wants to go to America!' exclaimed Francis Joseph. 'I 'm real vexed!'

'The apple cake!' cried Mrs. Hennessy. 'The apple cake ye promised, Bridie!'

Mrs. Hennessy peeled and sliced four big green apples while Bridie made the pastry. I watched her fingers mixing the bread, the soda, and the flour, then the water, taking the wet lump from the wooden bowl, rolling it in a heap of flour on the clean, scrubbed table, patting it out. She put little pieces of butter over it, folded the floury mass in three, rolled once more, scattered the bits of butter, rolled, more butter, and a final roll. This time was the last. The pastry was a long oval. Mrs. Hennessy piled half with the cut apple, sprinkled large spoonfuls of brown sugar, a scattering of cloves, and Bridie, with careful fingers, drew over the other half. I was breathless as Mrs. Hennessy held a sheet of greased paper so that the whole cake would slide on to it. Then in with it to the pot oven.

'And now for the news,' said Bridie. 'What's happening in the big world?'

She drew up a creepie to one side of the hearth. Mrs. Hennessy sat at the other. The pot oven was doing its work on the glowing hearth between them.

I picked up my rag doll and carried her out to talk to Mr. Hennessy. I trod softly in my bare feet, but he knew I was there, though he stood with his face upturned, listening to the blackbird.

'Is it yerself, Tricia, come to keep me company?' he asked. 'Sure I'm a lazy old fella. I should be makin' me creels.'

'Tell me about the fairy thorn, Mr. Hennessy,' I coaxed.

The blind man shook his head at the twisted thorn bush and his face was very severe.

''Tis that has us on the wrong side of the boreen, allanna. The spring is ours be rights an' 'tis over yonder the cabin should be. But ye daresn't build a cabin where *they* are comin' an' goin'. Ye daresn't do it.'

'Bridie would!' I declared.

'Mebbe she thinks she would,' said Mr. Hennessy. 'An'
I'm not denyin' she's a gran' little gerrul. But there's
some class of things even Bridie O'Callaghan daresn't do!'

'The dinner's on the table!' called Bridie over the
half-door.

The pig's cheek was cut thin, the cabbage was tender as
butter, and the potatoes were balls of fluff. I ate so much
I feared I wouldn't be able to eat any apple cake. But
when it came from the pot oven, golden brown, with
thick, sweet juice oozing through the crust, I knew I could
eat all Mrs. Hennessy would give me.

There was cream for our tea—Bridie had brought it.
I spooned the sugar in the bottom of my cup and sat
licking the last flaky crumbs from my fingers, feeling very
content.

'Are ye takin' Tricia along?' asked Mrs. Hennessy, as she
chopped pig's cheek and cabbage for Midgie, who stood
on his hind legs, purring and snatching.

'Where?' I demanded. 'Where?'

'The minit I've washed the delph,' replied Bridie.

'Sure, child, ye've no need to be botherin'. Haven't ye
enough delph to wash up at the farm?'

'The farm!' I cried. 'The farm!'

I jumped from the bench and ran to the door. Where
was the farm? My eyes fixed on Mr. Hennessy's fingers
poking the twigs in and out, I repeated to myself: 'Ye go
from here till ye come to the three birches. Ye'll know
them the minit ye set eyes on them. Sure the birch is the
daintiest of all the trees. Turn to the left an' folly the
stream till ye come to the plank bridge. Over ye go, careful now, up the boreen to the ruins. Round 'em, cross
Cassidy's two fields an', on the far side of the bank as ye
cross it, be the scarecrow in a green coat wid a gun on his
shoulder, starin' ye in the face is the farrum, O'Callaghans!'

'Let her start off!' said Bridie. 'I'll be after her.'

'Straight down the boreen, pet,' said Mrs. Hennessy.
'Turn to the right when ye come to the road and, when
ye reach the forge be the pond, ye 're there.'

I shut my eyes. I was trying to remember the short
cut. I thought of Judy Leahy's shop. But there were
shops in Cork.

'She 'll never find the way!' protested Mr. Hennessy.
'Let her stay an' talk to me. Then the two of them can
go together.'

I wanted to stay with Mr. Hennessy. I wanted to go
with Bridie into Judy Leahy's shop. But more than all
I wanted to go the short cut by myself. The basket for
the eggs was on the bench. I caught it up and ran down
the path.

'I 'll bring it back full up, Mr. Hennessy!' I called, for
I was ashamed not to stay with him. I went through the
gate and over the wall. I looked back, but no one was
watching. At the spring I stopped to look for the trout.
I could see his shadow but, as I had no crumbs, he wouldn't
come out for me, though I coaxed and coaxed. I tried to
peep into the cave which led to Tir na nOg. It was dark,
but I could see something white and shining, out of reach.
On I went. I swung the basket and tried to sing, but the
birds sang so much I listened to them. The path was
narrow and on that hot day the stones were cool and
pleasant to bare feet. Feathery plants rose above my head
and a small blue butterfly fluttered before me. When it
floated to a white flower beside the path I paused and saw
a big spider, half white, half green, walking sedately up a
slender stalk. I had seen only brown spiders in the house
and black ones in the shed. This spider was as beautiful
as a butterfly.

Wondering if there were blue-and-white or red-and-white
spiders as well, I went on, looking down, until I bumped
into a tree. It had mottled silvery bark and its long fine

branches were covered with tiny, rustling leaves. Then I saw there were two others just the same. I watched the branches tossing in the wind and thought of my mother brushing her dark silky hair. I turned to go back. I wanted home—Fair Hill—my mother and brother. I remembered they had gone from Fair Hill and, in my desolation, tears filled my eyes. A speckled bird, sitting on a rock, watched me with round surprised eyes.

'You 'd cry if your mammy and your Patrick Henry had gone away and left you!' I told him indignantly. He hopped off cheerfully and I thought how it was I who had come away.

'But they 've gone too,' I argued, following a brook which made a fuss about rocks no bigger than my fist and splashed down falls a few inches high. I was quite happy by the time I reached the bridge—a tree-trunk wedged at each end by large stones. The bark had been stripped off and the surface was green and slippery. The stream which had been so small now stretched before me as if it were the Lee. I put one foot on the bridge. Even with the sun blazing it was cold, slimy. I couldn't walk across it. I couldn't, I knew I 'd fall! Dinny was always walking on walls and daring me to follow. When I did, it was on hands and knees. And there was no Dinny to dare me now.

I looked down the stream, I looked up. The higher I looked, the narrower it became. Perhaps I would be able to jump across. Below a wide pool where yellow iris grew I saw a plank bridge with a hand-rail. Of course this was the one Mrs. Hennessy had told me about. I laid my hand on the rail and looked back to the green log, glistening in the golden light. There was no one to dare me; no Dinny to shout 'It 's as easy as easy! Folly me!' Yet I turned, ran to the green slippery log, and crawled across it on hands and knees, my head poked through the handle of the basket. The green slime clung to me and the front of my frock was dirty. But I danced along the bank, past the plank bridge, out to a boreen between stone walls neatly topped. I had crossed by a log bridge and felt so brave I climbed on the wall nearest the stream, and walked slowly along, my hands outstretched. I was sorry for Dinny left behind in Cork, while I was travelling the world. If only he could see me now!

The well-built wall stopped suddenly and I looked down upon heaps of stone and blackened timbers. A fire-place gaped, without a chimney, and a window space looked from a fragment of wall. The ground had dropped and lay so far below I shut my eyes. I couldn't go on, I couldn't go back, I couldn't jump down.

I opened my eyes. Nothing had changed. High overhead a huge bird drifted with widespread wings. If I had wings I wouldn't be in such a fix. The basket slipped from my fingers and, bouncing against the wall, landed right side up in the long grass. Carefully I sat down. I lay across the wall and searched for a foothold with my toes. Slowly, scraping my knees, I clambered down. As my feet touched the grass a voice called, and there was Bridie coming from the other side of the ruins, a basket on each arm.

'Aren't ye the limb!' she cried. 'I've been hunting the village. And then I thought mebbe Francis Joseph told ye the short cut. Was that the way of it?'

I nodded.

'An' me plannin' to buy ye a Peggy's Leg in Judy Leahy's!' said Bridie.

'Oh, Bridie! I love Peggy's Leg!'

Bridie laughed.

'There, Tricia, we'll visit Judy before ye go back. But look at the frock! Tricia, ye never crossed the log bridge?'

'I did!' I declared proudly.

'Ye might have tumbled in and deſtroyed yerself!' cried Bridie. 'Ye little ſtrap!'

My toes were sore, my knees scraped. But I didn't care. No one had ever before called me a limb or a little ſtrap!

We crossed Cassidy's fields. On the bank a scarecrow in a green coat with a gun on his shoulder kept guard.

'That's a shocking fierce scarecrow, Bridie,' I whispered.

'Not fierce enough!' declared Bridie. 'Will ye look at that!'

A cloud of birds flew up, and one of them perched on the scarecrow's head, its tail going up and its head down as if it made a mock of the scarecrow.

'That's a bold bird!' I said indignantly.

Bridie laughed.

'I never heard tell of a crow that wasn't bold. Now who'd want to be a farmer?'

We climbed the bank and at the far side of the meadow ſtood a farmhouse with golden walls, its back to the road and the mountains.

## 8. O'CALLAGHANS

O'CALLAGHANS was a grand farm! The thatched roof came down so low over the yellow walls I could almost reach it when I stood on tiptoe. Windows poked out from the straw and Bridie showed me which was her window, which the boys', the attic, and the old granny's. There were other windows on the far side of the house, but we didn't see them. By a green pond inside the gate six ducks were resting on the flat wet stones. One with a green head and a yellow bill slid in and out of the water, quacking every time it made a splash.

'That's Mr. Drake showing off,' said Bridie.

The door was open and we went into a big dark kitchen. The hearth was so large the glowing fire had as much turf piled on it as would serve Aunt Kattie for a week. Four big pot ovens stood in a row among the hot ashes and a great black kettle swung steaming in the chimney. When my eyes were used to the faint light I could see long pieces of bacon hanging from the rafters. The more I looked the more I saw, and up along with the bacon dangled flat dried fish, ghostly white, nets of brown onions, rolls of spiced beef, and queer bundles in brown sacking.

'That's a grand way to keep the food,' I declared. 'I'll tell me Aunt Kattie.'

'What name is on the strange child?' asked a sharp voice from the chimney corner.

A tiny woman, wrapped in a black shawl, was perched on the settle. To my amazement I saw she was smoking a short clay pipe.

'Her name is Tricia Lynch,' said Bridie, drawing me over to the settle. 'You remember, surely, Granny? She lives on Fair Hill, over in Cork city.'

The old woman held her pipe in her hand and gazed at me.

'So ye're Tighe Lynch's grand-daughter! Ah, he was the grand lad! A champion hurler of Munster and he only a slip of a lad when he went out wid the Fenians. 'Twas in Cork gaol they put him and I was the young gerrul that poked him in a long toffee-stick through the bars. Ah, them was the times. God be wid the old days!'

'He's writing a book!' I said proudly.

'Whisha, a book!' cried the old woman scornfully.

'A history book!' I told her. 'All in poetry and Irish!'

Now she was impressed.

'D'ye tell me?' she said. 'And for why d'ye stare so?'

'I've never seen an old lady smoke a pipe,' I answered.

''Tis a great comfort,' said the old woman. 'A pipe and a good fire of dry turf and a cup of strong, swate tay—what could be better?'

'There's apples and Peggy's Leg!'

'There is indade, and they're grand for a girsha like yerself. And be that same token—Bridie! When ye're down in the village—get two Peggy's Legs, one for me and one for the child. Now, where are ye taking her?'

'Me mother will be wanting to see her,' said Bridie, giving me a pull.

'Ah, well, and why wouldn't she? Nora Lynch's little gerrul! And it seems only yesterday Nora herself was a child and she here talking to me. But she was like yerself, Bridie, mad for the cities and no wish at all for the country. Tricia, are you like that?'

I stood silent. I wasn't sure. I loved Cork and my mother lived there. But there was so much more to see in the country.

'Bridie said there'd be little turkeys in the orchard, I whispered.

'Ah, God help her! Sure she's given her answer!' chuckled old Mrs. O'Callaghan. 'Go along, Tricia, and remember when ye're rale old—a pipe, a settle, and a cup of tay!'

'Come to me mother in the dairy,' said Bridie.

I looked back and saw the old woman picking up pieces of hot turf with a long iron tongs and packing them on the lids of the pot ovens—they called them 'bastables' at the O'Callaghans.

'The men will come in starving for their dinners,' Bridie told me. 'Farming's hard work, Tricia!'

We went into a wide yard. A red-roofed barn stretched along one side and a haystack rose next the turf pile. We had to step carefully, for slender white hens, elegant and quick; fat, speckled ones; comfortable brown hens and long-legged chickens were everywhere, pecking and scratching. I wanted to stay, but Bridie hurried me past a sty where pigs lifted their pink snouts and grunted at us.

'I hate pigs!' said Bridie. 'Their eyes are so mean.'

I liked the way they grunted. But we went on to a stone building sunk in the ground. We jumped down a flight of steps, shaded by an elderberry-tree with its white circles of blossom, fragrant and noisy with bees. A grey

cat stretched in the shade of the elder and a black kitten
played with her tail, while she washed a grey one very like
herself. Two black-and-white kittens sat up, boxing, and
I was so delighted I sat down to watch them.

'You wouldn't want me mother to think you 'd sooner
look at a lot of silly kittens than talk to her?' asked Bridie.

She pushed a door and we stepped into a long, low room.
The walls were stone, the floor was stone, and I think the
roof was stone too. A woman with curly red hair like
Bridie's, but bigger and more serious, was turning the handle
of a churn. A tall girl in a white pinafore was beating
butter into rolls at a long table and a smaller girl squatted
on the floor, counting eggs from a big basket into little boxes.

'Here she is, mammy!' called Bridie. 'Here 's little
Paddy Lynch!'

I remembered how my mother hated pet names or nick-
names.

'Tricia Nora Lynch!' I corrected. 'From Fair Hill.'

'Ye dote!' cried Mrs. O'Callaghan. 'Come over to me
and give me a hug, and tell me all the news!'

I went to her and as she kissed me I saw the two girls
had stopped working to smile over their shoulders.

'Good day, Mrs. O'Callaghan,' I said. 'I hope I find
you well.'

'And how is yer mammy?' asked Mrs. O'Callaghan.
'Did ye ever hear her talk of me? We were at school
together when we were young. Over in foreign parts it
was. And her cousin Kate was with us.'

'She didn't talk of you, Mrs. O'Callaghan,' I said. 'But
she told me all about Bridie and how she put too much
salt in the butter and she 'd sooner hear a donkey singing
in the moonlight than go to the opera in Cork!'

Mrs. O'Callaghan leaned over the churn to laugh. Bridie
sat on the table and the two other girls laughed until they
choked.

'If that don't beat all!' gasped Mrs. O'Callaghan. 'That Nora's a villain. But 'twas me, pet, she meant. Ye see, I'm Bridie too. And when ye're all back home again, tell her I'll make butter the way she wants if she'll watch me churning it. But you shall have a roll without the least speck of salt and you shall make it yourself.'

Bridie taught me to churn. I held the handle and, her hands guiding mine, churned my first butter. I beat it into a roll with two wooden bats dipped in water. Mine would not go round and smooth like those piled on the table but was thin in one place and thick in another. The girl in the white pinafore offered to shape it for me, but I wouldn't agree.

'It's my roll!' I said.

I let her mark my name before she wrapped the mis-shapen little roll in clean, thin muslin and laid it in Mrs Hennessy's basket with the eggs.

'Will you stay here with me, Tricia, when Bridie runs off to America and leaves the O'Callaghans without a daughter?' asked Mrs. O'Callaghan.

'I looked at her laughing face and friendly eyes. I thought of the hens and the pigs, the cows over the fence, the cat and the kittens in the yard. If only Fair Hill could be at the top of the road, how happy I would be, for then I'd have everything in the world! But Fair Hill was miles away.

'Me Aunt Kattie is saving up to go to America,' I told them. 'She's saving in the tea-caddy, the middle part.'

'How much has she saved?' asked Mrs. O'Callaghan.

'Seventeen shillings, four pennies, and one halfpenny. She counted it last Saturday.'

'How long has she been saving?' Bridie wanted to know.

The girl in the white pinafore never stopped beating the butter. But the little one forgot all about the eggs while she listened.

'Ever since I can remember!' I answered.

'There you are, Bridie!' cried Mrs. O'Callaghan. 'And she's years older than you!'

'Some must go!' exclaimed Bridie impatiently.

'They do!' I assured her. 'They come down Fair Hill, and Dinny and me go to the boat and wave, and some of them cry.'

'They're the ones who don't want to go!' she explained. 'But I do! Every time me passage money is ready something happens—the best milker dies, or the farm needs a new plough, or a horse, or a shed, or the roof of the barn is blown off!'

'You'll make Tricia think you don't love your home,' sighed Mrs. O'Callaghan.

Bridie tossed back her red hair.

'But I do!' she said fiercely. 'I do! Only I want America as well.'

'You'd best be taking out the buttermilk,' her mother told her.

Bridie carried the buttermilk in a big white jug, so heavy she had to walk slowly with it. Mrs. O'Callaghan gave me a basket with six tumblers lying on their sides and I followed Bridie up the steps, across the yard into a meadow. A narrow path had been trampled across one corner, and on each side the grass, spangled with flowers, stood up tall and thick. The sun drew out a sweet honey scent, but as I trod in Bridie's footsteps another scent overpowered this. I shut my eyes and felt waves of hot fragrant air sweeping against my face.

'Bridie O'Callaghan!' roared a voice. 'I'm parched wid the drought!'

I opened my eyes and hurried. The meadow sloped. Below me a giant of a man was making great cuts into the standing grass with a shining, curved scythe. One moment the grass stood high and proud. Then it lay in sweeps behind him. In the next meadow, where the grass was all cut, following one after the other, came three young men, tall as the older reaper, but not so broad. Two tossed the grass with broad forks, the third drew it into little heaps with a wooden rake.

'Buttermilk!' called Bridie.

The young men flung down their tools and came striding towards us. The older man laid his scythe carefully on a heap of grass.

'Here's Patricia Nora Lynch from Fair Hill, Cork!' said Bridie, laughing. 'And for pity's sake don't call her Pat or she'll murder you!'

''Tis bad manners making game of a visitor, Bridie!' said the big man. 'Ye're welcome, Tricia. Sit down here beside me and tell me how are they all at home. These lads are Tim, and Michael, and James. But don't mind them.'

They shook hands with me and we sat on the grass. They were burnt brown with the sun and they drank the glasses of buttermilk at one draught. I sipped mine, for I didn't like the queer, sour taste.

'Did you never drink buttermilk before?' asked Bridie. I shook my head.

'Aunt Kattie mixes the soda bread with it. But we don't drink buttermilk,' I told her.

They all looked very serious as if they had never heard of such queer ways before, but as I sipped and sipped, I began to enjoy the cold, sharp taste, and when my tumbler was empty I held it out for more.

'That's the girl!' said Mr. O'Callaghan.

I told the news over again. When they heard about the letter from my father they looked at one another very gravely.

'Isn't it the world's pity when a man can't stay in his own country!' said Mr. O'Callaghan, turning his tumbler upside down.

'There's something to be said for seeing more of the world than lies between here and Bantry!' muttered James, the youngest of the boys.

'Say it!' ordered his father.

James rubbed his head and looked away. Then I knew Bridie wasn't the only O'Callaghan who wanted to go to America.

'If the two of them went they'd be company, Mr. O'Callaghan!' I said.

'Take that child out of me sight!' exclaimed Mr. O'Callaghan, laughing. 'Is she a changeling, or what?'

He stood up, a mountain of a man, with dark thick hair, and brown heavy eyes. Two of his sons were like him. James had Bridie's red hair and freckled face.

We went back with the empty jug and the glasses. When we came in sight of that golden farmhouse and saw the blue smoke rising from the chimney and a great grey dog rushed barking to meet us, I wondered how Bridie could have the heart to leave it. I had a cup of tea and a cut of hot plum cake with the old woman. I sat on the settle beside her and she told me the way things were when she was young.

'Sure we knew black hunger then,' she said. 'As ye go back home to Brigid Hennessy's, when ye cross the wall, let ye look along to the south and ye'll see a great black bare mountain filling the sky—Hungry Mountain they call it, and 'tis there I was reared. Put more sugar in yer tay, pet. 'Tis gran' tay—a mouse could dance on it—gran' tay! An' sugar was sixpence the pound, God help us!'

Bridie took me back by the road. The village was just round the corner from the farm, but you wouldn't know you were there until you were in it. The lane had a bank on each side, topped by a stone wall. All along the bank grew yellow flowers, glistening as if they were polished every morning, white ones like stars, blue pincushions, and sturdy purple bells climbed and crowded. The dark mountains folded on one another, and the lane, white and dusty, marched right into them. A narrow stream trickled at the foot of the bank until suddenly it spread out under a wide bridge and there was the village. I heard the clanging of iron on iron, looked up, and, through a horse-shoe doorway, saw the smith, his shirt sleeves rolled above his elbows, hammering a horse-shoe, scattering sparks at every blow. A fire gleamed behind him and, his head deep in his nosebag, a pleasant solid horse stood munching. At one side of the doorway sprawled a white cat, at the other side a white dog sat bolt upright, its ears pricking, and there wasn't a speck on either of them! I went towards the cat but never reached her, for my eyes, wandering about this strange place, discovered Judy Leahy's shop.

In the middle of the village was a three-cornered island, the forge at one corner, a grocer's at the other, and Judy's at the point looking up the main street. The cabins were whitewashed, with thatched roofs. Before every door sat a dog, and cats lay comfortably on the window sills. Men, caubeens tilted over their eyes, leaned against the walls, and women, sitting on low stools, looked out from their half-doors.

I knew Judy's shop without Bridie telling me, and I knew the sharp little face peering at us through the thick glass was Judy's. I was acquainted with every huckster's shop on the north side of Cork, but Judy's was better than any of them. The little square window was so crowded with toys and lucky packets it was no use at all as a window, but the door opened right back and the sun streamed in, showing the walls, the counter, the space in front, the shelves at the back crowded with bottles, jars, boxes. The ceiling was hidden by cards with little bottles and packets stuck on to them. I looked about me in wonder.

Dolls sat on heaps of apples, ships sailed across a sea of
Peggy's Leg and toffee-apples; boxes of bricks, boxes of
tin soldiers, boxes of wooden furniture were piled on story
books and picture papers. Packets of playing cards mingled
with bunches of carrots and gleaming oranges. A block of
shining brown dates was almost hidden beneath a heap of
lemons. Reels of cotton had fallen down into a barrel of
apples, and potatoes rolled across the floor. Skeins of wool
hung on a rod, and poked through them were knitting
needles and crochet hooks. Sugar-sticks and brandy balls
glistened in tall glass jars and, on the counter, blue bags of
sugar, packets of tea and cocoa leaned against a great slab
of salt. Standing at the counter, so small she could have
rested her chin on it, was a little wizened woman with
peering eyes, Judy Leahy.

'Two Peggy's Legs, two oranges, and a box of furniture,
Judy,' said Bridie. 'Here's Tricia Lynch from Cork.
She's staying with Mrs. Hennessy.'

'Didn't I see her wid me own two eyes comin' down
through the village in the middle of the night on Peadar
Keeley's turf cart? Dead asleep she was!'

'How did you see her? Weren't you sound asleep in
your bed?' demanded Bridie.

'An' if I was, Bridie O'Callaghan, haven't I the windy
over me bed? There isn't much goes on in these parts,
night or day, widout Judy Leahy larnin', me lassyo!'

'I don't doubt it!' said Bridie scornfully, as Judy put
down three boxes of dolls' furniture on the counter.

'Choose!' said Bridie. 'Blue, green, or yellow!'

'A present!' I cried, and chose at once.

'Green was me favourite colour too!' sighed Judy
''Tis the fairy colour an' 'tis that has me the way I am.
'Deed! If I'd only chosen blue, or mebbe yella!'

'Are you sure you want green?' asked Bridie.

I was sure. I was delighted to have any of the sets, but

the tiny green chairs, table, and dresser were lovely. As we went out of the shop I carried the cardboard box of furniture, a Peggy's Leg, and an orange. I had to let Bridie carry the basket with the eggs and my roll of butter. Judy Leahy's voice followed us.

'Ye 'll be takin' the young one to the Fair on the Saturday, Bridie?'

'The Fair!' I cried, tumbling down the two steps into the roadway with excitement. 'Does she mean a real Fair?'

## 9. TO THE FAIR

So much happened the days must have been very long, yet when Mrs. Hennessy said it was time for me to be in my bed I couldn't believe her. She'd show me the sun low in the west before I felt sure she wasn't joking. Every morning I went up to the farm for the milk in a round tin can with a lid. One day Mrs. O'Callaghan taught me to milk the red cow Molly. To please her I pretended to like milking, but I much preferred helping to make butter or feeding the pigs and fowl. There were three young calves, two red and one quite black. I held the bucket while they gobbled and breathed hard until the last drop of their feed was finished. The little turkeys in the orchard had their grown-up relations with them and one old cock turkey was so spiteful I was scared even when Francis Joseph carried me past them on his shoulder.

Soon I knew all Judy Leahy had in her shop better than any of the village children. She let me make the twisted pokes of newspaper and tidy the shelves, and every time I went in for a Peggy's Leg or a lucky bag she gave me a bull's-eye—the only sweet she ate. She told me about her young days when she lived on the far side of the mountain,

63

where from the door of her mother's cabin she could see the great ships going west or south and fleets of fishing boats with red and brown sails. Yet she never tasted fish until she came to live in the village, and then only the salt fish dried on the rocks. She liked drisheens best of all, and though at Fair Hill we often had drisheens for dinner, when Aunt Kattie was in a hurry, I never tasted such drisheens as Judy Leahy's.

I was impatient to go to the Fair and I began to wonder if Saturday hadn't come and gone without any one saying a word. We had eaten our dinner—a meat pudding boiled in a cloth, dished up with white turnips and mashed potatoes—and I was nibbling an apple and listening to Mrs. Hennessy telling a story of the lost silver mine, when I heard a horse and cart coming down the boreen. Whatever happened when Mrs. Hennessy was telling a story no one bothered. But this time she stopped.

' 'Tis Mr. O'Callaghan coming to take Tricia to the Fair,' she said, as calmly as if she told me Francis Joseph was bringing the water or the kettle was boiling.

'The Fair!' I cried.

'The Fair!' repeated Mrs. Hennessy.

'It must be Saturday!' I declared, jumping up so hastily I bumped my head hard against the wall. I didn't stop to rub it, but off with me down the path to the gate. There was Mr. O'Callaghan sitting up in a side-car far above my head. The horse drawing it, the biggest brown horse I had ever seen, looked over the gate and snorted at me.

'Bridie's taking the short cut,' said Mr. O'Callaghan. 'So you'll have time to put on your cape and bonnet and say farewell.'

'But I will be coming back, Mr. O'Callaghan, won't I?' I asked anxiously.

The horse snorted again and Mr. O'Callaghan folded his arms.

'Sure, child, when ye set out on a journey, who can tell if ye 'd ever come back again? Isn't that what I 'm always after telling Bridie? But sure, where 's the use?'

'Oh, that 's America!' I told him, and went in cheerfully to put on my coat.

Francis Joseph was standing ready, his fiddle under his arm, and Mr. Hennessy was buttoning up his thick tweed coat. Mrs. Hennessy held out my coat, but I was so excited I couldn't get my hands in the sleeves until the third try.

'Aren't you coming, Mrs. Hennessy?' I asked, for she was still wearing her indoor slippers and her cloak hung on the peg. She laughed.

'Sure, I 'll be wanted over yonder to help wid the ceilidhe.'

'A ceilidhe!' I cried. 'Where?'

'At O'Callaghans, pet. And don't vex yerself. Ye 'll be in on it!'

I asked no more questions. I couldn't talk. A Fair and a ceilidhe in one day! It was almost too much. I didn't wait for Francis Joseph but ran out and swung back the gate.

'Isn't Bridie here yet, Mr. O'Callaghan? We 'll be late!'

'Hold the gate, child, while I back in the mare, and keep away from her heels or ye 'll be murdered. Betsy Grey 's nearly as impatient as yerself.'

I hadn't realized that this was Betsy Grey towering above me, for at work on the farm she seemed only half the size. Now I saw how high the side-car was from the road and suddenly I wished I was staying with Mrs. Hennessy. There was no frightening stairs down here, no Aunt Hannah to tease me, but I knew there were terrors everywhere. I couldn't sit up on that side-car! I couldn't!

'Up ye go!' said Francis Joseph, swinging me into the air. 'Hold tight, now!'

I sat sideways, clutching the rail.   Looking straight ahead
I couldn't see the ground, only the mare's body between
the shafts, but when I turned my head there was the ground
so far below I felt dizzy and shut my eyes.   Mr. Hennessy
came out, a shawl round his neck and a new green caubeen
pulled low over his eyes.   I expected Francis Joseph to
help him, but the blind man put his foot on the iron step,
caught hold of the rail, and pulled himself up.   He moved
along and sat beside me.   Bridie, breathless from running,
came scrambling over the wall.

'There's the short cut for ye!' chuckled Francis Joseph,
tucking a thick rug round us, and was going to climb in
next to Mr. O'Callaghan when Wolf, the big grey dog,
leaped over the wall and tried to get in with Bridie.

'Now, Bridie, ye know well ye can't have that wild animal
in the car,' her father warned her.   'Betsy Grey wouldn't
stand for it.'

'I didn't tell him to come!' protested Bridie.   'But you
know he loves a drive!'

'Let the poor crathure sit between the child and me,'
urged Mr. Hennessy.   ''Twill keep Tricia safe in her seat
and Betsy Grey will never know what's going on behind
her.'

'Ah, well,' said Mr. O'Callaghan.

Wolf put his forepaws on the car and whined.   Francis
Joseph lifted the dog's hind legs and up he scuffled, sitting
underneath our legs so that he was like a cushion.   Francis
Joseph took a piece of rope from his pocket, tied it to the
back of the seat, drew it across me, and made a knot on
the other side.

'Now ye'll not fall off!' he declared.   'And ye're not
afeard of old Wolf, are ye?'

I wasn't afraid of anything now.   I shook my head.

'He's a lovely dog, Francis Joseph.'

He gave Bridie his fiddle to hold while he stepped in.

Mrs. Hennessy came to the gate and waved a towel as the mare tossed her head and trotted carefully down the boreen. Once on the road, Betsy Grey galloped. My tammy came off, but Bridie caught it. At every turn and twist my feet swung out.

'It 's like flying!' I told Mr. Hennessy.

We came to a cross-roads and here I knew we really were going to the Fair. A flock of sheep spread before us, heads of bullocks tossed in a wave as they marched at the heels of the sheep, and, along the other roads, more sheep and bullocks, carts, men on horseback, girls and boys on bicycles, were swarming towards us. Betsy Grey went slowly. I was very proud to be looking down on sheep and bullocks and sitting on the same level as crates of hens and ducks piled on yokes. I peered over the sides of wagons where pink, grunting bonaveens lay on straw with nets stretched above them.

'Won't we be late for the Fair?' I asked, as cows with calves filled the roadway.

''Twill be only getting into its stride,' Mr. Hennessy told me. We were in the mountains and the road was rising at every step. Rocks leaned out over our heads and furze blazed golden in the sunshine. Amid a patch of purple heather, a goat with a white kid, standing up against the sky, gazed down at us.

'Will ye look!' said Mr. Hennessy. 'Yonder is the Deer's Leap.'

I looked up at the towering walls of rock.

''Twas long ago,' Mr. Hennessy told me. 'And a deer was being hunted. It raced the hounds on the roads and took to the mountains. A wild crathure will always do that. It followed the river, but they cut across and when it thought 'twas safe and sound and its troubles over, up on the wind came the cry of the hounds. They caught up to it at the edge of the rocks and, thinks they, 'tis the end of the hunt, when the deer rose in the air and leaped to safety, for there wasn't a horse or a hound could folly it. And to this day they call it the Deer's Leap.'

I wondered at the deer flying across that space and squeezed closer to Mr. Hennessy.

'That was a brave deer. I'm glad he got away,' I whispered.

'I'm terrible glad,' said Mr. Hennessy.

Wolf poked out his head. When he saw another dog he whined or barked and shuffled uneasily, and then Betsy Grey tossed her head and neighed with indignation.

'There were dogs like Wolf in Ireland in the ancient times,' said Mr. Hennessy. 'Finn MacCool and Oisin and all them lads went hunting with them.'

I wanted to tell Mr. Hennessy all I had heard from my mother about the ancient heroes only Bridie was singing *The Jackets Green* and I had to listen.

Below were the roofs of a town and a great open space crowded with stalls and carts and a multitude of people. The road dipped, twisted, and ran across a low stone bridge. Betsy Grey trotted gaily, her hoofs rattled on the stones. The roadway was crowded; the pavements were crowded; shops were on each side of us and I saw one with an open front filled with red cabbages—round and glowing like enormous roses. The mare swung up a side street and stopped so suddenly I fell sideways. Wolf barked and Bridie screamed.

Mr. O'Callaghan jumped down.

'Well, I've brought yez here and, plaze God, I'll take yez all back. Good luck to the Fair!'

## 10. LOST

WE stood in the roadway with Wolf scampering to the corner and back again, jumping at Bridie, and barking until Mr. O'Callaghan threatened him.

'Now weren't ye the foolish girl, Bridie, to bring that animal!' he grumbled. 'Ye daren't take him into the Fair. He'd as well stay with me. There's a plough I want to see about. Will ye be happy with Bridie and the child, Mr. Hennessy?'

'I will, indeed!' replied the blind man cheerfully.

He let me carry the market bag he had brought and away we went, Wolf whining to come too. I was sorry for the poor dog when I looked back and saw his mournful expression. Mr. O'Callaghan beckoned and I ran to him hoping he meant to let me bring Wolf, but instead he gave me a sixpence.

'Wasn't I young meself once?' he asked. 'And don't I know well there's no pleasure or comfort in a Fair widout a penny piece in yer pocket.'

This was my first sixpence—and it was a lucky sixpence, with a hole in it! Uncle Liam gave me a penny every

time he saw me and Aunt Kattie let me keep all the farthings.
But sixpence! Bridie tied it in a corner of my handkerchief
to keep it safe and I could feel the coin there, hard and
round. I looked in all the shops as we went down to the
market-place, for I didn't want to spend my money until
I had seen every shop in the town and every stall in the Fair.

Most of the sheep and cattle had been sold earlier in the
day, but a few bargains were still being made and I heard the
slapping of hands as buyer and seller agreed. A dozen
sheep were in one of the pens, and as I stopped to look
they raised their heads and baaed at me. Next a young
sow was rooting in a trough, grunting with satisfaction.
Bridie caught my hand.

'Sure we didn't come all the way to Bantry Fair to look
at sheep and pigs! And you're not a farmer wanting to
buy stock, Tricia Lynch!'

But she couldn't pass three little calves who looked at
her and called plaintively. They took turns at sucking our
fingers and I know Bridie was sorry to go away from them.
The stalls were in rows with narrow lanes between. I
wished Francis Joseph would let me ride on his shoulder
so that I could look over the people's heads, but he wasn't
staying with us.

'There's money in this Fair!' he said to Bridie. 'I'm
for wheedling some of it into me own pockets wid this fiddle.
Have a good time now. I'll be seeing yez!'

'Sure he couldn't have ye on his shoulder an' he playin'
the fiddle,' Mr. Hennessy told me, as if he knew what I had
been thinking.

'Keep close to us, Tricia!' Bridie warned me. 'This is
a terrible crowded Fair.'

It wasn't easy to keep beside Bridie. She didn't walk
like an ordinary person, but her feet danced even when she
was standing in one spot. We stopped to listen to an old
man singing *The Old Bog Road*. I watched Bridie's face

growing sad as she heard about the emigrant in America thinking of his mother at home. A sulky boy with a cap too big for him stood beside the ballad singer, selling green and red song sheets.

'I 'll have two,' said Bridie, holding out sixpence.

'I 've no change!' growled the boy.

'I want two of each,' Bridie told him impatiently. 'Two green, two red! That 's sixpence, and no change asked for.'

'Why didn't you say so!' snapped the boy, snatching the sixpence before he would let her take the sheets.

'You 're a bold, rude boy!' I said under my breath, wishing I had the courage to say it out loud. I forgave the boy when Bridie folded a green sheet inside a red one and gave them to me.

'Now you can learn all the songs,' she told me. 'Hurry up and learn to read before you lose the sheets!'

'Oh, I will, Bridie!' I promised. 'I will!'

Mr. Hennessy hummed the sorrowful ballad as we pushed through the crowd. Neither he nor Bridie glanced at the strong man, but I clung to their hands so that they stopped.

'He 's as big as me father!' said Bridie. 'He 's a lovely man!'

The strong man was draped in a spotted fur rug, with bare arms and legs. His fair curly hair was rough and his face streaked with dirt. Above his head he held a bicycle with a big boy sitting on it. First he held the bicycle with two hands, then with one. Slowly he lowered it to the ground and the boy stepped off, looking very proud.

'Now I 'll do something a bit harder!' said the strong man. 'Come along, half a dozen of you, and take a seat.'

He pointed to a small wooden bench which stood against the wall. I tried to tug Bridie forward. But she held me back and no one else moved. The strong man stood with his clenched fists on his hips.

'Ye 're an oncomin' lot, so y' are!' he jeered. 'There 's a fine strapping lad wid the slane on his shoulder! Come along, me young turf-cutter, and rest yerself!'

The tall boy with the brown face and staring eyes strode over and settled himself on the bench, a bald, bearded man followed, then a small man, no bigger than a boy, and the seat was crowded.

'That 's as heavy a load as I 've handled yet,' said the strong man. 'An' me cap 's still empty!'

He picked up his cap from the ground and shook it in our faces. Mr. Hennessy gave him a penny, so did Bridie. I felt my lucky sixpence and wished I had two. The people were generous and soon the strong man was satisfied. He emptied his cap into a leather bag and walked up and down in front of the men on the bench. They began to laugh at him. Suddenly he stooped, seized the legs of the bench, and, inch by inch, raised it from the ground—as high as his waist, to his shoulders, on a level with his head. His face was red, sweat poured down his cheeks, and his mouth twisted. The crowd cheered and flung pennies on the ground. Some threw threepenny and sixpenny pieces.

'This isn't the Fair!' said Bridie, and we pushed on.

Pedlars, with trays slung from their necks, sold packets of pins and needles, thimbles, studs; girls with a bucket of water and a tray of tumblers were calling: 'Fizz drink! Fizz drink, white or pink—halfpenny and penny the glass!' Musicians played fiddles, mouth-organs, melodeons; tinker women with lazy, drawly voices cried: 'Tell yer fortune! Tell yer lucky fortune!' There were games of chance and throwing rings on hooks to win prizes. I wanted to try them all but I wouldn't risk my sixpence. One stall had toys all made of wood. There was a Noah's Ark painted green with a red roof and a white dove sitting on the chimney. Noah, in a yellow robe, stood at one side, and Mrs. Noah, in a blue frock, at the other. Their children, all painted yellow, and the animals, were in a heap. I could only make out the elephant and the giraffe, who had green spots.

'I 'll have that!' I said, pointing.

Bridie wasn't listening. Her eyes were on a stall where a woman, with a plaid shawl over her head, was selling dresses.

'Look at the gorgeous green one!' cried Bridie. 'I must have it. I 'm ashamed to go dancing in me old one!'

'Is it the American money ye 'd be spending?' asked Mr. Hennessy.

'Indeed I would not!' said Bridie.

So we went on past the dresses. I stopped at a cart loaded with the old dingy kind of books my grandfather read, but standing proudly in the middle was a green-and-gold story book with a mermaid on the cover. Wouldn't it be grand to go home with that under my arm, even if I couldn't read?

'Bridie!' I called. 'I 'm buying the story book.'

But Bridie was fingering the stockings at the next stall.

'They 're so thick!' she grumbled. 'Nearly as thick as the ones my mother knits. When I make me fortune in America I 'll never wear anything but silk! silk! silk!'

'Even wid silk from top to toe, ye 'd be desprit lonesome in America!' Mr. Hennessy told her.

They stood with me while I admired the shell necklaces. There were all kinds of necklaces on that stall, rings, too, and bracelets—with red, green, blue, and yellow stones blazing in the sunlight. But the shell necklaces were the best.

'One for me mother; one for Mrs. Hennessy!' I almost decided.

Still I didn't want to part with my lucky sixpence—yet! I wanted to see all the Fair, though I was tired of being pushed and poked. My head had been knocked by market baskets. It was sore, even though I pulled my tammy right over my ears.

'I'm thinking we'd all be the better for a cup o' tay an' a cut of hot apple cake!' said Mr. Hennessy. 'That's a powerful great smell of cloves!'

We sat on a bench beside a turf fire kept in place by stones where a big woman with a red face and short black hair was making tea. A thin little fellow, with shoulders so hunched his head was sunk between them, was heating an apple cake on a frying-pan. When it was hot he tipped it out on a box, sprinkled white sugar on the crust, and cut three pieces. The cake wasn't as good as the one Bridie had made in the pot oven, but I ate every bit, crumbs and all. It was grand to be sitting there watching the Fair and looking out at the harbour where a steamer was being unloaded at the pier. I saw a crate rising from the hold and slowly, slowly dropping down on to a waiting cart. A distant boat with a red sail was tossing as it met the ocean swell, and row boats, like spiders walking on the water, were travelling to and from the island. Little waves danced and glittered, and sea-gulls came screaming overhead. I wondered what they thought of the Fair. What fun it would be if a sea-gull swooped down and snatched a necklace, or Mr. Noah, or the green silk dress Bridie wanted.

'But that would be stealing!' I reminded myself.

'Mebbe we'd as well be doing the shopping, Bridie,' said Mr. Hennessy.

'I'll not be forgetting,' replied Bridie.

Yet we sat on with the sun warming our backs and the sea breeze blowing the smoke of the fire away from us, until a woman with two little boys carrying her basket stopped for tea and we gave up our seats.

'Herself's wanting some taycups as well as the bit of tay and sugar,' said Mr. Hennessy, as we pushed and squeezed along by a platform with rolls of stuff standing on end.

The seller had a long piece of flowered cotton draped over his arm and billowing round him. He was a long thin man with a round angry face and fierce blue eyes. His voice rose like a trumpet over all the other sounds.

'Here's the very bit of stuff for a young gerrul's best Sunday frock!' he shouted when he saw Bridie. 'Lookit! Five yards—not a ha'penny more than a shilling a yard! Five shillings for the makin's of a frock that 'll turn every head yer way. Lissen now! Four an' six—three an' six! Wait now—don't be in such a tearin' mad rush! I 'll throw in enough to make a pinny for the chiseller!'

''Tis the green silk or nothing!' muttered Bridie.

She sounded very determined, but she looked wistfully over her shoulder at the gay stuff, so lovely in the clear air. I couldn't pass one stall. It had oranges and apples in rows, rising to a gleaming slab of sticky dates. There were figs, too, in pressed slabs, and nuts and little flat tangerine oranges wrapped in silver paper. There had been two in my stocking at Christmas and I remembered the scented smell and the soft sweet taste.

'Bridie! How many can I buy for sixpence?' I asked.

There was no answer. Bridie wasn't in sight; neither was Mr. Hennessy. They had kept on, thinking me with them, and here was I—alone at the Fair. I left the fruit stall and wriggled and squeezed among the people. I could get along much faster now that I hadn't to keep with the others and I was very pleased. Still I couldn't find Bridie or Mr. Hennessy. I called them but no one answered; no one even looked at me for all the noise I made.

Suddenly I thought of the red cabbages. The oranges in silver paper were delicious, I knew that! The shell necklaces were beautiful. But I had never before seen red cabbages! Surely I 'd be able to buy two for sixpence. I knew Mrs. Hennessy would be proud to have one. I wasn't sure about my mother, but I could see myself bursting into the kitchen at Fair Hill and displaying the red cabbage I had bought with my own money at the Fair. At once I turned and fought my way back. I knew I had to get out of the market-place into the main street. Then up! up! up! I had been told time and again never to walk in the roadway. But I was soon pushed from the pavement. Now I could only see men and women crowding on every side and rising above me like trees in a forest. But these trees did not keep still. They made way only for horses and cattle. Then the nearest people thrust me to one side for safety. I climbed on—up! up! up! At last I managed to scramble back to the pavement and discovered myself outside a sweet shop. The best sweet shops in Cork kept their sweets in boxes and bottles. Dinny and I bought ours in the hucksters' shops at the foot of Fair Hill, where bulls'-eyes, allsorts, Peggy's Leg, Spanish bootlaces, and bars of chocolate cream were mixed up with loaves of bread, apples, and onions. The window of this shop came down so near the footpath that I looked on a bank of coco-nut kisses—pink and white curls with white sugar crystals glistening on them. They were dear sweets—two ounces a penny—and exclusive to Sunday. Striped sugar-sticks, tied in bunches, filled the corners. Spanish bootlaces and ladders hung at the back, and a pile of everlasting toffee-sticks, wrapped in tissue-paper, had mixed sweets on one side and fat, shiny, satin cushions on the other.

My sixpence made me rich. If I bought a farthing's worth of each how many kinds would I have? I didn't bother long about Spanish bootlaces, or toffee-sticks, or satin cushions, for, in the centre of all this luxury, was a white dish and on the dish a huge block of honeycomb toffee—all holes and bubbles, golden, golden-brown, toffee-brown—crisp and rich. I determined to spend the whole sixpence on honeycomb toffee!

I was in the doorway, my foot on the step, when I remem-

bered the red cabbages.  Out I came, swinging the market
bag to show I didn't care.  But I did!  My feet dragging,
my head down, the market bag trailing in the dirt, I walked
on slowly until I bumped into something soft yet un-
yielding.  I looked up at a tousled woman, with a tattered
coat slung over her shoulders, sitting on a broken chair.
Her tangled hair fell over her forehead, and her mocking
eyes made me think of Aunt Hannah.  But in the open
front of the shop behind her were the red cabbages I had
come seeking—round and hard and glowing.  They were
so much lovelier than I had imagined I no longer regretted
the honeycomb.

'I want two red cabbages, please,' I said.  'Big ones!'
'Where's yer money?' snapped the woman.

I knew she didn't believe I had any, but I had my sixpenny piece with the hole in it, tied in the corner of my
handkerchief, and the handkerchief was fastened to my belt.
With my eyes fixed on that jeering face I felt for my handkerchief.  It wasn't there.  I looked down.  Belt, handkerchief, lucky sixpence were all gone.

'I've lost me money!' I cried in horror.

'Sure ye have!' agreed the tousled woman.  'If ye can
lose what ye never had.  Now go down the main street
the way ye came up an' don't never again be after en-
deavourin' to chate a dacent, hardworkin' widda wumman
of her red cabbages!'

I wept as I toiled down the hill, but I kept a sharp watch
for my shiny belt and the red-and-white handkerchief.
I had been so proud of them and now they were lost and
my lucky sixpence with them.  I heard kind voices asking
what ailed me.  I couldn't tell them.  Grief and disappoint-
ment so bewildered me I couldn't see where I was going;
I could only blunder on and on, seeking Bridie and Mr.
Hennessy.

An angry hiss close to my face made me stop.  I had

reached the far side of the Fair near the harbour wall. Blinking away my tears I saw a fierce gander, its head poked between the bars of a crate, hissing at me. Piled on top and all around were other crates of ducks and hens. In the corner between the pier and the wall a tilt cart was drawn up, the white horse between the shafts munching in a nosebag. On the seat lounged a tall, dark man, smoking a blackened clay pipe while he gazed thoughtfully over the Fair. He was the tinker who had laughed at me and Dinny, the one I had met when I was coming away from Cork with Mrs. Hennessy. I was no longer afraid of him. Among a horde of strangers he was someone I knew, almost a friend. I ran over and clung to the wheel of his cart.

'Tinker!' I called. 'Tinker! I'm lost and I've lost me new shiny belt and me hanky and me lucky sixpence. Find Bridie and Mr. Hennessy. I'm lost!'

He took the pipe from his mouth and stared.

'Find Bridie! I'm lost!' I insisted, beginning to cry all over again.

He scratched his head.

'Come up along out o' that!' he said, and, leaning over caught me by the wrist and hauled me up beside him I didn't like that way of being lifted and I frowned at him while I rubbed my aching wrist.

'Sit up here beside me and cast a glance round the Fair,' he growled. 'Sooner or later ye'll see yer friends. Now, quit screechin'!'

He leaned back and puffed a cloud of smoke over me. I looked over the Fair, but I looked more at the terrifying tinker and wished I had not ventured quite so near. He was brown and cross-looking, and his long, thin face seemed as if it could never smile. Though he sat so still, his bright eyes were restless. I felt they could see what was happening in the harbour at the back of us as well as all that went on in the Fair. The tobacco smoke had a strong stifling smell, but I sniffed another smell which grew more savoury and tempting every moment. I peeped over my shoulder. Below the cart, by the stone steps, an old, old woman, wrinkled and bent, sat singing to herself beside a fire of driftwood. I saw the black saucepan, big as a pot oven, perched on two stones beside the blaze. An appetizing smell of onions, rabbit, and herbs came from it, conquering the odours of stale fish and harbour mud.

'I'm hungry,' I said.

Two boys, crouching in the shelter of the wall, looked up. I hadn't noticed them before and their scowling faces were frightening. I clutched the tinker's sleeve.

'If it's their dinner, I don't want any,' I whispered.

He knocked my hand away.

'Hand up a tin of stew!' he ordered.

'Is it feedin' all the beggar's brats in the Fair ye are?' screamed the old woman.

'Hand it up!' repeated the tinker, while I wiped my eyes on my frock.

Grumbling and muttering, the old woman took an empty tin lying on the ground, and plunging it in the saucepan brought it out steaming and dripping. She hobbled round and held it up to me.

'Beggin' off tinkers!' she snarled. 'Beggin' off tinkers!'

'I'm not begging off tinkers!' I retorted indignantly, and put my hands behind my back.

'Eat the stew!' commanded the tinker.

I took the tin. It was so hot I nearly dropped it.

'Put the can on the seat, ye young eejit, ye!' snapped the tinker. 'Wrap this round it!'

He flung me a rag from the floor of the cart and I managed to hold the tin.

'Here's bread, yer ladyship!' jeered the old woman.

She stretched up her skinny hand, clutching a hunk of white, golden-crusted bread, so fresh it was still warm.

With my fingers and the bread, I managed to eat the ſtew and I drank every drop of the thick gravy.

'Paudeen!' roared the tinker. 'Leg it along to the polis an' tell him there's a young gerrul loſt an' we're carin' her!'

The old woman flung back her head and cackled.

'The polis!' she cried. 'The polis!'

'I'm not loſt now!' I declared. 'Tell the boy to find Bridie and Mr. Hennessy and Francis Joseph and his fiddle and they'll come for me!'

The tinker grinned.

'Will ye liſten to her! The size of her and the way she gives her commands and she sittin' up there like a cock fairy! But the young one's right. Bein' a mitcher she's no fonder of the polis than we are. Off wid ye, Paudeen, an' tell the fiddlin' chap that's playin' in Daly's the little Lynch gerrul is safe be the harbour wall.'

The boy ran off, dodging from cart to cart as if he didn't want to be seen.

'Would ye like to jine us an' be one of Yalla Hankercher's tribe,' asked the tinker without looking at me.

The old woman was eating ſtew. She put down her tin and spluttered with laughter.

'What ails ye now?' growled the man.

'She's a rale dacent little gerrul,' the old woman told him. 'But she'd want a clane pinny every day an' a feather-bed an' a chair to reſt her bones on!'

I saw Francis Joseph ſtriding along paſt the ducks and hens and looking very anxious.

'Francis Joseph!' I called. 'I'm here! I'm not loſt!'

'An' I thought I could truſt Bridie!' he exclaimed, putting an arm round me as I ſtood up in the cart.

'It wasn't her fault!' I told him, and I explained about the red cabbages.

As I spoke, tinkers were gathering from all over the Fair. They came quickly and silently. When I began there were only Yalla Hankercher, the old woman, and Francis Joseph. When I finished a crowd of dark faces with glittering eyes looked up at me. Yalla Hankercher laughed until he was doubled up and the others laughed with him so that I thought the whole town would hear.

'Listen now!' said the dark tinker. 'If ever ye 're tired of houses an' city folk, an' ye want to mitch for good an' all, come an' jine us! Just say "Red cabbage" an' there 'll always be room be the fire an' a helpin' from the pot. Red cabbages!'

I heard him and his followers still laughing as I rode away on Francis Joseph's shoulder.

## 11. NEWS FROM CORK

WE met Bridie and Mr. Hennessy with the tallest policeman I had ever seen. Bridie was crying and Mr. Hennessy was shaking his head sorrowfully, though I could see he was doing his best to be cheerful.

'Here's herself!' roared Francis Joseph. 'No need to call her through the Fair—brown eyes, fair straight hair, red-and-white frock, no belt, no hanky, no lucky sixpence, socks coming down, strap shoes thick with mud! Here she is!'

'Oh, Tricia!' cried Bridie, hugging me. 'What happened you? We were petrified! We're dead with searchin' the Fair! Me Aunt Brigid 'll ate me when she hears!'

'She went huntin' red cabbages,' explained Francis Joseph.

'That one should be wid the tinkers!' said the policeman severely.

'Sure, they're her friends!' Francis Joseph told him. 'She's a wild young one, always strayin'. 'Tis the Spanish strain in her!'

I sat up on his shoulder, looking over the Fair and feeling

quite pleased with all the fuss. How I wished Dinny Foley could see me! But not my mother! She 'd be ashamed of such goings-on.

We had to do Mr. Hennessy's shopping in Mr. Daly's crowded Stores and every one there knew I was the little girl from Cork who had been lost and found by the tinkers.

'They 're a bad lot, tinkers!' declared Mr. Daly, a fat, red-faced man in shirt sleeves and a white apron, leaning across the counter. 'But they do be good to the childer.'

'They stole me mother's washin' on her!' said Bridie.

'Not my tinkers!' I protested. 'It couldn't be them!'

'That 's the gerrul!' cried Mr. Daly, thumping the counter. 'Stand by yer friends!'

He gave me another sixpence to make up for the one I had lost, though this hadn't a hole in it. Mr. Hennessy pulled out all the pennies in his pocket and, when we went from Daly's Stores, I did my marketing. I bought two green enamel mugs, one for Mrs. Hennessy, one for Aunt Kattie. Even then I had enough money to buy Patrick Henry a pencil with a shiny cap and the best shell necklace on the Stall for my mother.

'I 'll not give you a farthin',' Bridie told me. 'But tell me everything you want and you shall have them all!'

I studied her laughing face to see if she really meant this. She did, and I had a banana, a pear, a Peggy's Leg, a Spanish bootlace, and an everlasting Stick. I kept the sweets for Dinny Foley, the banana and the pear I ate, while Mr. Hennessy bought six cups with red tulips on them for Mrs. Hennessy.

The cows and sheep were all gone. So were the pigs. Now the last of the hens and ducks were riding off in their crates with lighted lanterns hanging from the carts. I saw the white-tilted tinkers' cart swaying out of the market-place, a red lantern swinging from the tilt. The tinkers Streeled after it, every one of them loaded. My dark friend was driving and I watched the red light going up the road above the sea until it vanished in the darkness of the mountains. Candles in glass chimneys flickered on the stalls and, at the delph stall, two flares blazed and spluttered, while the man selling tea sets and covered dishes bawled so loudly, people rushed in terror lest they might be missing a great bargain.

Bridie bought a piece of blue stuff for a Sunday coat and the sounds of singing and music and dancing rose from three sides of the square. On the fourth side, beyond the harbour wall, the tide was coming in and the fishermen were clearing their boats.

'When I hear the music and I think of that lovely green silk frock I could cry!' grumbled Bridie.

'Ye 'll look a drame in the blue coat,' Francis Joseph consoled her. 'An' isn't there dancin' waitin' for us and haven't I the music under me arrum?'

My feet were so tired I couldn't lift them: my eyes were closing. A dog charged towards us down the lane of empty stalls and I saw it was Wolf. He was silent until he reached Bridie. Then he barked and whined, raced round and round her, stood on his hind legs, paws on her shoulders, and licked her face. As she coaxed him to stand still a voice hailed us, and there, coming down the main street, was the side-car, with Mr. O'Callaghan smoking a long pipe and looking very contented.

'Up wid ye, Mr. Hennessy!' he said. 'An' will ye hand up the child! She 's droppin' wid the tiredness. The rest of yez can walk the hill.'

Betsy Grey was fresh, and willing to rush the hill. But Mr. O'Callaghan held her back. When we reached the top, Francis Joseph and Bridie clambered in beside us and away we galloped along the dark road. I looked back at the lights. Even when they were out of sight the music followed us. I snuggled close to Bridie. Wolf had his head on her knee, and it was well we kept one another warm, for the night wind was bitter. My eyes closed and I was back at the Fair, looking over the shell necklaces. I put out my hand and took three, one for Bridie, one for Mrs. Hennessy, one for my mother. The woman in charge of the stall was the woman from the red cabbage shop. She made a grab at me and screamed: 'Ye little robber! I'll set the polis on ye!' I kept a tight hold on the necklaces and jumped into the air. Up I went, just above the heads of the people, who were all shouting and trying to catch my feet. I floated over the fruit stall and snatched a whole bunch of bananas. I saw the green silk frock Bridie had admired and, stooping, gathered it up. My feet knocked against the tops of the stalls and, though I tried to fly higher, I couldn't. I stepped on a man's hat. He looked up, laughing, and it was the dark tinker with the yellow handkerchief tied round his head. Suddenly the bananas slipped from my hand. I tried to swoop after them, the way the gulls dive for fish. But I woke with a bump!

'Tricia! We're home!' cried Bridie.

Still I heard music. But it came from the O'Callaghans' kitchen. The white lamplight shone through the windows and the red glow of the fire streamed over the half-door. I was puzzled about the necklaces and the silk frock. Had I dropped them, and when had we left the Fair?

'Sure the child's dramin'!' said Francis Joseph to Bridie. 'I'll slip down wid her an' pop her into her own bed. I'll not be gone above half a minit!'

'No!' I cried. 'No!' For now I was wide awake and knew there was a ceilidhe in O'Callaghans. 'I want Bridie to dance and you play the fiddle, Francis Joseph! I won't go to bed!'

'Why couldn't she lie on the settle?' asked Bridie. 'Hasn't she a right to her share of the fun?'

So into the kitchen I went with them.

That was a real ceilidhe.   A young lad stood up against the dresser playing a melodeon and an old man was drawing such music from a tin whistle I thought it a shame he hadn't a fiddle and a bow.   The place was crowded.   There were old men and women sitting on chairs and benches against the walls: children younger than myself running about with cuts of soda bread and butter; so many boys and girls were dancing, they knocked against one another at every step. But no one minded.   I saw Mrs. Hennessy over by the fire making tea.   Old Mrs. O'Callaghan was still perched on the settle, and when Mr. Hennessy seated himself beside her I followed, for I was shy of so many strangers.   Every one called for Francis Joseph to play.   But he turned to the boy with the melodeon and the old man with the whistle.

'What's wrong wid the three of us knockin' out a bit of a tune?' he asked.

The boy flushed and the old man looked very happy.

'Is it me wid the old box to be playin' alongside Francis Joseph O'Dwyer!' exclaimed the boy.

'Indade we'd be rale proud an' plased to play along wid a musicianer like yerself,' said the old whistler.

'So ye were at the Fair, Tricia?' asked old Mrs. O'Callaghan.   'Sit up here alongside me an' tell me the latest news.'

'Sure the poor child was lost,' Mr. Hennessy told her. 'Listen now!'

I fell asleep while he was telling my adventure at the Fair.   In my sleep I could hear the thumpings and scufflings of the sixteen-handed reel, then the light tapping and sliding of two good dancers.   I half woke to see Bridie and a fair-haired young man dancing up the room.   Mr. Hennessy sang *The Snowy-breasted Pearl* so plaintively I cried myself back to sleep.   When I opened my eyes again, Mrs. Hennessy was sitting in an arm-chair by the fire and luckily she was beginning a story.

'There's some laugh at leprechauns,' she was saying. But I know what I know an' I'm tellin' ye.'

The old people and children listened seriously. The young people were smiling. I heard about old Micky Dooley setting off from Ballincollig to tramp to the Mallow races. He had been walking only half an hour when he overtook an old fellow with a beard down to his knees and a kish of brogues on each arm.

I looked up at the pictures on the walls—'Our Lady and the Holy Family' in gleaming blue and crimson. On the opposite wall were Wolfe Tone, young Robert Emmet, Parnell, and O'Connell side by side. The Hennessys had them too. So had we in the kitchen on Fair Hill.

Once more I fell asleep and, when I woke, the story was ended and Bridie was dancing, this time with another girl as well as the fair-haired boy. A little fat woman with a cup of tea in her hand sat on a creepie close beside me.

'Will ye look at me little gerrul, pet,' she said. 'She's showin' Bridie O'Callaghan how a young gerrul should dance. Sure, if her father was a snug farmer instead of a poor clerk, 'tis me Eileen would be called the best dancer in Cork county!'

'Bridie is the best dancer!' I declared. 'And Francis Joseph plays the best music and Mrs. Hennessy tells the best stories and Mr. Hennessy is the best singer!'

But the fat little woman never heard me.

When the dancers sat down Mrs. Hennessy began another story.

''Twas the time of the Famine, God between us an' harrum,' she said. 'An' a dacent widda woman be the name of Mary Molloy set out from Skibbereen wid her four young childer to go to her brother, a pudden-maker at Killaloe.'

I lost the next part of the story, for Bridie came over to

me with a thick piece of hot drisheen on a cut of bread and I was too busy eating to listen.

'She'll tell me all the stories to meself to-morrow,' I thought comfortably.

Mrs. Hennessy had just brought Mary Molloy and her four children successfully to Killaloe when there was a commotion at the half-door.

'Is it yourself, Peadar Keeley?' cried Mr. O'Callaghan. 'Come in, man, ye're welcome! An' who's this ye have wid ye? Why, Patrick Henry! 'Tis a long time since ye were in these parts! Now who's the little lad? An' how are all on Fair Hill?'

I stood up on the settle so that I could see over the heads. Coming across the crowded room, along with Peadar Keeley, were my brother and Dinny Foley. I was so excited I fell off the settle, bruised my elbow, and scratched my knees. But I had my brother's arm round me and Dinny's red friendly face grinning with delight.

'Is it bad news from Cork, allanna?' asked Mrs. Hennessy. 'Or what brings ye, when ye should be far away on the salt say?'

'It is bad news, but not from Cork,' replied my brother. And every one stopped talking or even moving. 'My father will never come back. He is dead in Egypt! So we shan't be going there now.'

Mrs. Hennessy flung her arms above her head and cried out in sorrow. Then I heard that terrible wail of desolation—the Caoine. One voice after another joined in and Patrick Henry sat there, his face grave and cold.

'Come away, lad!' said Francis Joseph, pulling him to his feet. 'Ye're tired out an' the two childer are terrified. Come away now!'

We went out into the starlit night and, as we came to the road, Mr. Hennessy was with us. He and Dinny and I walked hand-in-hand. Like shadows before us Francis

Joseph and Patrick Henry were visible on the road, then
vanished in the darkness of the banks. As we passed
through, the village was still; not a light showed. A cat
ran swiftly across the street and a dog howled mournfully.
My brother was talking. His voice came back to us—a
muffled whisper, but here and there a word rose clearly.
Dinny stumbled over the stones.

'That's Judy Leahy's shop,' I told him. 'She's me
friend.'

'I want me mammy!' burst out Dinny, and there he was
roaring and lamenting until I was ashamed of him.

'The poor gossoon!' said Francis Joseph, turning back.

He picked Dinny up and set him on his shoulder. Now
I was ashamed of myself, for I was jealous. I didn't want
any one, not even Dinny Foley, to ride on Francis Joseph's
shoulder, only myself!

## 12. GOING BACK

DINNY was asleep beside me. Francis Joseph and Mr.
Hennessy sat on each side of the fire with my brother
between them, while he told the news. I lay awake listening
and trying to understand. I would never see my father.
He would never come to Fair Hill. I couldn't remember
him, but there was always so much talk of him and his
letters that I had been sure he would come walking in one
day, a bag of gold in his hand and a boy pushing a truck
after him loaded with presents. Now he would never
come!

Then I heard something that made me sit up so that
I wouldn't miss a word.

'This Miles Justin Blanchard was my father's friend. 'Tis
he has all his money and papers and he's in London, so
we're going there to meet him.'

'Mebbe 'tis all for the best,' muttered Francis Joseph
doubtfully.

'An' for why can't Mr. Miles Justin Blanchard send the
money and the papers?' asked a voice from the door.

Mrs. Hennessy had entered so quietly no one had heard.

The three by the fire turned and looked at her.  But I was too anxious to keep silent.

'Me too, Patrick Henry?' I demanded.

'Whist, child, whist!' said Francis Joseph.

My brother nodded at me.  I lay back contented.

'Young an' all as ye are, ye want to be off to London. I thought better of ye!' exclaimed Mrs. Hennessy re-proachfully.

'I want to be with Patrick Henry and me mammy, and I want to be here!' I explained.

'God forgive me for a fault-finding suspicious old woman,' sighed Mrs. Hennessy.  'But I do be sick an' sorry to see the young people flying away.  They're all goin' an' none comin' back!'

'We'll come back,' promised my brother.

'Ah, yer poor mother, me darlin' Nora!  God help her!' said Mrs. Hennessy.  'Is there any more news?'

'Aunt Hannah has left Fair Hill!' announced my brother.

'Left Fair Hill!' echoed Francis Joseph.

'Why?' asked Mr. Hennessy.

'So she's taken Mike Keiran in the heel o' the hunt!' exclaimed Mrs. Hennessy.  'If that don't bate all!'

'Ye knew she was marryin' that bog-trotter!' cried Francis Joseph, his eyes blazing.  'An' ye never let on to a soul!'

'Why would I?' asked Mrs. Hennessy.  'Isn't it well for her to be goin'?  There was never an argyment in that house, barrin' talk of politics, but Hannah raised it.  They'll have peace now!'

'Now that we're going,' my brother reminded her.

'What's wrong with politics?' demanded Francis Joseph. 'Isn't it natural to talk politics?'

'It leads to argyfyin', an argyfyin' leads to quarrellin',' said Mrs. Hennessy.  'Ye can have all the talk on histry ye want, but not politics in this house.'

'Sure hiſtry's only dead an' gone politics!' objeꞔed Francis Joseph. 'An' I've seen 'em sit up all night on Fair Hill debatin' hiſtry, an' ye couldn't tell the differ!'

'Then 'twas hiſtry so near our own time ye wouldn't know it from politics!' Mrs. Hennessy pointed out triumphantly.

Francis Joseph laughed.

'Have it yer own way, Brigid! But to think of Hannah marryin' Mike Keiran! Ah, well, he has a bit of a farm an' that's what 'll plase her!'

I thought of Fair Hill without Aunt Hannah. I was ſtill thinking how wonderful it would be when Patrick Henry went off to bed with Francis Joseph and Mrs. Hennessy turned down the lamp.

''Twill be a lonesome house wid four gone,' she said.

'Sure, three will come back,' Mr. Hennessy reminded her.

It was dark and I couldn't see, but I knew she shook her head.

Next day I was very happy. I showed Patrick Henry and Dinny the apple-tree, the way up the rocks, and the way across the road to the wishing well. Dinny wished for three toffee-apples. My brother wished to himself and I wished all over again.

''Tis only the firſt time that counts!' declared Dinny scornfully.

'There's never any harm in wishing,' my brother told us. So I thought of everything I could possibly want and wished one big wish.

I took them by the short cut. I was surprised that neither Dinny nor my brother wanted to walk on the log bridge. They preferred the proper way, and they wouldn't walk on the wall. I couldn't underſtand Dinny. Back home he walked on every wall he came to. Then I noticed he put his hands in his pockets and tried to whiſtle—like Patrick Henry. He was pretending to be a big boy. Even

in the orchard when the turkeys came rushing at us, Dinny
didn't run. My brother waved his arms and shouted. He
wasn't a bit afraid, but Dinny hid behind him.

I showed them the scarecrow in the green coat with the
gun on his shoulder.

'Who's afraid of an old scarecrow!' jeered Dinny.

'You would be, if you were all alone with him,' I
declared indignantly.

But they were both excited when I took them into the
barn to meet Mr. O'Callaghan and his big sons. Even
Patrick Henry looked small and young beside them.

'Well, lads!' said Mr. O'Callaghan. 'Will ye be good
farmers when the time comes?'

Dinny looked at my brother. Patrick Henry shook his
head.

'I'll have an office in Patrick Street,' he replied.

Mr. O'Callaghan flung down his fork and put his hands
on his hips.

'An' what good will that do ye?' he asked.

'I'll be a rich man and buy the house on Sundays Well
where me mother used to live,' said Patrick Henry. 'I'll
rebuild it and make it grander than ever. When I've done
that, I'll have time to think of being a farmer. You see,
me father promised me mother and I'm going to do it
for him.'

''Pon me word!' exclaimed Mr. O'Callaghan. 'The old
chat of him! What are the young ones comin' to?'

He looked hard at Patrick Henry and Patrick Henry
looked back, smiling but firm.

'So yer mind's made up?' asked Mr. O'Callaghan.

'It's made up!' agreed my brother.

'Ye didn't make it up for yerself, lad!' Mr. O'Callaghan
persisted. 'Someone told ye a fairy tale about all the power
there's in a bag of gold. Mebbe there is power, but, often
as not, there's little happiness.'

'Every one can't be a farmer,' said Patrick Henry. 'Most people must live in cities and I want me mother to have that house!'

I admired him for answering up to Mr. O'Callaghan, and the four men stood there looking at him seriously as though he were a man too. I thought how grandfather and Mrs. Hennessy and all the old people talked to him as if he were one of themselves.

'He's right!' exclaimed James O'Callaghan fiercely. 'We can't all be farmers! I'm not cut out for farming; neither is Bridie! We want crowds and lights and noise and streets, not fields and cows and the desolation of the country in winter! We want life, an' 'tis only in cities ye get life!'

'Well, young lad,' said Mr. O'Callaghan to Patrick Henry, 'ye've made James open his mouth at last. But ye're very young to be so sure. An' yer little sister wouldn't agree wid ye, if she'd only speak up. Ye like the old farrum an' the pigs, an' the cows, don't ye, Tricia?'

I nodded, but I put my hand into my brother's. I cared for him more than the farm or the pigs and cows all put together.

We had dinner with the O'Callaghans, and the Hennessys and Francis Joseph came over. The table was so big there was room and to spare. If only my mother had been there I would have wished never to go back to Cork, but to stay here always.

'There's a circus on Saturday,' I told Dinny as we were going back through the village. We went very slowly, for Mrs. Hennessy was proud of Patrick Henry and brought him to shake hands with all her friends.

'We won't be here Saturday!' said Dinny. 'Didn't we come to take you home?'

I tried to tell my brother about the tents which would be put up at the cross-roads, but he was talking to Judy

Leahy, who told him he was the spit of his father, only he had his mother's eyes.  She was so excited she wouldn't even look at Dinny and she forgot the bull's-eye she always gave me.

As we stood looking up the main street, a man carrying a pot of paste and a brush came along.  He had a roll of bills under his arm and, putting them on a window sill, he pasted a long green strip on Judy Leahy's wall.  Farther on he put up a red one.  Out from the cabins and houses, the children came running to read them.  I tugged at a big girl's frock.

'Is it the circus?  The Saturday circus!' I asked.

'It is indeed!' she answered.  'There's lions and tigers, an elephant, monkeys, and a clown!  I do love a clown! And there'll be a band and a procession!  It's the greatest circus in the world!'

Dinny listened, as excited as I was, but Patrick Henry wasn't interested in the circus.

'I must go to the circus!' I told Mrs. Hennessy.

'Sure, child, I'd love to keep ye here always,' she said. 'Only yer mother couldn't spare ye.  Don't fret, love! There'll be another circus one day!'

'This is the greatest circus in the world!' I cried, and wept so loudly that Dinny began to roar too.  For all the talk and good-byes, I couldn't believe I was going back to Cork before the circus until Peadar Keeley looked over the half-door and said:

'God save all here!  'Tis only a small load I have and Moddy can carry the three of them, aisy!'

'God save ye kindly!  Come along in and welcome, Peadar!' answered Mrs. Hennessy.

Then I was up on the cart with my bundle and Dinny beside me, kicking his heels against the seat.  My brother was stroking Moddy's ears and looking straight at Mrs. Hennessy, for he was nearly as tall as she was.

'You've been very good to Tricia, Mrs. Hennessy. She'll never forget you. Neither will I!'

'Listen now,' said Mrs. Hennessy. 'If ever she needs a home—there's one here for her.'

'We'd love to have her up at the farm,' said Bridie. 'Isn't it a terrible pity her mother wouldn't leave her, an' she crazy for the country?'

'We'd best be going,' muttered my brother. 'Say good bye!'

I waved good-bye until the bend in the road. Even then I could still see Francis Joseph's fiddle held aloft like a banner. Judy Leahy came to the door of her shop with a Peggy's Leg for me and one for Dinny. The red and green circus bills were everywhere on walls and doors. At the end of the village a great hay-cart filled the road, and there was Mr. O'Callaghan sitting up in front.

'So ye're takin' our little friend from us,' he said. 'I'm tellin' ye, Tricia, if London is too much for ye, pop into the first train ye meet an' tell the driver "O'Callaghans, West Cork." We'll be waitin' on ye!'

I had stopped crying now. The great moving haystack rose above us. Moddy reached out for a mouthful of hay and munched contentedly. We followed Mr. O'Callaghan and at the cross-roads he waved his hat.

'We've a gran' long day for the journey, thank God!' said Peadar. 'I'll tell ye one thing about cities—them that's never seen 'em don't know all they've to be thankful for. Did ye never think of that, Patrick Henry?'

'I never did,' answered my brother, laughing.

Peadar laughed, so did Dinny. I couldn't laugh.

'You're not sorry to be coming back home?' asked my brother.

I shook my head. No, I was glad to be going home, but desperate sorry to be leaving the Hennessys and the

O'Callaghans. Why hadn't I wished properly when I had the chance?

We saw the last of the circus bills and came out on a road between rocks and gorse bushes. The sun drew out the sweet coco-nut scent and Peadar, reaching into a box under the seat, gave us each an apple. They were big red apples with thin skin and full of juice like those in the Hennessys' barn.

Late in the day we came to Mrs. Flanagan's. It seemed so long ago I had been there with Mrs. Hennessy, I didn't expect her to remember me. But she held out her arms as if we were friends who met every day. I was glad of her welcome, for although I had my brother and Dinny I was tired with lonesomeness.

'So ye 're goin' back?' she said. ''Tisn't many young ones go round seeing the world this way! The people ye meet! The places ye see! The stories and songs ye hear!'

I stood in the dark kitchen looking up at Mrs. Flanagan. All my loneliness vanished. Patrick Henry and Dinny were with me. The Hennessys and the O'Callaghans were in their own place. My mother was on Fair Hill. As I sat up to the table before a saucer of thick hot stew I couldn't understand why I had been unhappy.

## 13. AUNT HANNAH AND COUSIN KATE

PATRICK HENRY went first when we came to the old house on Fair Hill. I lingered outside, staring up at the windows. But Dinny was impatient.

'Will ye come along in, Tricia! I haven't seen me mammy this long while!'

So I went down the broken steps with him and in at the open door. There on the settle was Dinny's mother, wiping her hands that never seemed dry on her apron, and there sat my mother. I didn't run to her as Dinny did to his mother, but went slowly and timidly. She looked different. Her hands lay in her lap, idle. I was sorry and frightened

'The poor child!' she said. 'We three must always keep together now.'

I ought to have been glad then, for wasn't that what I always wanted? Instead I looked around, wondering who was missing. There was a feeling of desolation in the house.

''Pon me word!' said Aunt Kattie, kissing me. 'I do believe ye 're fretting for yer Aunt Hannah and she always tormenting ye!'

'She 'll be seeing her to-morrow,' said my mother.

'Sure, ye 're not trailing the child over to Hannah's!' protested Aunt Kattie. 'Isn't she worn out from journeying the roads? And what harm if she doesn't bid farewell to every one?'

'Will it be in a train?' asked Dinny.

'It will!' my mother told him with a friendly smile. She always liked Dinny.

'Then Tricia should go!' he declared. ' 'Tis the chance of a lifetime!'

'The dote!' cried Aunt Kattie, as if he had said something clever.

I liked being back home, and the Hennessys and the O'Callaghans seemed to be going farther and farther away. I was very excited when we climbed into the train. The carriage was full, but a thin man in a yellow coat pushed two dogs from the seat to make room for us. He was smoking a pipe but, after one look at my mother, he knocked it out.

'Would ye like the winda shut or open, ma'am?' he asked.

'Open!' she answered. 'It might clear the air!'

'An' the little gerrul could stand here an' have a look at the countryside.'

I was delighted. The dogs sniffed at my ankles, then slumped on my feet. The trees ran, the houses ran. I waved my hand to some boys sitting on a wall. They waved, and on rushed the train while backward rushed the world outside.

And my mother was asking the thin man wouldn't he like to smoke his pipe?

At every station some of the passengers got out and others scrambled in, but the thin man and his dogs remained until my mother looked out and said: 'Here 's where Hannah lives. Be careful now, Tricia!'

'Which way would I go for Mrs. Keiran's farm?' my

mother asked the man who, sitting on a truck, held out his hand for her ticket.

He rubbed his chin with the back of his hand.

'Mrs. Keiran's farm! Mrs. Keiran's farm! It wouldn't be Mrs. Mike Keiran, would it, up on the high bog?'

'Mrs. Michael Keiran!' said my mother stiffly.

The man stood up and took off his cap.

'No offence, ma'am! If ye'll come along I'll show ye the best way. Are ye good at short cuts?'

'I am!' I said proudly.

'There's the gerrul!' and he patted my shoulder. 'Ye see, ma'am, short cut an' all, 'tis a matter of three mile or more.'

'Isn't there a side-car?' asked my mother.

'There is not, ma'am. If ye take the road ye might get a lift an' then again ye mightn't, for the horses is all workin'.'

'We'll take the short cut!' decided my mother. 'Listen now, Tricia, or we'll be losing our way.'

I listened my hardest.

'Count it on yer fingers!' the man told me. 'Here—up across the wall. One—the path straight across three fields. Two—over the stepping stones. Three—lave the wood on yer left till ye enter the Rocky Valley, which makes four. Up wid ye on to the bog. Folly the new road be the old cuttin', an' right forninst ye is Keiran's Dump—I mane farm!'

'Can you remember all that?' asked my mother.

I repeated it, counting on my fingers.

'Isn't she the great little child!' exclaimed the man. 'Ye must be very proud of her, ma'am!'

But my mother was climbing over the wall.

'Thank you! Thank you very much!' she said, over her shoulder.

The man leaned on the gate.

'D' ye think the young one can walk that far?' he asked suddenly. 'Sure, she's only a wheeshy scrap! Lave her here wid me an' I'll care her.'

I was determined not to be left behind. I ran along the path while my mother and the man were talking. She came treading daintily in her black button boots, clutching her rolled umbrella in one hand and holding up her skirt with the other. We crossed the first field and climbed a wall. My mother took off her tight kid gloves.

'This is ridiculous!' she exclaimed. 'Why wouldn't they leave a gap for people to go through. My new boots will be ruined!'

A high gate barred the entrance to the third field. My mother was quick and active, but she was wearing her new black clothes, and when she looked down from the top of the gate she saw a trampled stretch of mud.

'I'm not stepping into that!' she declared.

I sat beside her, gazing out over the small fields, thin patches of oats and barley guarded by stone walls.

'We'll go by the next field!' said my mother. 'It looks a nice, tidy, decent kind of a field!'

'The path straight across three fields!' I quoted.

'Path indeed!' exclaimed my mother. 'If we go in the same direction it won't make any difference at all!'

We climbed back and followed the wall until we came to a rough stile. This field dipped down half-way across and a black bull with shining white horns raised his head from the long grass and glared at us.

'I never did like bulls!' said my mother, stopping suddenly.

She called a month-old calf a bull, but this really was one. She gave me a push.

'Go back!' she whispered. 'Don't run until you're near the wall. He mayn't see you.'

I obeyed, went a few yards and turned.

'You come too!' I called softly.

My mother's face was white. She held her umbrella as if it were a sword. The bull swung his great head, pawed the earth, bellowed, and trotted up the slope.

'Run!' ordered my mother. 'He'll be after your red frock!'

I ran, stopped, and looked back. The bull had paused, his angry eyes staring round the field. My mother was walking quietly towards me, not straight, but sideways, so that she could watch the bull. He tossed his horns and thundered across the grass. He was coming nearer and nearer. I was sure he would catch my mother. I could not move. Now she was running. She came up with me, caught my hand, and dragged me along. At the wall she pushed me over, then scrambled after, tearing her dress. The bull reached the wall and halted so close to us the foam from his mouth was thrown in our faces. My mother reached across and gave him a whack with her umbrella.

'You nasty creature!' she cried. 'Frightening the child and tearing me new skirt!'

The astonished animal swung round and lumbered away.

'Hannah would choose the country!' exclaimed my mother. 'Bulls and mud! Fields and stone walls! We'll have to go the other way!'

We went back to the high gate and climbed over it into the mud. It was even deeper than it looked and this made my mother more indignant with the bull.

'The great bully! Driving us into the mud!' she cried, using her umbrella as a stick, while I tried to hop across.

I was wearing strap shoes and, in one of my jumps, a button came off and I left the shoe behind. My mother dug it out with her umbrella and, when we reached dry ground, bound it on my foot with the ribbon from my hat. We found the stepping stones across a shallow stream, washed away the mud, and went on to the wood.

'I 'm tired!' said my mother. 'This is the longest three miles I 've ever walked.'

We sat on a log, but a huge red spider swung down from its web and my mother wouldn't stay another moment. The wood was lovely—birches, slender and graceful, tossed in the wind and a giant beech had dragged its roots so far out of the ground it seemed on the march. An oak, with its green acorns hardly formed and fantastic leaves, surprised my mother into interest and wonder.

'Isn't it queer how the leaves are different shapes on different trees?' she said. 'Your dadda was always drawing trees. He might have liked this place, poor Timothy! God rest his soul!'

'Did me dadda draw pictures?' I asked.

But she didn't hear me. I could tell she was thinking sad thoughts so I plodded along, guiding her away from the trees down to the rocky valley. At a distance I had seen the rocks, not grey, but gold and purple, silver and copper, and I discovered tiny plants growing out of the dry, harsh rock, delicate bells, silver foliage studding every rock with jewels. All about us was the sweet, hot scent of the gorse.

'Mrs. Hennessy has lovely rocks like these at the back of her house,' I said, watching my mother's face and trying to make her smile.

'Were you happy there?' she asked.

I nodded.

'Away from Fair Hill?' she persisted.

I was ashamed. But I had been happy.

'Didn't you miss me?' she wanted to know.

I hadn't the words to tell her how much I had missed her; but she understood, and we went through the Rocky Valley hand-in-hand.

As we slipped and scrambled she talked of Mrs. Hennessy and the O'Callaghans, then of Fair Hill and grandfather.

She made all she spoke of so real that I could see people and events I could not remember.

'Do you remember?' she kept on asking, and told me of her own childhood and of grandfather's boyhood, of how the Lynches had once been rich and grand. Down, down we came to a waterfall, and there was a bridge, no handrail, just a wide plank laid across the stream with the water foaming far below. Now I was glad I had crossed that slippery green log over the stream beyond the Hennessys' wishing well. I marched on to the bridge, still holding my mother's hand but keeping in front. When we were safely over she looked down at me.

'You're a very brave child!' she said. 'You're growing more like Patrick Henry every day.'

I was bursting with pride as we climbed out of the Rocky Valley. I hoped there was another bridge so that she would call me brave again. But we had reached the bog.

'Hannah can't live here!' exclaimed my mother. 'It's a wilderness—a great brown desert!'

There were cuttings and high banks, like a giant's feast of chocolate. Jagged heaps of brown sods rose along the paths, and the paths were brown too. Men were cutting and the long narrow blades of their slanes gleamed in the sunlight. Women stood the sods on end and barefoot children were helping them or running madly along tiny tracks. There were golden pools and white tufted bog cotton grew in patches. The air was golden and the singing of unseen larks made me clutch my mother's hand.

'There's nothing to be afraid of!' she said, then shook her head with a laugh.

'I know—it's not fear but happiness you're feeling. Why, Tricia—how can you be happy for no reason at all?'

We came upon a group of the turf-cutters. Their skin was ruddy and their eyes gleamed. They all stopped working to show us Mike Keiran's farm. At first we couldn't see it—only a cluster of stunted trees. Then we made out a ramshackle wooden hut and a few sheds.

'Hannah can't live there!' exclaimed my mother. 'Mrs. Keiran is my sister,' she explained to the turf-workers.

'Sure, ma'am, ye'd be surprised the way people can live!' said a big dark woman with laughing eyes. 'But if yer sister is city bred I wouldn't say but it might go hard wid her.'

We went along a path soft and crumbly underfoot with the dry powdered turf, by a deep cutting half filled with water. The children we met stared at me and I stared back. I hoped we would stay a while at Aunt Hannah's so that I could run over the bog.

A fence of branches like those in the Hennessys' fence, only white and withered, separated the farm from the bog. But the Hennessys' fence was well made. This had gaps and, instead of a gate, part of an iron bedstead was hung on a post. As we pushed in, my Aunt Hannah came to the door of the hut. When she saw us she did not move but waited, hands on hips, her eyes watchful and unfriendly. Her face was burnt brown and her sleeves rolled to the elbows. She wore a man's cap and rough boots.

'So it's yourself, Nora, and the young one! I wasn't expecting to see you here. But, as you are here, you'd as well come in!'

We went into the hut. Mike Keiran was sitting on a box, a cat on his shoulder, a dog between his knees.

'This is kind, Nora!' he exclaimed, going red with pleasure. 'Ye're very welcome, an' the little one too! Hallo, Tricia! I'm yer uncle now!'

'How do you do, Uncle Michael?' I asked, going to him at once.

My mother sat in the only chair. Aunt Hannah perched on the table and swung her legs.

'What's wrong?' demanded my aunt. 'What brings you all this way from Fair Hill?'

My mother did not answer.  She took out her handkerchief and began to cry into it. .

'Will you take yourself out of it, Mike Keiran!' snapped Aunt Hannah.  'And the child with you.  Show her the pig!  This is a family affair!'

I wanted to stay and comfort my mother.  But Uncle Michael clutched my arm and led me out.

'Hannah's right!' he said.  'Sure we'd no manners to stay there, pimpin' an' pryin'!  Come along now!  An' I'll show ye round the place.  Here's the pig!  I'm after strivin' to make a sty for the crathure.'

Mike Keiran used to come into the kitchen at Fair Hill. I had heard him talk of his 'little bit of a farm.'  Aunt Kattie had laughed at his bragging, but I know she never dreamed what a forlorn place it was.  The pig was fenced into the corner of a tumbledown wall with one end of an iron bedstead.  I often wondered where Uncle Michael found all these bedsteads.  He used them for gates and fencing, and even for a bridge over a wide drain with planks laid across.

'A handyman like meself could build a grand house wid bedsteads, if he'd a quantity,' he told me, running his fingers through his faded fair hair.  'But they're no use wid hens.  Would ye like to stay here wid us for a time, Tricia?  You and me 'ud get on fine.  I'd put in a word for ye wid Hannah.'

There was no donkey, not even a goat.  The hens followed us, and the cock, a dingy black bird with scarcely any tail, flew to Uncle Michael's shoulder.  The pig grunted appealingly, so my uncle turned back, shifted the bedstead, and on we went, the pig trotting in company with the hens. I wasn't sure if I liked Uncle Michael.  I was quite sure I didn't want to stay on his farm, though he offered to make me a wheelbarrow of my own.  I was hungry, I was tired, I was terribly thirsty, and I was about to ask would there soon be something to eat or a drop to drink when the door of the hut was flung open and my mother marched out. Her cheeks were flushed, her eyes angry, and I knew at once Aunt Hannah had been tormenting her.

'Tricia!' she said. 'We 're going! I thought I had a sister here!'

I was frightened. Aunt Hannah was standing in the doorway.

'Sure, there 's no call to be that touchy!' she protested. 'Haven't I a right to me opinion?'

'You 've no right to talk as you did about poor Tim and he dead in Egypt, or your own father. Hannah, you should be ashamed!'

'I 'd be ashamed if I let that child run around in a red frock when she should be in mourning for her father!' retorted Aunt Hannah, and, stepping back, she slammed the door.

'Tricia!' called my mother, walking so quickly I had to run to keep up with her.

'Sure, ye can't go widout a sup of tay, or anything at all!' cried Uncle Michael. ''Tisn't dacent nor lucky!'

My mother didn't answer and, when I glanced over my shoulder, I saw him leaning on the bedstead he used as a gate, looking after us with a foolish smile on his brown face.

Instead of turning to the left we went to the right, and my mother's face was so stormy I didn't dare warn her that we were going wrong, even when we came out on a road which led away from the Rocky Valley. The shoe tied on with my hat ribbon kept slipping and soon I had a blister on my heel. I limped painfully, clutching my mother's hand and wishing she hadn't quarrelled with Aunt Hannah, then we might be sitting down, drinking hot, sweet tea. My mother began to walk slowly. She, too, was limping. Her tight, elegant boots weren't made for such a tramp.

We came to a stream flowing over stones and splashing up against clumps of forget-me-not.

'Thirsty!' I cried, and made for the water. My mother held me back.

'You mustn't drink that!' she said. 'It might poison you. It's dirty! It's flowing over stones and mud.'

I looked at the clear, sparkling stream and longed to kneel down and drink.

'Sit here now,' said my mother. 'Maybe someone will come along and we'll ride to the station on a side-car.'

'Thirsty!' I complained.

'Be a good girl and I'll tell you a story,' she coaxed.

We sat on a low flat rock. I had my back to the stream but I could hear it leap and gurgle. The air was cooler and the sun's heat pleasant.

'Did I never tell you the story of the dark sailor who sailed with Columbus?' asked my mother. 'He was a man from Youghal.'

I listened drowsily, leaning against her. The dark sailor without a ship, wandering forlorn along the coast until he came to Galway—I had heard about him before, but not about the silver earrings in his ears, the green scarf about his neck, and the queer foreign money jangling in his pockets. I heard the splashing of the waves against the little row boat when he set off to board the strange ship lying in Galway Bay. I could feel the rocking of the boat and hear the sailor singing. No! It was the rocking of a cart and the song was the sound of horse's hoofs on a stony road and the rattle of wheels. I opened my eyes. I was lying on a heap of straw in the bottom of a cart. Gazing up I could see my mother, sitting beside the driver, looking happy and excited. She looked round and saw that I was awake.

'Aren't we terribly lucky?' she called. 'This good, kind lad is driving us to Cousin Kate's over by Macroom.'

I sat hugging my knees, still sleepy, wondering how I came to be riding to Cousin Kate's, when we had been sitting on a rock near Aunt Hannah's. There would be no quarrels at Cousin Kate's. She thought the world of my mother; everybody knew that. There would be lovely food and lashings of tea and Cousin Ulick to talk to. Maybe we'd stay there and not have to limp along hard dusty roads. I fell asleep again, and when I woke once more the cart had drawn up outside the pleasant white house with the trees all round it and Cousin Kate was coming down the steps, crying out:

'Nora! It can't be you! And is that Tricia in the straw?'

Cousin Kate was lovely! She had big brown eyes, piles of dark hair, her dress was of blue silk, and her shoes had buckles. Her voice was like my mother's, only deeper, and you could tell they were terribly fond of one another.

A girl in a black frock with a white apron and a cap on her curly hair took me off with her, sewed a button on my shoe, mended the hole in my sock, bathed my blister, and washed my face and hands with warm water and scented soap. When I was tidy we went down to a big room where all the chairs were arm-chairs and I sat on a sofa so comfortable it was like a bed. Cousin Ulick sat beside me. He was as big as my brother, but not so serious. He put cream in my tea, piled one plate with sandwiches, another with little cakes, and put them on a chair before me.

'When you've eaten all you can, we'll find some ripe plums,' he said. 'Would you like a ride or a swing?'

'On a horse?' I asked.

'A pony!' said Cousin Ulick.

My mother and Cousin Kate sat on another sofa holding hands. They weren't bothering about tea or cakes, though I had never eaten such cakes and they were all different.

I was sorry to go out of that pleasant room, but Cousin Ulick had his hand on my shoulder and gently pushed me the way he wanted me to go.

'There's the swing,' he said.

It hung low, a wide seat with thick ropes, disappearing into the leafy branches of a beech. But a light brown pony put his head over a fence and called Ulick.

'Give Sandy these,' he said, pulling some lumps of sugar from his pocket and putting them in my hands.

He showed me how to hold my hand open loosely with the sugar on the palm. I liked the feel of the pony's lips and forgot the swing.

'I'll ride!' I said.

Ulick lifted me up before him and we rode down a long avenue and across a meadow. The pony jumped a fence and then a stream.

'Frightened?' asked Ulick.

I shook my head. Sandy galloped. I leaned against my cousin, wishing my hands held the reins. Suddenly we stopped and I had only to put up my hand and draw down big red plums. When we came back to the house my mother was sitting in a carriage and Cousin Kate stood talking to her.

'You'd like to go to school, wouldn't you, Tricia?' asked Cousin Kate.

'It's no good!' interrupted my mother. 'I'll never part with her! She's too little to put into a school. Hannah offered to keep her.'

'Hannah!' cried Cousin Kate scornfully.

'Let her stay here!' said Ulick. 'I'll teach her to ride and she can have the swing. It's years since I used it! I'd sooner have a brother, but I'd put up with a sister when she'd be Tricia!'

I scrambled into the carriage and clutched my mother's hand. She looked pleased and laughed.

'That's her answer!' she said. 'Good-bye, Kate! Good-bye, Ulick!'

I wouldn't say good-bye, I wouldn't even wave my hands, but I sat up proudly and looked at the two horses prancing before us.

'Cousin Kate's my dearest friend,' my mother told me. 'We were schoolgirls together and had everything alike. Now her son goes to a grand school, has a fine home, and rides a horse; my poor boy must emigrate and all I can do is go with him!'

'Why?' I asked.

'Because they're rich and we're poor!' said my mother bitterly.

I wasn't very troubled. I'd had a great tea, eaten six big plums, ridden a pony, and here we were being drawn to the station by two fine horses.

## 14. GOING AWAY

THE big black chest was tied crossways with a new straw rope.  A label:

MRS. NORA LYNCH, passenger from CORK to LONDON

was fastened to each handle.  My bundle sat on top and the rag doll Poosie had a new frock.  Mrs. Foley made it, and what with her damp hands and the way she wept over it the frock had to be dried before the fire.  My ticket had been bought—a half-ticket.  There was no doubt this time. I was an Irish emigrant!  I was so excited and proud I couldn't keep still in the house and, as there was no school, Dinny and I roamed the quays and bridges, looking at the boats and wondering which could be taking me to London. We told every one who would listen to us.  Strangers we had never set eyes on before were friendly and gave us pennies to buy apples.  We spent the money with Mrs. Sally Nugent, who sat on a step along Pope's Quay, near the Dominican church, with her basket in the gutter.  She had so many apples her basket was piled to the top of the handle.  They filled her lap and she ranged them on her bare arm from the wrist to the shoulder.

'Twelve sweet red apples for one penny! Twelve juicy 'Merican apples for de penny!' shouted Mrs. Sally, stretching out her arm without letting one fall.

When I told her I was going over to England she gave us a whole armful of apples and shook her head at the penny.

'God's holy angels watch over the poor innercent childer!' she prayed, looking at us sorrowfully.

'She thinks I'm going too!' boasted Dinny, as we strolled away munching apples.

While my mother was still packing, Captain O'Connell arrived at Fair Hill. He was a cousin on the O'Neill grandmother's side, the one who came out of a castle, though I could never understand about relations. I loved the Captain the moment he stumped into the kitchen, one leg shorter than the other, a face so brown it might just as well have been black, and a loud hoarse voice. He let himself down on the settle with a thud, stared at us all, and shouted:

'Here I am, Kattie! Can't get a ship! Me! Kattie! Can't get a ship! Now laugh! I've stopped laughing. Saved twenty pounds. Will they let me stay?'

Aunt Kattie had a meat pudding in the saucepan swinging from the chain in the chimney. It was wrapped in a cloth and I could hear it bubbling and tumbling. She turned her head without moving.

'God in heaven! 'Tis the Captain!'

I sat up on the settle as close to the Captain as I could squeeze. His thick blue clothes smelled of salt and he wore a clumsy silver ring with a green stone on his left little finger. Dinny leaned against his knee and waited. The Captain gave Dinny a poke and Dinny roared with laughter.

'Whose kids?' he asked.

'Tricia is Nora's. Dinny's a neighbour's child,'

explained Aunt Kattie. 'They're hoping you'll tell them a story.'

'So I will!' declared the Captain. 'Dozens!'

'Dinny's mother will fix you for the present,' said Aunt Kattie. 'Nora's going to England with Tricia and the boy. Poor Tim is dead—in Egypt.'

'Heard it!' said the Captain. 'So I came along. She'll need a man to handle that swindler. He cheated Tim. He'll cheat her!'

'Nora won't thank you!' Aunt Kattie told him. 'She'll never believe Miles Justin Blanchard is a swindler! She has a great regard for him. He writes lovely letters!'

'A brigand!' shouted the Captain. 'A land shark! Him and his French cook at three pounds a week and his poor wife and two lovely boys starving in Paris. Found 'em in an attic, Kattie, and lent her four hundred francs. I hadn't five hundred! It was five hundred she needed.'

'You'll never get it back!' said Aunt Kattie. 'The pudding's ready!'

'Who gave ye the ring, mister?' asked Dinny.

'I'll tell ye,' answered the Captain.

'Not now!' objected Aunt Kattie. 'You can stay for a bite, Dinny. Your mammy knows where you are and there's plenty for all. Run, Tricia, and bring down your mother. God knows where Patrick Henry is!'

'He's in with grandfather,' I told her.

'Then leave him so. I'll hand them theirs on a tray. Come along now, Captain. Where in the wide world is Liam?'

When Aunt Kattie had emptied the teapot, and the kettle was empty too, Dinny and I went off with the Captain. He walked with one foot in the gutter, the other on the kerb, so that his legs were even, but he was in a fix when we had to cross a road. He helped us to read the names over shops and the words on newspaper posters and outside the Opera House. When we made mistakes in spelling he said it didn't signify, for words were spelt differently in every country.

'I've friends on every quay and alley in Cork!' shouted the Captain. 'We'll see them all!'

'Who gave ye the ring, mister?' insisted Dinny.

'Ye never heard how my *Connemara Girl* sank in sight of Wexford harbour?' the Captain asked at the top of his voice. 'What do ye larn in the school at all? Every man saved, but I've walked with a limp ever since. God help me! And did I get a pension? There's one man in every ten in this country has a pension. But would they give Captain O'Connell one? They would not!'

'Was it a pirate gave ye the ring, mister?' cried Dinny.

'The ring!' repeated the Captain, looking puzzled.

'The ring wid the green stone,' explained Dinny.

''Twasn't in Cork I had the ring given me,' said Captain O'Connell. 'And 'twasn't in Dublin. Now I'm warnin' ye. Never go to Dublin! 'Tis the wickedest city in the world! Some say London and some say Paris, and I have heard a sailorman that lives down in Dominick Street say Amsterdam beats 'em all! But I'm tellin' ye 'tis Dublin!'

Dinny was getting desperate.

'Did ye steal the ring, mister?' he roared.

Captain O'Connell stopped. He bent down, put his hands on his knees, and stuck his face against Dinny's.

'I did not steal the ring, ye impident young limb!' he growled. ''Twas given to me for the bravest deed of me life! Steal, indade!'

I was cross with Dinny. He had vexed the Captain and now we would never know who had given him the ring.

We heard all kinds of stories, or bits of them, from the Captain's friends. They were battered old seamen, and there wasn't one of them would start a story at the beginning and go on to the end. We heard beginnings and we heard ends, but never an end that would go with any of the beginnings.

A morning came when I sat on the chest in the hall waiting. Dinny sat beside me, looking very important. I had on my best coat, new shoes, and my brother's leather school bag. The hall door was propped open and an old black closed-in cab—a jingle—stood out in the street. The horse, a white bony creature with drooping head, reminded me of the tinkers' horse and I began to feel alarmed. We were going away from Fair Hill, from all sight or sound of the Hennessys and Peadar Keeley. I was leaving Dinny and Aunt Kattie. The driver was dragging a trunk down from the attic—bump! bump! bump!

'Don't want to go!' I told Dinny.

Suddenly the hall was crowded. Aunt Kattie, her hair tidy, her sleeves rolled down, was buttoning her Sunday coat. My mother and Patrick Henry, both carrying bags, came down the stairs. My uncles, Mrs. Foley, Peadar Keeley, neighbours from up the hill and down the hill were on the steps, out on the pavement, pressing against the white horse and clambering into four side-cars that had followed the jingle.

'It's like a funeral!' sighed my mother.

Grandfather's door was flung open and he came out. He was the only one not dressed for the street.

'I shall never see you again, Nora!' he said.

'I'm coming back! A little while and everything will be as it used to be!' my mother told him. 'Only there'll be money for all the books you want.'

'I shall never see you again!' repeated grandfather.

Then we were in the jingle—the three of us—with Aunt Kattie and Dinny. I waved my hand to every one we met or passed. Dinny waved too. The side-cars rattled along behind us. I wished we were on one. The jingle was dank and stuffy.

'Want to be on a side-car!' I grumbled.

Dinny nodded, ready to agree. The jingle stopped. We were late, the last to reach the ship. I was kissed, hugged, pushed up the gangway, and stood there looking down on a strange small Dinny, Aunt Kattie, Uncle Liam, and the neighbours. Captain O'Connell was there, every one except grandfather. They were being carried away. No! We were! The great ship, screaming and wailing, was steaming away from Cork, down the Lee, past Blackrock Castle, past Spike Island—a blazing hill of light. I was cold and frightened and the lowing of cattle in the hold made me sad. A man in a blue jersey stood beside me at the rail.

'Ye 've looked farewell long enough, girleen! Where 's yer mammy?'

I didn't know.

'We 'll try walking. We might happen on her. One day ye 'll be coming home to Cork, a fine, fat lump of a woman wid a bag full of gold. 'Tis a thing poor Joe Doyle could never do. That 's meself!'

'For grandfather?' I asked.

'For yerself!'

'I 'll give it to Dinny!' I declared. 'There 's Patrick Henry looking for me.'

## 15. EMIGRANTS

My mother and I had a cabin to ourselves. The top bunk was mine, and when I climbed up the waves dashed against the porthole so close I expected to feel the spray on my face.

There were four bunks, two at each side. The black chest crowded the floor. My bundle, the school bag, a big cardboard box, and a straw hamper were piled on the bunks on the far side. In between there was a wash-basin with clean towels swinging on a rail and, in the rack above, I saw two tumblers and a bottle of water. A small settee, not big enough for me to lie down on, had a long mirror at the back and already my mother's coat was hanging from a hook on the door. It swayed gently at every movement of the ship.

'Can we live here always?' I asked, for I wanted to untie my bundle and empty the school bag.

My mother sat on the settee and smiled up at me.

'For three whole days and nights, Tricia! It's a long time, but we 'll manage.'

'Make some lace,' I said coaxingly.

I was so used to the ball of thread and the shining crochet hook in her white fingers, she seemed strange without them.

'I 'll never make another inch of lace as long as I live!' she exclaimed. 'When we come back we 'll be rich. May be we 'll go back to Sundays Well, or we might build a house of our own.'

Her eyes were bright and excited as if she were telling a story or saying poetry.

'Tell me!' I cried, excited too.

Suddenly she was sad again.

'Maybe I 'm only dreaming and, if we ever are rich, it 's because of your father,' she told me. 'No one else believed in him. But I did, poor Timothy Patrick!'

She was silent. I watched the waves. I watched her. The little cabin was dark, but there were lights on the ship and they shone out over the sea. There were tramplings and creakings, shouts and splashings until I could stand being away from it all no longer.

'Can I go upstairs?' I whispered.

I knew I should be under the bedclothes and asleep, but a ship wasn't a house, and, often, at home, hadn't I stayed up until my eyes wouldn't keep open? She nodded without speaking. I could just see her white face. I was scrambling down when there was a tap on the door and my brother came in.

'There 's tea and hot toast in the saloon,' he said. 'That 's where the people go. I know the way.'

We went out together, the three of us, into the narrow passage. Glittering rails stretched against the walls to cling to when the ship dipped or rose. I was laughing when suddenly the passage tipped the other way and I had to run.

The saloon was a long bright room with so many looking-glasses that, whichever way I looked, I saw myself. The seats were cushioned, and a pleasant young man put a cushion under me and another at my back, so that I was wedged in with comfort.

'The little girl can have hot bread and milk,' said the young man.

'Sure, she's no baby!' retorted my mother. 'She'd be lost without her cup of tea!'

I was ashamed to tell her I would sooner have the bread and milk. The toast was cut in fingers, very hot and soft with butter. It was piled in a silver dish and the teapot was so big and heavy my mother had to take her two hands to it. Patrick Henry leaned back.

'Isn't it grand to be on a ship again?' he said.

'But you do miss Fair Hill?' my mother asked him anxiously.

'Ah, we'll be going back one day,' he answered, looking round him.

My mother put her elbows on the table and clasped her hands under her chin.

'I wonder what they're doing at home!' she said.

Patrick Henry pulled out the silver watch Uncle Liam had given him.

'They're eating hot potato cake and drinking stewed tea,' he told her.

'It's the first time we've had Tricia with us. I'd love a cut of Kattie's potato cake,' sighed my mother. 'And her tea was never stewed—only strong!'

'So strong a mouse could dance on it!'

They both laughed and I thumped the table with my spoon and laughed along with them.

'Will you be a good sailor, Tricia?' wondered my brother. I nodded.

'Isn't she her father's daughter?' demanded my mother. 'Why wouldn't she be a good sailor?'

When there was no more tea in the pot, or another finger of toast left, we went out of the long room, past the other passengers, and went on deck. I walked in the middle, clutching warm hands, seeing the waves, the stars, the lights on the ship, and, far off across the waves, other lights.

The ship was very noisy, hooting, scuffling, straining. I saw so much I didn't understand. Small boats, carefully covered, sat high above our heads, little houses stuck up out of the deck, strange curved shapes, masts, funnels, coiled ropes, gangways, were revealed and hidden as the lights swung with the motion of the ship. An old man played a tin whistle on the deck below. Out of the darkness young men and girls came running. A few scrapings and shufflings, and a sixteen-handed reel was being danced.

'We'll go down!' said my mother. 'Weren't we very foolish to spend so much money on grand travelling when we might have been with friends!'

Indeed they were friends! Two girls moved along a bench to make room for us and a young man spread his coat to save my mother's dress. When the dancers were tired they sat with the others and sang *O'Donnell Abu*, *On Lough Neagh's Banks*, and then these Irish emigrants sang *I'm sitting on a Stile, Mary!* Its sadness made me cry, and I was glad I could hide my face until I saw the tears falling down my mother's cheeks. Patrick Henry pretended he had a cold and pulled out his handkerchief. Some of the girls were crying out loud. The old man polished his tin whistle on his sleeve and shook his head sorrowfully.

'Sure, 'tis very hard on the young ones,' he said. 'Maybe ye'd give us a bit of a song, ma'am? I can tell by the big grey eyes of ye, ye have a lovely voice.'

'She has!' I cried. 'She has!'

My mother shook her head.

'My little girl will recite,' she told him.

So I stood out in the middle and began *The Irish Widow's Message to her Son in America*. The smoke from the funnel poured down on us and a cold wind swept the boat, but

I was too proud to care. I forgot some of the words and Patrick Henry whispered them to me, but when I had finished the people clapped and stamped until all the other passengers came hurrying to discover what caused the tumult.

'Arish! Arish!' shouted the old man.

'That means you'll have to say another piece,' said my brother. 'What else do you know?'

'Battle of Font—of Font——' I stammered, trying hard to remember.

'Too long!' decided my mother. 'Besides, you always forget it.'

'I know!' I said, and too excited to wait I ran back to the middle of the deck and began:

> 'At the sign of the Bell,
>    On the road to Clonmel,
> Paddy Heggarty kept a neat shebeen;
>    Sold pig's meat and bread,
>    Kept a neat feather-bed
> And well liked in the country he had been.
>    Himself and his wife,
>    Long struggled through life,
> On weekdays Pat mended the ditches.
>    But on Sunday he dressed
>    In his suit of the best,
> And his pride was——'

Every one on the lower deck, except my mother, roared out:

'HIS OLD LEATHER BRITCHES!'

I didn't forget one word! Uncle Liam had taught me *Paddy Heggarty* and given me a penny for each verse I learnt properly. I longed to recite *The Battle of Fontenoy*. But, though the name had come back to me, the laughing faces, the old man with the tin whistle, the ship, were growing misty.

'I wish you hadn't give them that old thing!' complained my mother. 'It's terribly vulgar!'

'I'll carry her to the cabin!' said Joe Doyle, appearing out of the darkness. 'Isn't she the great little gerrul! Her and me had a great collogue an' we comin' out of Cork!'

I had a grand dream that night. I stood at the foot of Father Mathew's statue on Patrick Street and recited *The Battle of Fontenoy* to an enormous crowd! Every one I knew was there; every one of them from grandfather to the dark tinker. But as well there was Peadar Keeley's donkey Moddy, the bull who had chased us when we were going to Aunt Hannah's, and all the calves and sheep I had ever seen going down Fair Hill. The people clapped and stamped, Moddy roared, and the bull sat back and laughed.

'That child's a great one for her bed!' said a voice.

I opened my eyes and blinked. I wasn't in Patrick Street, but in the ship's cabin. There was no sign of Moddy or the bull, only a jolly fat woman in a black dress, with silky black hair piled up.

'Let ye go to yer breakfast, ma'am,' she said to my mother, who was standing up, ready dressed. 'I'll care the young one.'

'I'm Mrs. Flannery, the stewardess,' the fat woman told me. 'I heard the piece ye gave out last night. I haven't finished laughing yet!'

I didn't speak. I was listening to the tramping and lowing of cattle and I was bewildered.

'Is it the poor bastes ye're after hearin'?' asked Mrs. Flannery. 'Sure, they're a bit upset in themselves. But they'll have peace now. Don't mind them. Aren't they emigrants too? Will I bring ye breakfast in yer bunk for a treat? An' ye can tell me all about yerself. I have a little gerrul of me own in the convent at Limerick. Ah, wisha! These little bits of hairpins is no use at all!'

'I had breakfast in bed every morning at Mrs. Hennessy's,' I told her as she went out, a tail of her hair falling over one eye and another coming down at the back.

She returned with the tray and, propped up with pillows, I drank hot tea, much milkier than I liked, and ate a great round of toast. I heard all about Mary Flannery, who could play pieces on the piano with two hands and who had three prizes for good conduct.

'An' now ye 'll see Plymouth!' said Mrs. Flannery, as, sitting on the black chest, she combed my hair. '"Tis a dote of a town! Ah, ye 're the lucky child to be goin' on shore for a whole day!'

Mrs. Flannery taught me not to say 'upstairs' or 'downstairs' or to talk of the 'window.' As we went out, Joe Doyle, in blue jersey and carpet slippers, came shuffling along.

'Is it yerself, Joe Doyle?' asked Mrs. Flannery. 'Here 's little Tricia Lynch.'

'We made acquaintance coming down the Lee, an' I heard her givin' out last night,' said Joe Doyle. '"Twas that had me dramin' I was back on me stepfather's farm from beyond Bantry, below Hungry Hill. Have ye ever been in them parts, Tricia?'

'Maybe,' I answered. 'Me mother wouldn't go away without me, would she?'

'God help ye, child! She would not!' declared Mrs. Flannery. 'She 's up on deck this very minit waitin' on ye.'

'And Patrick Henry?' I asked quickly.

'Come along now!' she chuckled. 'Joe Doyle, take the tray, will ye? And for pity's sake put on a dacent pair of shoes now we 're in port. 'Pon me word! I don't know how the Captain bears wid ye at all an' ye disgracin' him before the English!'

'Sure, I 'm not goin' on shore, Mrs. Flannery!' objected Joe Doyle. 'An' when I do I 'd be sorry for the people of Plymouth if they haven't anything better to do than look at a dacent man's comfortable slippers!'

'Up wid ye! Will ye keep yer mother waitin' on ye till the ship's sailin'?' demanded Mrs. Flannery, giving me a push.

I scrambled up the steep steps and saw Plymouth, clean sparkling, with a lighthouse on land gazing out towards the lighthouse at sea. At first I couldn't catch a glimpse of my mother and brother. Then I saw them sitting close together, their heads bent over a paper Patrick Henry was holding steady on a book. He was writing and talking at the same time and their backs were turned to the lovely city. I ran over to them and tugged my mother's hand.

'Look!' I cried, pointing at the lighthouse along the Hoe. She looked up smiling.

'Run about the ship and play,' she told me. 'But don't touch anything and don't open any doors.'

I stared in amazement.

'Mrs. Flannery says it's Plymouth!'

My brother jumped up.

'I'd like to see Plymouth,' he said.

So we climbed the gangway and went on shore. I kept in the middle and they talked over my head. On the Barbican we stopped at a bookshop which reminded my mother of Massey's in Patrick Street. We walked and walked. Sailors swaggered past us, fishermen carrying nets, ladies just looking at the shops. There were flower shops and sweet shops and shops with gay new books. I saw children with bare legs and sandals carrying painted buckets and wooden spades, or bowling wooden hoops. One little girl pushed a pram with two grand dolls in it and I was sorry for my rag doll left alone in the cabin.

I discovered my mother was talking to me.

'It's time you were able to read, Tricia!'

'I can read!' I told her. 'I can read everything.'

'Can she?' my mother asked Patrick Henry.

'Read that!' he commanded, pointing at a word on the wall.

'B—a—r Bar, b—i bi, c—a—n can, Barbican!' I spelled triumphantly.

'You shall have a book,' said my mother proudly. 'Any book you like!'

There was a book of fairy tales in the school satchel which Uncle Liam had bought for me, but I hadn't tried to read it. I found it pleasanter to listen to my mother telling stories or to Patrick Henry reading them out. I marched into the shop and we looked at the rows and rows of books on shelves and on tables, and I wondered which I liked best.

'A book for the child?' asked a girl behind the counter 'There's *Nursery Rhymes* with pictures and an *Animal Alphabet*, or can she read?'

'Of course she can!' said my mother scornfully.

'Then buy her *Brer Rabbit*,' advised the girl. 'I bought it for my little brother's birthday and I sat up for hours reading it myself.'

So I had *Brer Rabbit*.

We had meat pie and tea in a grand shop where the tables were made of marble. I usually ate with a spoon, but now that I was old enough to have books I tried to eat with a knife and fork. I sent scraps of meat flying over the table and one bit stuck in my hair.

'Do try to behave yourself,' whispered my mother. 'You're shaming us!'

It was marvellous meat pie with thick jelly and crust that crumbled between my teeth. Then we had jam puffs so light the flakes floated all down the front of my coat, but I managed to brush them off before they were noticed.

'Well, Tricia from Cork! How did ye find Plymouth?' asked Joe Doyle when we came on board. He was cleaning the deck with a mop and bucket and I dropped behind to talk to him.

'It's gorgeous!' I told him. 'And I can read and I have a new book!'

'Ye don't say!' cried Joe admiringly. 'I'm not much of a scholar meself. I like a nice quiet game of cards. Can ye play cards?'

'Indeed no! Grandfather wouldn't have them in the house. You lose all your money if you play cards!' I told Joe.

'D' ye tell me? I'll remember that!' he exclaimed.

We were in the saloon drinking coffee when the coffee-pot slid to the other end of the table and the coffee in my cup slopped over into the saucer.

'I didn't do that!' I said quickly.

'The boat's going down!' my mother gasped. 'We'll be drowned at sea like Uncle Henry, and before we've done any of the grand things we set out to do!'

The young man who looked after us came over.

'We're just going out, ma'am, and there's a bit of a swell. But you're all grand sailors and you won't feel it in five minutes. I'll bring you more hot coffee.'

'I don't like this at all!' exclaimed my mother. 'I never was a good sailor. I'm going to the cabin. Take care of Tricia! Thank God! There's Mrs. Flannery!'

Patrick Henry and I sat looking sadly at one another until Mrs. Flannery came back.

'Let ye not be worryin' yerselves!' she said. 'Yer mother's grand now. She'll have a sleep and when she wakes she'll never know what happened her. Listen now! The ladies and gentlemen are having a bit of a concert to rise their hearts in the little saloon and they want the child to recite for them. Come along now!'

The concert was very grand, not like the ceilidhe on the deck. There was loud music on the piano and singing, but I didn't know any of the tunes and the words had no meaning. I recited, but I was shy. A tall man in a splendid uniform gave me a box of chocolates, yet I knew I hadn't recited nearly as well as I had the night before.

'She mustn't take presents, captain!' said my brother.

The tall man laughed.

'I'm not the captain, lad, only the chief steward. But at sea orders must be obeyed or it's mutiny, and orders are—Miss Patricia Lynch receives a box of chocolates!'

We went up to the covered part of the deck where we could look through glass windows at the stormy sea. We found Joe Doyle there folding deck-chairs and stacking them in a corner.

'Do you think we'll be wrecked, Mr. Doyle?' asked my brother.

Joe sat on the pile of chairs.

'We might, young lad, and then again we mightn't! Can ye swim?'

Patrick Henry nodded. He was the best swimmer at his school, where Brother Joseph was always taking the boys off to the sea.

'A pity!' said Joe, shaking his head. 'Us old sailors never larn to swim, an' I'll tell ye for why—because it prolongs the agony!'

A wave caught the deck. Spray dashed against the windows. I moved closer to my brother and he squeezed my hand.

'Tricia recited again to-night and the chief steward gave her that box of chocolates!' he told Joe Doyle.

'"Twasn't chocolates they gave me on my first ship!' growled Joe. 'But then I wasn't a clever little gerrul!'

'Why did you be a sailor, Joe Doyle?' I asked.

Joe screwed his face up, trying to think.

'Ah, I'd been readin' rubbishin' books about pirates an' the like, an' one day when me mother sent me wid me father's dinner I hid away in a nice dry cowshed to find out did the cabin-boy beat off the buccaneers or didn't he? When I did turn up me father gave me a jacketin', for the man was ragin' mad wid the hunger an' starvation. An' when I went home me mother gave me another. So I slipped off wid meself to Bantry. I got a job on a boat; the boy had skipped, but I didn't take warning from that. Before morning I'd another jacketin' that knocked the others into a cocked hat—and here I am, an' that's cuttin' a long story short!'

'I like the long stories best!' I told Joe Doyle.

'Sure I've me work to do!' he protested. But he didn't budge.

My brother opened the box of chocolates and we sat eating them. I noticed Joe took all the ones in silver paper without even looking at them.

'Do you like being a sailor?' asked Patrick Henry.

Joe sniffed.

'Sure, I'm all for ships and sailormen. Where'd we be widout 'em? Mind ye, I'm gran' in harbour or when I'm just sittin'. But the minit I feel the first lift of the ship I do be quare, an' a cattle boat's the worst torment of all. What wid the crathures themselves and the smell of the chloride, sometimes it does be shockin'! I know what yer poor mother's sufferin'! I seen her go below along wid Mrs. Flannery. Ah, there's the gran' wumman. The worst storm yet never took a rise out of her. But she's a terrible tongue on her! Now for why are ye goin' to London, if you won't think it too bad of me to be axin'?'

My brother was quite pleased to tell Joe Doyle, and we settled ourselves comfortably beside him on the deck-chairs.

'We're going to collect my father's money,' said my brother. 'You see he died in Egypt and his friend brought all the money and papers to London, so we're going there to meet him.'

'An' why not?' demanded Joe Doyle. 'Doesn't every one know all the money of the world is gathered together in London! But why wouldn't the gentleman come over to Cork and save yer mother this terrible journey?'

Joe Doyle cocked his head inquiringly and my brother looked puzzled.

'I don't know,' he said at last. 'We're going to find out.

'An' have ye friends there?' asked Joe anxiously.

Patrick Henry smiled.

'Indeed we have. Good friends. They were poor in Cork and they emigrated to England. Now they're doing fine in London. We're going to them.'

'Thanks be for that!' said Joe. 'Now off wid ye to yer bunks, for to-morrow will be a jewel of a day!'

## 16. END OF THE JOURNEY

THE next day was a jewel! The sky was blue with white ship-like clouds speeding over it to join white mountains piling up to the east. The sea was a deeper blue with white tips tossing, and the ship danced through the waves. There was such lightness in the wind and warmth in the sheltered corners that every passenger came on deck the moment breakfast was ended. We were so close to the shore we could see harbours and houses, boats drawn up on the beach, and people walking on neat promenades, their clothes fluttering. I waved my handkerchief until the wind snatched it and it flew away, curling and twisting.

'Ye should have yer hankies pinned to ye!' advised Joe Doyle.

'I used to,' I told him. 'But I'm too big for that now.'

'Ye'd best not say a word about it, girleen. Ye'd be murdhered! Ye're not too big to be murdhered, are ye?'

I went with him into the galley and saw the covered range with holes in the top where saucepans fitted snugly. I stood on a wooden chair without a back and washed up in a tin bucket. The cook, a fat man with a smooth, shiny

131

head, taught me to make soap bubbles by forming a circle with my dripping thumbs and fingers and blowing gently between them.

'Would ye like to ſtay here with us always, Tricia?' asked Joe Doyle.

I nodded. I hated the thought of going away from the ship.

When I went to the cabin and, unbuckling the leather school bag, looked for the book of fairy tales, it was gone, though Poosie, the rag doll, ſtill sat on guard. I had intended to read a ſtory from it to Joe Doyle and the cook, to let them know how clever I was. *Brer Rabbit* was there, but I hadn't the same friendly feeling for the Plymouth book as I had for the one I had brought from Cork.

'Here 's the Thames!' said Joe Doyle.

'The Thames, two hundred and ten miles long,' quoted my brother.

'If ye 're not the great young scholar, lave it so!' cried Joe admiringly. 'Ye know something about everything!'

'The Lee 's beſt!' I declared crossly.

I thought of the river at Cork in sunshine, little boats, big boats, Blackrock Caſtle, all gay and gleaming. I couldn't remember it in rain or ſtorm.

''Tis not too bad a river, mind ye—the Thames,' Joe told us. ''Tis the miſt an' the hooters make it that diso-late. Then ye muſt remember the summer 's over an' no river 's worth lookin' at once the summer 's gone. Now there 's some say the Thames is the grandeſt river in the world. Don't ate me—I 'm not one of them! But ye 'll see for yerselves!'

A thick miſt hid the shores and clung about the ship. I saw Patrick Henry's face blurred and dim, and I longed for the warm kitchen and Aunt Kattie, the lovely reek of burning turf, and the thick smell of hot potato cake.

'Want to go home!' I sobbed.

'Whist now! whist! A great little gerrul like yerself to be bawlin' an' roarin'!' scolded Joe. 'An' ye're vexin' yer big brother.'

'She isn't vexing me!' declared Patrick Henry. 'I feel just the same way!'

'Then don't let yer poor mother hear that, or the young one ochonin'!' said Joe sternly. 'D'ye think her heart isn't broke an' she leavin' home an' country an' goin' out to face the world wid a pair of childer clingin' to her skirts!'

'I'm not clinging to her skirts!' exclaimed Patrick Henry indignantly. 'I'm going to work and take care of her!'

Joe put his hand on my brother's shoulder.

'I believe ye, lad! I believe ye! An' mebbe ye will be goin' back soon wid a bag of gold. Mind ye, there's great chances in London, but 'tis a sad lonesome place for all that.'

He vanished into the mist, shaking his head dolefully.

'We should be making ready,' said Patrick Henry.

He led the way to the cabin he had shared with three other passengers. The door was open and a pile of trunks blocked the entrance. Patrick Henry scrambled over them, gathered up his brush and comb, toothbrush and box of tooth powder, and the book he had been reading, and crammed them into his trunk. He forced it to shut and was trying to drag it out when Joe Doyle leaned across and took it from him.

'Ye shouldn't struggle wid a load that's beyond yer strength!' he exclaimed. 'Amn't I here for them jobs, an' haven't ye lashin's of time! Go along to the saloon an' I'll gather all yer luggage.'

My mother was sitting alone in the saloon gazing straight ahead. We sat one on each side of her.

'We're nearly there,' said Patrick Henry. 'I wonder will the Cadogans meet us?'

'Of course they will!' declared my mother. 'Maybe with a carriage.'

'Like Cousin Kate's?' I asked.

'Wouldn't you think they'd have gone back home long ago if they are rich?' said my brother.

My mother looked vexed.

'Don't be always doubting! Why wouldn't they be rich? Haven't they written time and time again how well they're doing? And who would they come back to? There isn't one of their twelve children left to them. Tell the young man to bring us tea and toast!'

Patrick Henry frowned.

'I'm tired of tea and toast. Look now! Let's have fried ham and eggs.'

'It's sure to be shocking dear!' objected my mother.

'In a few days we'll be having all the money we want!' he coaxed.

She had never refused Patrick Henry anything in his life, so we had ham and eggs with fried potatoes, a big pot of coffee, and crisp little rolls which had been brought on board by a rowing boat from the shore. The young man told us all about it as he cut my ham into strips.

'Isn't it queer?' said my mother as he went away. 'I never knew a ship steward that wasn't kind and friendly.'

Patrick Henry and I didn't talk. I wasn't exactly tired of tea and toast, but I had never tasted such ham, and the eggs—I had two of them—were crisp all round and the yoke was firm, the way an egg should be. I cleaned up the gravy with my roll and ate two lumps of sugar. I didn't want to stay there another moment.

'Maybe I should say good-bye to Joe Doyle?' I suggested.

'Don't lose yourself,' my mother warned me.

Other passengers were drinking coffee; but most of them were hurrying up and down the narrow passages carrying bags. All the cabin doors were open and in one I saw Mrs. Flannery taking blankets and sheets from a bunk.

'Good-bye, Mrs. Flannery!' I called. 'I'm going to London!'

She sat down and beamed at me.

'Not yet, pet. 'Twill be a good hour or more before ye set foot in London. Come here an' talk to me! Have ye any pennies to spend? Ye'll need a terrible amount of money in London.'

'We're going there to find a bag of gold!' I said. 'Miles Justin Blanchard has it for us.'

'Good luck to him!' replied Mrs. Flannery. 'Hide these three new pennies in yer pocket. Ye'll need 'em, an' sure they look every bit as good as gold.'

Joe Doyle came along, set down the two bags he was carrying, and leaned against the door. I liked being there, but who could tell what was happening on deck?

'Off wid ye!' cried Mrs. Flannery. 'Don't I see the two eyes of ye dartin' this way an' that? Ye're mad to be in London. Give me a kiss an' God go wid ye! Joe Doyle! Will ye take up them bags to the misfortunate passenger that's waitin' on 'em!'

I found my mother and Patrick Henry on deck. The mist was thick as ever, but we moved slowly between ships with lights along the sides, lights on the masts and rigging. Beyond were more lights and great sheds, and, farther, blackness where no lights showed. The three of us stood together beside the black chest. The two trunks and all our bags and boxes were piled on top. Suddenly the ship stopped with a jerk and shivered. Gangways were thrust out and men rushed on board seizing luggage and shouting words we could not understand.

'Will yer friends come on board, ma'am?' asked Joe Doyle, coming up behind us.

Before my mother could answer a huge young man with very long arms and his head sunk between his hunched shoulders slouched down the nearest gangway.

'Mrs. Lynch, I'm Bill Crouchman,' he said. 'I'll tike yer to the Ciddigins. Come on!'

He gathered the bags in one hand, the biggest tin trunk in the other, and pushed through the crowd. Two men seized the black chest and the rest of our belongings.

My mother followed him, her chin as high as it would go, her face very white. My brother held my hand. He had slung the school bag over his shoulder and carried my bundle. I had the rag doll. Our luggage was loaded on to a cart. My mother looked at it in dread.

'Don't worry, lidy!' said Bill Crouchman. ''Ere's a keb!'

We went away from the ship and the river, leaving behind sheds and lines of carts and cabs, great lorries, and plunging horses. A thick fog pressed against our faces and the lights looked dim and choked.

'Keep your mouth shut tight, Tricia!' my mother warned me.

She didn't say another word, and Patrick Henry didn't speak at all. I peeped round my mother at him. His face was flushed, his eyes were very bright, and he looked happy.

We stopped at last before a small shop with a door in the middle. The windows were gay with apples, oranges, and bananas. Outside, cabbages were piled on the pavement, potatoes tumbled from gaping sacks, and bunches of carrots and sticks of rhubarb were built up, leaving a narrow pathway to the door. The cart with our luggage was already there and Bill was waiting. He lifted me from the cab and carried me through the shop into a hot comfortable room, where gas lights with rose-tinted shades helped to keep out the fog.

''Ere's the Ciddigins' frien's, ma!' he said.

A red-faced woman in a purple woollen coat came across
the room from a blazing coal fire.

"'Ow are yer, missis?' she said. 'I'll tike yer up, but
I can tell from yer looks yer won't stay 'ere long. Bill'll
tike yer things up.'

A man sitting in a big wooden arm-chair was eating at the
table, his head close to the plate, and he shovelled the food
into his mouth with a knife.

"'Allo, missis!' he said. 'Mike yerself at 'ome. Bill!
Give the little gel a coco-nut!'

Mrs. Crouchman led us up a narrow staircase. She filled
it from side to side. Hugging the rough, hairy coco-nut,
I followed last, puzzled and wondering. It seemed a queer
place for rich people to live, but I was sure we would find
something wonderful at the top. At last Mrs. Crouchman
thumped on a door.

"'Ere's yer friends, Mrs. Ciddigin!' she called, nodded,
and went heavily downstairs.

The door was flung open, a tiny woman rushed at my
mother and threw her arms about her.

'Oh, Nora Lynch!' she cried. 'Nora! Why did you
come to London? Why did you?'

## 17. THE CADOGANS

THE Cadogans' home was a big room with three windows. From one I could see over the fog which pressed on the huddled roofs and chimneys and beyond to the great river and its streets of lighted ships. Far from the bank a steamship rode high and, forging behind, came a tug with a string of barges. A smaller window at the side looked on a crowded market-place, and through the gloom the fluttering flares showed stalls of fruit and vegetables, brightly coloured clothes, and shining delph.

Tomas Cadogan had a long trestle table in front of the big window. Here he mended broken boots and I heard Mrs. Cadogan tell my mother he was such a clever workman he always had more cobbling than he could do. My mother sat still and silent, staring into the fire, listening and thinking. Patrick Henry had gone with Bill to arrange our luggage and find out where we were to live. The Cadogans had fixed it all. Mrs. Cadogan had promised grand lodgings with pleasant people.

'Mary! Why didn't you tell me?' cried my mother. 'Why did you let me think you had money and a fine home?'

'It is fine compared with some of the places we lived in, and I was ashamed!' confessed the little woman. 'Did ever a letter come to Cork that told of hardship and failure? Sure, Nora, you wouldn't want me to let Tomas down? Tomas Cadogan a cobbler! The neighbours would laugh at us!'

'I wouldn't laugh!' said my mother reproachfully.

'I wouldn't blame them for laughing,' sighed Mrs. Cadogan. 'But I couldn't bear their pity. You know they always called Tomas a dreamer.'

My brother came in quietly. He sat beside Mrs. Cadogan and I stood against the window, looking now at the river, now at that little group by the fire. A wind had risen and was scattering the fog, so that gaps appeared and every moment I saw more of London.

'Come to the fire, child!' said Mrs. Cadogan. 'You'll be perished with the cold.'

They all looked at me. Mr. Cadogan pushed back the dark hair which hung over his left eye and leaned forward.

'Are you the messenger?' he asked me.

I shook my head.

'They didn't send you?' he asked eagerly. 'But no! You're only a child. When the messenger comes 'twill be a fine handsome man on a black horse, or a beautiful woman with yellow hair falling round her like a cloak. Up the stairs she'll come and in at the door. I'll be sitting over by the window, hammering away, when I'll look up and see her. "Rise up!" she'll say, "and come back to your own people! Rise up, King Cadogan!"'

His wife rocked in her seat, her thin hands clasped and her eyes shining.

'That's a lovely dream,' said my mother kindly.

'A dream!' muttered Tomas Cadogan. 'You think 'tis only a dream?'

He gazed appealingly from her face to Mrs. Cadogan's, to Patrick Henry's, and to mine.

'Sometimes dreams come true,' stammered my brother. The old cobbler's hand clasped his.

'There's a deal of knowledge in young people,' he said.

'Only sometimes,' said Mrs. Cadogan, 'I do be wondering what has a poor old woman like meself to be doing with lovely young men and beautiful ladies, and galloping black horses. I'd sooner the messenger was someone like little Tricia here.'

She gave me a shy friendly smile and I wished my hardest that I could be the messenger.

A gas light over the mantelpiece buzzed like a bee and the coal fire glowed a deep red. A black kettle steamed on the hob and a frying-pan began to give out the familiar smell of potato cake. Tomas Cadogan cracked the shell of the coco-nut with his big hammer and my brother cut the nut into chips with a new pocket knife Captain O'Connell had given him. I was drinking my third cup of tea when there came a rattling of the door handle. Mrs. Cadogan ran to open it and in walked the Cronins. I had heard often of them, but they had left Cork before my time. Mr. Cronin had owned a little trading steamer which went to Bantry and Youghal and even as far as Waterford. But he was dissatisfied. He sold the steamer and came to London, determined not to return until he had bought the biggest steamer that could come up the Lee. He was a tall, thin man with spectacles and a straggling grey beard. He didn't look through his glasses but over them, and he carried a hooked umbrella on his arm. Mrs. Cronin was thinner but not so tall. She was dressed in black and her cold grey eyes looked at me so severely I disliked her at once. Besides, Aunt Kattie always said she was a 'craw thumper.' I didn't know what this meant. But now I knew I could never be friends with a 'craw thumper.'

Mary Cronin and her brother Jim came in, pushing one another. They were as big as Patrick Henry, but both wore sailor suits and the name of Mr. Cronin's ship—*Cluna* —was worked on their caps. Since I had known Captain O'Connell I had wanted a sailor suit. Now I didn't mind.

'How are ye, Nora?' asked Mrs. Cronin, and they all shook hands. 'So ye 're a widda woman now! Ah, well, 'tis all for the best!'

'It isn't for the best!' exclaimed my mother indignantly. 'It 's wrong for Timothy Patrick to die in Egypt when he was coming home to us. It 's wrong that Tricia, poor child, doesn't even know what her father looked like!'

'There! there!' coaxed Mrs. Cadogan, stroking her hand.

We sat round the fire. Fresh tea was made and Mrs. Cadogan cut a big loaf into slices.

'That 's a very quare smell!' muttered Mr. Cronin, sniffing.

We all sniffed. I could discover only the pleasant smell of potato cake, made with caraway seeds. Mrs. Cadogan looked at the Cronins uneasily.

'I thought Nora wouldn't feel so homesick if she had a potato cake,' she said.

'Respectable people don't demean themselves by eating potato cake!' declared Mrs. Cronin. 'Only the poor ignorant people of Cork know no better!'

'Nonsense!' exclaimed my mother. 'And you know it 's nonsense, Mrs. Cronin! Mary couldn't have given me anything I 'd like better!'

'Whisht! whisht!' whispered little Mrs. Cadogan.

Mrs. Cronin began to talk politics. I could tell from my mother's face that she didn't agree, and Patrick Henry sat very straight and watched her. If there was to be an argument he 'd be on her side; so would I! So would the Cadogans, both of them.

The young Cronins sat at the table and ate the whole of

my coco-nut.   They ate the big plateful of bread and butter
and emptied the teapot.   But their father and mother loved
arguing better than eating or drinking.   So did my mother,
and she had a great backer in Patrick Henry.   Tomas
Cadogan went over to his trestle table and I tiptoed after
him.   I could listen to an argument if there was nothing
better to hear, but I wanted Tomas to tell me more about
the messenger.

'Did you live on Fair Hill, Mr. Cadogan?' I whispered,
leaning on the table.

He made room for me on the seat beside him.

'I come from the island,' he said.   'A Cadogan was
always king there!   And one day I'll be going back.   I'm
longing for the day.'

'Was it the island at Bantry, Mr. Cadogan?' I asked.

He looked puzzled, but didn't tell me.

When the Cronins went away Mrs. Cadogan took us to
our rooms—a big one with a bed at the end and a small
slip of a room leading from it up two steps.   Our luggage
was piled there and, sleepy as we were, some unpacking
had to be done.   The only light we had was from the
candle Mrs. Cadogan stuck on the mantelpiece.   While the
others opened bags and pulled out clothes I looked from the
window.   I could see right across into a lighted room.
A red-haired woman sat there making flowers from bits
of silk and velvet piled before her.   She was a big rough
woman with a face nearly as red as her hair, and she sang
so loudly I could hear her although both windows were
closed.   Suddenly she laughed and clapped her hands.
Then began singing again.

'Good night!   God bless you!' said Mrs. Cadogan.

She closed the door softly and the three of us were alone.

'This is a queer home!' said Patrick Henry.   'But I
like it!'

'Not our home!' objected my mother.   'We won't unpack anything we don't need at once.   To-morrow we'll find Mr. Blanchard.'

'Shall we go home again when we 've found him, if he gives us the money?' asked Patrick Henry.

My mother was silent.

'No!  Not at once!' she said at last.  'Wouldn't that be foolish now we 've come so far?  We 'll see a bit of the world.   London 's a wonderful city.   Houses on every side, stretching for miles; grand shops.   We 'll have a look at them to-morrow.'

Patrick Henry went into his room.   It had a sloping roof and the only furniture was a stretcher bed, with a chair and a wash-stand.   Ours was far bigger, but we were supposed to live as well as sleep there.

All night long carts rumbled by.   Shouts and running footsteps came up to us, singing and laughter.   I slept and woke, and slept again.   There was never silence.   Even in my sleep I heard strange sounds and my dreams were frightening.

## 18. THE CORNER

In the morning we had breakfast with the Cadogans and, when my mother and Patrick Henry set off to find Mr. Blanchard, I stayed behind.

'Would you like to come?' my mother asked.

She was pleased when I shook my head, but the moment the door closed and I heard her light steps descending the stairs, following the clatter of Patrick Henry's strong boots, I was lonely.

'I'm coming! I want to come!' I called, running to the door, but Mrs. Cadogan held me back.

'Wouldn't you want to help me make the place look like home for your mammy?' she asked. 'An' then I'll take you round to see the neighbours.'

'There was a lady making flowers,' I said. 'I saw her through the window.'

Mrs. Cadogan put her head on one side and blinked her bright blue eyes.

'Miss Tilly, that would be. Her shoes are ready. Now I wonder would your mammy be vexed if I let you come wid me to take them back.'

'She'd want me to. I know she would!' I declared.

Mrs. Cadogan taught me to make beds. We swept the rooms, laid a fire in a queer high grate with hobs, filled a kettle, arranged the table with cups and saucers. I stood on a chair and put my mother's books in a row on the mantelpiece. I couldn't read all the names, but Mrs. Cadogan helped me—*Knocknagow, Tom Burke of Ours, The O'Donohue, David Copperfield*, the big green-and-gold book of *Moore's Melodies, Gulliver's Travels, Faith and Fatherland, The New Ireland*. We went down the steep stairs to the shop and found Mrs. Crouchman sitting behind the counter, twisting onions into a rope.

"'Allo, little gel!' she said. 'Like apples?'

I nodded. She reached out to a heap of apples, picked out the biggest and reddest, polished it on her apron, and handed it to me.

'Thank you, ma'am,' and I clutched it safely.

'Looks poorly,' said Mrs. Crouchman. 'Best let 'er run round wiv young 'Arry! Get 'er up early termorrer, an' Bill can take 'er to the gardin along o' 'Arry. Do 'er all the good in the world! 'Arry! Come 'ere!'

A little boy crawled out from under the counter and lay on a heap of cabbage leaves staring at me.

'Like the little gel to go along o' you an' ole Bill termorrer, son?' asked his mother.

'No, I wouldn't!' declared the boy.

'That ain't friendly, 'Arry!' said Mrs. Crouchman.

Harry scratched his head.

'Orl right. She c'n come!' he agreed, and crawled back.

'They won't st'y long, Mrs. Ciddigin!' and Mrs. Crouchman shook her head dolefully. 'It m'y be cheap, it m'y be clean, it m'y be comfortable. But it ain't their style. You mark my words, Mrs. Ciddigin, they won't st'y!'

I ate the apple as I trotted along with Mrs. Cadogan out of the shop into the alley at the side. Stalls were being put up and the pavement was so crowded with boxes and bundles we had to walk in the roadway. There were dark men with hooked noses draping dresses neatly and very quickly. One fixed his stall, opened a packing case so large I could have walked into it, pulled out cardboard boxes, and had each with its lid standing beside it, displaying ladies' shoes, as we loitered by. The women were big, with brilliant eyes and lovely red cheeks, so that Mrs. Cadogan looked like a ghost beside them. Two young men put their stall in a corner, little polishing brushes in front, then hand-brushes and long-handled brooms at the back, head in air. I looked at dolls—baby dolls, sailor dolls, dolls with silk frocks, dolls with real hair, sleeping dolls, until I wouldn't have taken any of them—there were too many. The hoops and skipping ropes were better, and coloured balls as big as my head set me wondering if Mr. Blanchard would give my mother so much money that she would buy me one. Rows and rows of cups and jugs stood in the gutter, framed pictures gleamed in doorways, and feather dusters swung overhead. Every one talked quickly and I couldn't understand a word they said.

'Jew boys!' explained Mrs. Cadogan.

At the end of the alley we entered a big gateway. I hung back, for a man was making cough sweets in a huge cauldron, and I liked the smell, and the way he lifted out a ladleful, poured it on a dish, beat it with a wooden spoon, pulled the mass out in his hands until it was long and thin, folded a strip again and again, then, seizing a big scissors, clipped it into little lumps.

'Catch!' he called, and flung me one.

The sticky sweet was still warm and the taste was very comforting on that cold, damp morning.

'Nothing mean about them lads!' Mrs. Cadogan told me. 'Look now! This is the back of where we live. Ye need never go through the shop. The passage at the bottom of the stairs comes out yonder. See, Tricia! There 's the window where Tomas sits. You looked across and saw Miss Tilly at the other side of the courtyard.'

We pressed against the wall to let a milk cart pass in.

''Twas all showrooms once upon a time,' explained Mrs. Cadogan. 'Sure 'tis a quare place to live, wid no proper doors or gardens, or anything at all. Beyond at the far side—that 's the dairy.'

Shining churns stood in a row and the gutters ran with milky streams where two men were washing out the last churn. The big brown horse who had brought in the cart was shaking his nosebag and munching steadily. A ladder leaned against the wall and beside it a heap of new straw gleamed in the pale sunshine.

'Here 's Mr. Miles's shop!' Mrs. Cadogan told me. 'He 's a good friend to his own.'

We went into the shop. It was like Judy Leahy's—only far larger—a wonderful place! I had never seen so many different tins and packages before. And two men were carrying in more from a cart outside. At the counter a man was cutting bacon. He wiped the long shop knife on his white apron and rubbed his nose with the back of his hand. He leaned over and peered down at me. His keen eyes had bushy brows, his hair was sleek, and he had three chins. The white apron bulged in front.

'Who 's this new customer you 've brought me, Mrs Cadogan?' he asked.

'Tricia Lynch! They came last night and I 'm minding the child while her mother and brother are about their business.'

'So you 're the last of the Lynches,' said Mr. Miles thoughtfully. 'Welcome to the Corner!'

He smiled and, reaching across, shook hands with me

'Is this the Corner?' I asked.

'That 's right, little Paddy from Cork!'

I liked him, but I remembered what I'd been told.

'Me name is Tricia Nora Lynch,' I said firmly.

'And don't I know it well? Hasn't Mrs. Cadogan here been telling me all about you this long time? How about some sweets?'

I had Mrs. Flannery's new pennies in my pocket.

'I'll have a halfpennyworth of mixed sweets, please, Mr. Miles,' I said.

'Have bull's-eyes,' he coaxed. 'Then you'll have scent and sweets in one. Ah, 'tis grand to hear a voice fresh from Cork!'

He weighed a big bag of bull's-eyes and pushed it across to me.

'I said a halfpennyworth!' I objected.

'That's the right weight, when you're a Paddy from Cork,' said Mr. Miles; 'and, at the Corner, we never take money from a new customer. 'Tisn't lucky! And I need all the luck that's going.'

'Why?' I asked.

Mrs. Cadogan sat close to the counter where bundles of short sticks, neatly tied with string, were piled. They made a fine seat, but I perched on a high square box so that I could listen comfortably to Mr. Miles and look over the shop. Barrels of apples and of broken biscuits formed a barrier against the side window: boxes of Spanish onions, their crinkled, silky skin peeling from them, were stacked at the back, and a monstrous block of brown, shining dates stood on the counter flanked by loaves of bread and half a Dutch cheese, round, with a red rind. The loaves were different shapes, square, oblong, round with a smaller round stuck on top, and long loaves like large twisted bananas. A brown pan of milk covered by a clean check cloth kept company with a cooked ham, a slab of corned beef, and a piece of seed cake. There were tins of salmon, crayfish, lobster, sardines, pineapple, and pears; bottles of sweets, sherbet, and lemonade powder. Overhead swung hanks of small brown onions, bunches of bananas, and cards with penny packets and boxes of pills and ointments stuck on them. There was a smell of paraffin and tarred wood. I could see drawers with printed labels, unopened boxes, and great jars and canisters ranged on the shelves at the back. I looked at Mr. Miles and remembered Judy Leahy.

'Why do I need luck?' he asked. 'Because me ambition is to go back where I came from. One day, please God, I'll have a shop on the North Wall in Dublin. There's a city worth living in!'

'Captain O'Connell says it's the wickedest city in the world!' I declared.

'Why wouldn't you be content wid a little huckster's shop in Cork city, Mr. Miles?' asked Mrs. Cadogan. 'We'd all buy from you an' you'd be a rich man in next to no time.'

'Mebbe I would and mebbe I wouldn't!' chuckled Mr. Miles. 'Are you planning to go back?' he asked me suddenly.

I nodded, my mouth full of bull's-eyes.

'We'll be friends, that's sure,' said Mr. Miles, for when I was a young lad I used to be giving the ram's challenge in just that same way. It's a grand saving of breath!'

'What is the ram's challenge, Mr. Miles?' I asked.

Other customers were coming in. Mrs. Cadogan stepped away from the counter and beckoned me to follow her.

'He's a grand man,' she whispered. 'A lovely man! An' ever since I've known him he's been planning to go back. Isn't that what we all do?'

'Some people do go back, Mrs. Cadogan, don't they?' I asked anxiously. 'Me mammy will go back and Patrick Henry and—and I'll go back, won't I?'

She smiled at me.

''Pon me word, child! I believe you will!'

We went in at one of the doors in the courtyard and climbed a rickety wooden stairs.   Above our heads a voice was singing.

'That's Miss Tilly,' said Mrs. Cadogan.   'She's terrible gay and cheerful, God help her!   Always singing she is—the queerest old songs you ever heard.'

She waited at the top of the stairs until Miss Tilly was silent, then tapped softly on the door.

> 'Come in, come in, come in! sez I,
>      An' don't yer be afraid,'

sang Miss Tilly.

We went in.   Miss Tilly wasn't making flowers.   She was trimming a hat.

'I've brought the shoes, ma'am,' said Mrs. Cadogan.

''Allo! 'allo!' said Miss Tilly.   ''Oo's the stranger?'

'A little friend from Ireland,' explained Mrs. Cadogan. 'She came last night.'

Miss Tilly pulled out a chair.   I stood at the table and saw velvet and silk flower petals, slender bright green tubes, leaves, coils of silk-covered wire, and a big jam-jar of paste with a brush standing up in it.

'Think you'd like to make flowers, nipper?' she asked

I nodded.

Miss Tilly held out the hat.   It was a saucer of straw crammed with flowers of every colour.

'Like it?' she asked.   'Made it meself!'

'It's lovely!' I cried.   'It's gorgeous!'

Her big red face grew redder with pleasure.   She tossed her head.

'There you are, Bert!   That's what the little gel from Cork thinks!'

I looked at Bert.   He was a pale thin boy with sandy hair. He leaned against the wall, his arms folded, his pale eyes scornful.

"'At 's all right, auntie!' he agreed. 'Never said it wasn't. But, Aunt Tilly, it ain't yer style!'

Tears came into Miss Tilly's eyes.

'Ye 're unkind, Bert, that 's what you are! I can wear colours! Ye 're just obstinit, that 's all!'

Bert leaned across the table.

'Black 's yer colour, auntie. I 'm a n'artis', an' I tell yer—black 's yer colour!'

'Black!' cried Miss Tilly. 'Black! An' let every one in the yard think I 'm a widder! No, Bert! Colours for me!'

'If you 'd look at the shoes, ma'am!' urged Mrs. Cadogan.

'No need!' declared the flower-maker. 'They 'll look like a new pair, I know! Bert! 'And over the cash— one-an'-six!'

She picked up a few flowers, twisted them together, added a leaf, and held out the tiny bunch to Mrs. Cadogan.

'Put it in yer Sunday 'at, Mrs. Cadogan. You like a bit o' colour, same as what I do.'

Mrs. Cadogan unwrapped the shoes and put them on the window sill. Miss Tilly stared.

'Buckles! My eye! 'Ere, Bert, another sixpence! That feller ought to be up the West End makin' shoes fer posh ladies—three guineas a time! 'E 's a n'artis'—that 's wot 'e is!'

Mrs. Cadogan's hands were trembling as she folded the piece of brown paper.

'Thank you, Miss Tilly. I 'll tell Tomas. You 're kind and generous. God bless you!'

In the darkness of the stairs I felt my way carefully.

'I like Miss Tilly!' I said.

## 19. THE CROUCHMANS

I was telling Tomas and Mrs. Cadogan about the Fair at Bantry when my mother and Patrick Henry came back. They were tired but excited.

'We've been all over London!' said Patrick Henry. 'We were lost a dozen times! It's a wonderful city! There's no end to it!'

'There's all the people in the world in London!' declared Mrs. Cadogan proudly. 'Doesn't every one say so? Did Mr. Blanchard give you the money?'

'Not yet,' replied my mother. 'We didn't actually see Mr. Blanchard. He's away. We were hours finding his office. If it hadn't been for a policeman who came from Kerry we'd be searching yet. He told us the business people in London have offices in the strangest old rookeries, and he was right. This is a grand cup of tea, Mrs. Cadogan, and I never ate better bacon and cabbage at home!'

'You're foolin' me!' muttered the little woman, and she looked at my mother with pleasure.

'One day I'll have an office in London,' said Patrick Henry. 'But not on the sixth floor!'

'You will! You will!' cried Mrs. Cadogan. 'An'
we'll all be proud of you!'

'Was Tricia much bother?' asked my mother. 'I was
wondering would you mind her another day. Now we
know where to find Mr. Blanchard we'll soon have the
money, and then——'

She stopped speaking and gazed into the fire. It was a
coal fire, very hot and clear. Mrs. Cadogan was making
toast—big, round, soft slices. She kept her eyes on my
mother's face, yet she didn't burn one slice. She cut one
into fingers and I sat on a soft high stool close to the
fender, with a cup of tea beside me and a plate of the cut
toast on my lap.

'I'll miss you terrible, Nora!' said Mrs. Cadogan, laying
her hand on my mother's.

My mother smiled.

'We won't be going back for a while,' she said. 'We'll
see a bit of the country while we're here. Patrick Henry
is going to study and Tricia must go to a good school and
learn to be a lady.'

'You should have a nice little home,' Mrs. Cadogan told
her. 'Mrs. Crouchman was telling me of a dote of a
house. But 'tis a long way from here. You will come
to see me, Nora, an' bring the child?'

'You and Tomas shall come to see us every Sunday,'
promised my mother. 'We'll have plum cake and tinned
pineapple for tea!'

'And muffins!' added my brother. 'All the grand people
in London eat muffins!'

'Would you mind the child going in the big van to
Covent Garden to-morrow?' asked Mrs. Cadogan. 'The
young man below takes his little brother once every week
an' he's made the offer for Tricia. He's a careful steady
lad for all his looks, an' he's terrible fond of children!'

'Do you want to go?' my mother asked me.

'You come too,' I whispered.  'You and Patrick Henry.'

'Don't vex your poor mother,' coaxed Mrs. Cadogan. 'Look now!  I'll make you another cut of toast.  Don't mind her, Nora.  She's a terrible good child, but she doesn't understand how you can't be with her as you used to be.'

My mother and Patrick Henry looked at one another.

'Why shouldn't she come with us?' he asked.  'We don't walk all the time and I can carry her if she gets tired.'

'Indeed you won't!' she said indignantly.  'You—a slip of a boy to carry a big heavy child!'

'I'll play in the garden!' I put in.  'I want to play in the garden!'

'You'll have to rise up before the dawn!' said Mrs. Cadogan.  'You should go along to your bed now.'

At home I had stayed up as late as any one.  I never wanted to go to bed.  Now I longed to be alone with my mother.  It was so long since I had watched her brush her hair in the attic.  She didn't seem to belong to me, and Patrick Henry was almost a stranger.  He held my hand as we went by the flickering light of a candle along to our own rooms.  I watched him standing on tiptoe to light the gas.  He was nearly as tall as my mother and his blue serge suit was too small for him.  He gazed down at me.

'Like London?' he asked.

I shook my head.

'Want to go home!' I murmured mournfully.

My mother frowned.

'Tricia—where we three are together—that's home!  If you can undress yourself, I'll tell you a story when you're in bed.'

A story!  I unbuttoned my strap shoes, pulled off my socks, and fumbled with the buttons of my frock.  Unluckily they were at the back and I couldn't reach them.

My brother was closing the door of his own room. His laughing eyes encouraged me and I pulled the frock over my head without unfastening a single button. At last I was propped up with pillows. My mother sat on the edge of the bed, her hair streaming over her shoulders like a cloak, her grey eyes thoughtful. I had heard people call her lovely. That night I understood what they meant. She was pale and her dark eyebrows were thick, so were her lashes. Her straight nose and firm chin made her seem severe. I looked at her proudly, waiting for the story.

'You must have heard stories galore when you were with Mrs. Hennessy,' she said slowly.

I thumped the pillows.

'I didn't! I didn't!'

'When I was a little girl and stayed with Mrs. Hennessy she told me stories all day long!' declared my mother. 'She is a storyteller! She always tells them!'

I tried to think of the stories Mrs. Hennessy had told me. But they were no comfort.

'You promised!' I sobbed indignantly. 'I undid me shoes and I took off me frock. You promised!'

'I'm ashamed of you!' said my mother. 'If you cry when there's nothing to cry about, what will you do when you meet real trouble? I'm going to tell you the story of the Swan Children and their wicked stepmother. They knew trouble, God help them! This story is one of the Three Sorrows of Storytelling. I'll tell you the others some time—the Fate of the Sons of Usna and the Quest of the Sons of Turenn.'

I lay back luxuriously. My mother brushed her hair and spoke softly. Carts rumbled, there were shouts and screams from the street below, but I listened only to that expressive voice telling one of the Sorrows of Storytelling. The noises outside became the waves of Moyle sweeping over poor Fionuala and her brothers, the throbbing gaslight became the candles they saw in happy homes they could not enter.

'Open your eyes, pet, an' creep out.   I have your clothes under me arm an' there's hot tay ready an' waitin'!'

I opened my eyes.   Mrs. Cadogan was bending over me. My mother's head lay on the pillow, her eyes closed, her hair in two long plaits falling to the floor.   I crept out, and my bare feet shrank from the cold oilcloth.   But the trials of the Swan Children were still grieving me and I would not complain.

'Sup it up!' said Mrs. Cadogan, pouring out the tea. 'Sup it up, there's the girleen!'

A candle stood on the table, for the Cadogans did not like the gas, and its pale flame was clear and steady in the warm room.   But for the coal fire I might have been at Mrs. Hennessy's.   There were the same pictures on the walls—Our Lady, the Holy Family, Wolfe Tone, Emmet, Dan O'Connell, Parnell.   Their eyes were friendly as they looked down on the two exiles—an old woman and a little girl, drinking hot tea in the early morning, while outside the great sprawling city began the day's work.

We came downstairs as Bill strode through the shop, Harry stumbling after him, rubbing the sleep from his eyes. The high cart with the big black horse in the shafts was waiting in the street.   A ragged boy, munching a slice of bread, held the reins and shivered in the cold river wind. Bill made a nest in a heap of hay behind the driver's seat.   He settled Harry and then me into it, then, pulling a horse-rug over us, he mounted the driver's seat, cracked his whip in the air, and away we clattered.

Harry leaned against me and slept.   I saw Mrs. Cadogan waving her apron.   We turned a corner, swinging out on a wide, straight road, and joined the line of motors and vans flowing in one direction.   Some were loaded with cabbages, others with carrots or onions.   One, piled with flowers, kept alongside us for a while, and, when it raced on, the air was still scented. The shops were shuttered, curtains drawn across windows, but trams rattled along through the mist and the pavements were crowded, mile after mile. I was falling asleep when I discovered, towering above me, a great wall of red cabbages. They were still wet with dew, and the sun, cutting through the mist, glittered on every drop. I thought of the red cabbages at Bantry and remembered Yalla Hankercher. Were we going to a Fair? No! To a garden!

The cart stopped. Bill clambered down and came round to us. He clutched his elbows and grinned down at his sleeping brother.

'Wot a nipper! Sleep, sleep! Eat, eat! But strong! You wait!'

He picked Harry up and set him in the gutter. Harry opened his eyes and rubbed his hands.

'I'm ready!' he declared, yawning.

'Keep close!' Bill ordered me.

I still remembered being lost at Bantry Fair. I caught hold of Bill's long blue cotton coat and clung on. Because of the great crowd he was forced to move slowly. He stuck out his elbows and forced a passage. Harry kept with me and kicked his way through. I admired his boldness but didn't dare imitate him. Bill stopped and, reaching down, caught me up and placed me on a wooden platform. Harry pulled himself beside me, and there we were, safe from the crowd. The platform was small, and above our heads at a kind of rough desk a man was shouting. There were other platforms with shouting men and, from the crowd, men shouted back. It was a long time before Bill shouted. As he called out the people squeezed together and made an open laneway. Along it came a line of men carrying baskets on their heads. Harry and I peeped out, one on each side of Bill. The baskets were piled so high

I couldn't see the top ones. As one man passed, his baskets swayed and I was sure they would fall on us. He swung his shoulders, tilted his head, and the baskets straightened themselves.

'Seventy!' muttered Bill. 'Just fancy! Seventy baskets! Takes brains to do a thing like that!'

Lorries, snorting and throwing up clouds of smoke, backed with their loads. Horses kicked and tried to plunge, but were tugged down. Some were steaming as much as the lorries.

'I wouldn't swop my 'orse, not fer a dozen ole steam engines!' jeered Bill.

'Brekfuss!' demanded Harry.

'Work fust!' replied Bill.

Again we pushed through the crowd. Now we came to where sacks of potatoes were ranged on one another in a great wall. From the back men came running, bent low, each with a sack on his shoulders. Bill's cart was close to the potato wall. A man with a long pencil and a book stood by, checking numbers. Bill seized a sack at one end and Harry caught the other. Between them they slung it up on the cart. The man with the pencil stared. Bill and Harry lifted another sack. As they started on the third, people were stopping to watch.

''Ow old's that kid?' demanded the man with the pencil.

'Seven and a bit!' answered Bill proudly.

'Show yer muscles, young 'Arry!' he added.

Harry took off his jacket, rolled up his shirt sleeves, and bent his arm slowly. Great bumps came on them and every one cried out with delight.

'A strong man, that's wot 'e 'll be!' said the man with the pencil.

'I saw a strong man at the Fair,' I said.

'Funny wy the little gel talks!' said the man with the pencil. 'Welsh, ain't she?' he asked Bill.

Bill was hauling down another sack of potatoes. After potatoes he tossed cabbages into the cart, then bunches of carrots and turnips.. I wondered where Harry and I were to sit. Harry wasn't bothering. He tugged his brother's coat.

'Brekfuss, Bill!'

'Onions fuSt, nipper!' Bill told him kindly.

The horse followed Bill as he moved from potatoes to carrots, to turnips, and now to where ropes of onions were coiled as if they were necklaces. A smaller heap, where herbs were tied in bunches, made Harry sniff happily.

'I don't 'alf like a smell!' he exclaimed.

Bill tucked the bundles of herbs in between the sacks.

''Arf a mo!' he said, and ran to a diStant part of the market. He came back with his arms filled with chrysanthemums.

'Yer mum do like a bunch o' flowers!' he told Harry.

'The garden, Bill?' I asked. 'I want the garden.'

He grinned at me.

''Ere it is, kiddo! Orl round yer! Coven' Gardin!'

Our hands in his, we crossed the road, dodging horses and vans. The fumes crowded out the pleasant smells of vegetables and flowers. All the shops here were eating-houses. Bill walked Straight into the firSt, up three high Steps, and we sat at a table in the window, looking out on the Struggling world. We had big mugs of hot coffee, very sweet and milky, big plates of chipped potatoes, each with a sausage and a fried egg on top. A dish of bread and butter sat in the middle of the table. I was hungry and the chips were golden brown, crisp but floury. The egg was sizzling and the sausage thick yet well cooked. I ate Steadily, but my plate was Still heaped when Bill and Harry Started on their second. They ate three platefuls each. Harry put his elbows on the table.

'Can't eat no more!' he said sadly.

Bill ate on. At last he leaned back, pulled out a pipe, lit it, and began to puff. The smoke was sweet-smelling and the matches he used were wax. Now that I had time to look about me, I discovered that the room was hazy with smoke from pipes and the steam of food. The tables were crowded with men, big, strong men, like Bill. There were a few women with red faces and loud, jolly voices. Harry and I were the only children. Half-way along the room the floor went down two steps, and at the far end, where doors swung ceaselessly, were two more steps. I caught glimpses of fires, shining steel, men in white caps and boys wearing long aprons, carrying dishes, buckets, or just running.

'Time!' Bill yawned, and rapped his pipe on the table.

'Like yer brekfuss, little 'un?' asked the girl who had served us.

'I did indeed,' I assured her. ''Twas a grand breakfast!'

The girl laughed.

'Don't she talk funny! Scotch, ain't she?'

I felt my face going hot. I had been thinking how strangely every one around me spoke, and hadn't I come straight over from Cork? Scotch indeed!

There was no room inside the cart. The driver's seat was high above the horse, and on a level with Bill's feet was a small space, big enough for Harry on one side, me on the other. I didn't like being so high up, but the road was crowded with carts and horses and I couldn't see the ground. We went back slowly. Now the shops were open and stalls were being put up in rows.

'Is this the Fair?' I called out. 'Bill! Is this the Fair?'

'Mile End Road!' answered Bill, swishing the whip. 'Longest road in the world, I 've 'eard tell!'

The longest road in the world! I was wondering how long that would be when we turned into a side road, then a smaller road, a road where two carts like ours couldn't pass, and there was the shop and Mrs. Crouchman standing in the doorway.

''Ow d' yer like our Coven' Gardin, little gel? Wot sort of a load 'ave yer, Bill?'

My mother and Patrick Henry came home so late that night I was in bed asleep. I woke to see her sitting by the window, brushing her hair.

'The longest road in the world!' I said.

She laughed.

'Dreaming again?'

In Cork I had explored the streets and quays with Dinny Foley. Now my companion was Harry Crouchman. Dinny swaggered, ready to be friends with the world. Harry never ventured beyond the shop without looking up the street and down. He peered round corners, he avoided dark doorways, and I imitated him. My mother gave me twopence a week, and I spent it in Mr. Miles's shop. Patrick Henry was always giving me halfpennies, and I spent these in the same place. Harry shared my sweets and broken biscuits, but he had so much more money that it was only from politeness. The shop money was kept in a drawer at the back of the counter. When we were going out, Harry opened the drawer and took out a handful of coins. His mother knew, his brother knew, I expect his father knew, for he was always watching from his wooden arm-chair. But Harry behaved like a robber and came from behind the counter on tiptoe, his finger on his lips, warning me to silence.

Mrs. Cadogan had a great regard for the Crouchmans and I could coax her to let me do anything. The moment my mother and brother climbed down the stairs I was after them, and as they walked out the passage way I ran into the shop. Harry never went to school. He didn't know his letters, but he never made a mistake with money or with weights, and he never lost his way. Every day he took me through fresh alleys, over strange bridges, and across neglected wastes where tins rusted among the weeds. Sometimes we strayed so far we were in danger of being back later than my mother. Then Harry scrambled up behind carts going our way and pulled me with him, without the driver seeing us. I knew my mother would be horrified if she knew where I spent my days. Every night I made up my mind to tell her. I would begin, but she never listened and I was thankful to have an excuse for my silence. Mrs. Cadogan knew, and so did Mrs. Crouchman, but they sympathized with my longing to explore London. I must be back, washed and tidy, when my mother and Patrick Henry arrived; for the rest of the time they trusted me with Harry.

Harry hated sitting at a table for meals. He ate apples, pears, and bananas in the shop. Most of his food he bought in fish-and-chip shops, wrapped in greasy papers. On Saturday he had pease pudding and faggots, and sometimes wally-wallies—small pickled cucumbers. I felt guilty as I shared his feasts, and longed to tell my mother of the strange food I was discovering, but I didn't dare. She never knew of our wanderings by the docks where dark men walked on the sides of their feet, yellow men shuffled along, their hands folded in their sleeves, and half-caste children played in the gutters. I saw queer-shaped letters over shops, I heard strange words, and I wanted to share my knowledge and excitement, but every day I delayed made the telling harder. I was beginning to find Mrs. Cadogan's simple cooking tasteless. Even on wet days there would be queer talk and people in Mr. Miles's shop, and he always welcomed me. Harry never went there; his own home and the streets—they made his world.

Miss Tilly taught me to make flowers, and I became so expert that she promised me full employment when I was fourteen.

'In a workroom, ducky! Real young ladies, they are. You'd like to be a 'elp to yer poor mother!'

The neighbours called her 'Carrots,' and Bert was 'Young Carrots'; but I remembered my manners. Bert let me fill in some of his pavement pictures with coloured chalks, but I hated his cap lying on the pavement for the pennies of the passers-by. I told myself it was just the same as Francis Joseph fiddling at the Fair, but I didn't believe it. People gave Francis Joseph money because they liked his music and listened as long as he would play, but pennies were thrown into Bert's cap without a glance at his pictures.

Suddenly I was taken out of this life. One evening I lay in bed, biting a huge pear Bill Crouchman had given me. My mother was rummaging in the big black chest. She turned, still bending, and I saw her pale face and sparkling eyes upside down.

'Tricia! We won't be here much longer. I've found the loveliest little house in the world! It's made of wood and it's in a wood yard. And you're going to a grand school!'

I went to sleep again and dreamed we lived in a tree. We swung up and down by the branches and no one could see us. The wind blew and all night long a bird sang.

## 20. THE HOUSE IN THE WOOD YARD

BILL CROUCHMAN carried down our belongings and piled them in the cart. He had scrubbed it and spread clean sacks to save the black chest from harm. I went with Mrs. Cadogan to say good-bye to the neighbours. Miss Tilly gave me a bunch of flowers—white with green leaves.

'For yer ma's Sunday 'at,' she said. 'Wouldn't dare offer 'em meself. You tell 'er. With Miss Tilly's respects.'

Mr. Miles was weighing dates in blue sugar bags.

'Any time ye 're passin', look in,' he said. 'Any time ye 'd like a bull's-eye, don't forget the glass jar in the winda. Ye 're not goin' that far an' I 'm hopin' I 'll be seein' ye. Good-bye, Paddy from Cork! I 'll miss ye!'

He gave me two bags—one filled with bull's-eyes, the other with sticky dates.

'One day ye 'll be comin' to me shop in Dublin,' he said, laughing.

I went in the back way and looked good-bye at the courtyard. The shining milk cans stood in a row and the gutters ran with warm milky streams. My mother was shaking hands with Mrs. Crouchman in the shop.

'You 've been very good to my little girl,' she said.

164

'Crouchman!' called Mrs. Crouchman. 'The lady's goin'!'

Mr. Crouchman was sitting in his wooden arm-chair close to the table, eating from a soup plate with a knife. I had never seen him any other way, and I didn't like him, but I envied him the wooden arm-chair.

'Give the little gel a coco-nut!' he called, his mouth full.

'Can she ride with 'Arry?' asked Bill.

Harry, from his perch on the black chest, gazed down at us, and my mother frowned at me doubtfully.

I nodded eagerly, wishing her to let me go.

'If it's not too much trouble,' she said.

Bill swung me up beside Harry. Mrs. Crouchman, her arms folded, stood between my mother and Mrs. Cadogan. I waved as the black horse plunged and slipped on the cobbles. My brother lifted his cap, Mrs. Cadogan fluttered a handkerchief, and Mrs. Crouchman stared solemnly in front of her. Only my mother smiled.

'Guess you're used to goin' orf!' said Harry mournfully.

I was disappointed at the shortness of the drive. We stopped at a black fence so high that the top was on a level with the neighbouring roofs. Carts, loaded with planks, trundled slowly through a wide gateway, but Bill drew up at a small green door set in the fence and opened it with a key my mother had given him. Harry and I scrambled down and were through the door before Bill began to unload. A tiled path led to a wooden house. The walls were brown, the door and roof bright green. A window on each side of the door had clean muslin curtains swaying in the wind and, beyond a low fence, planks piled on planks towered like mountains.

'Look!' said Bill.

He strode along a narrow lane between walls of planks. Harry and I ran after him. We came out on a canal with a barge drawn up at the side. Two men were loading this, each carrying a yellow swaying plank on his shoulder and running with the burden.

'Couldn't carry it if they walked.   Too 'eavy!' explained Bill.

We went back to the house.   He brought out another key and opened the house door.   There were four rooms, two in front and two, very small, at the back.   It was already furnished and, when Bill carried the chest into the sitting-room and stowed the bags and trunks and bundles in the front bedroom, our moving was finished.

I hadn't seen the house properly before my mother and Patrick Henry came walking up the path.   I rushed to meet them.

'There's a boat and a river!' I cried proudly.   'But there isn't a turf pile!'

'Who'd want turf with all this wood for burning?' asked my brother, and we all laughed.

'When you're movin' agin, missis, there's me an' the nag an' the cart at yer service,' said Bill, taking off the cap he wore always, even indoors.

'We're staying here!' replied my mother.   'I don't suppose we'll move for years and years.   But thank you kindly.'

I went to the door in the fence with Bill and Harry.

'Get a move on, nipper!' said Bill to his brother, who lagged behind.

'Kin I stay 'ere?' mumbled Harry.   'Along of 'er?'

His brother looked at him, at me, at the little wooden house and the towering heaps of planks, grinned, and shook his head.

'Come back where yer belong, 'Arry.   Say good-bye quick, an' come on!'

'Good-bye, Harry!' I said quickly, anxious to run indoors.

We stared at one another and I feared he was going to

cry, but Bill pulled him on. I was sorry to part with Harry, but he wasn't like my old friend Dinny. When the little green door closed it was Dinny, not Harry, I remembered. I heard the clatter of the black horse's hoofs and the rolling of wheels, but I thought what fine games Dinny and I could have among the lovely yellow planks, only Dinny wasn't here—he was far away in Cork.

My mother had a string shopping bag, bulging with parcels, and Patrick Henry carried a big basket. She unwrapped the soft brown paper from a loaf of bread, the kind I liked best—a big round cake with a little one on top.

'That's a cottage loaf!' she told me. 'You can have the top all to yourself.'

There was a lump of soft yellow cheese, a green packet of tea, a blue bag of sugar, six brown eggs, and a pot of whole-fruit strawberry jam. But before she had half emptied the basket she clapped her hands and looked round laughing.

'Isn't this the dote of a house!' she cried. 'It's the house I always wanted.'

Patrick Henry was lighting the fire in the small range. He was the best in the family at lighting a fire, better even than Aunt Kattie, but he wasn't used to a range. He blew and blew at the pieces of wood and paper behind the iron bars, for there was no bellows. As he looked smiling over his shoulder the wood began to crackle and there was a roar in the chimney.

'It's like a house in a fairy story!' he said.

'Tell me a story!' I demanded.

My mother caught my hands.

'Amn't I a good mother to find you such a splendid home?' she asked.

'You're a lovely mother!' I told her, and the three of us danced round the table.

We went on with the unpacking. There was a cupboard

built against the wall and we found the delph stored on its shelves. We had never had so many cups and saucers before, but I thought the room looked strange without a dresser. I laid the table, three cups and saucers, three plates, knives, forks, spoons. My mother filled the kettle at a sink in the corner and we gazed in amazement at one another when she brought out a blue enamel teapot from the back of the cupboard.

'It won't poison us for one day!' she said. 'I'll buy a brown teapot to-morrow if they have them in London!'

The milk was in a bottle. My mother had brought it with her and then she discovered a jug of milk on the window sill.

'That's a kind man I took the house from,' she said. 'He let me have it five shillings a week less than he asked at the beginning and we can have all the wood we want for burning. Mr. Forbes is his name.'

'Maybe we're lucky?' suggested Patrick Henry.

'Why wouldn't we be?' demanded my mother. 'God knows we've had enough trouble! Isn't it time there was a change?'

We had cooked ham and I wondered where was the cat to eat the fat I hated. I cut my own top of the loaf and saved the crust to spread with strawberry jam. When darkness came there was a lamp with a golden shade and black figures on it. The windows had thick blue curtains, and when Patrick Henry pulled them across, indeed it was a snug house!

'To-morrow we'll settle in properly!' said my mother. 'And, Patrick Henry, Mr. Forbes wants to talk to you. I told him how clever you are with figures. He used to live in this house by himself. He's the owner or the manager, or something important.'

I lay in bed in the front room, listening to their voices and to the rain falling with soft taps on the corrugated roof. I held the rag doll in my arms and told her all that had happened. Poosie was a warm, comforting doll, and I had neglected her lately.

In the morning a man with milk in a big can came through the door in the fence, and I held the jug while he poured milk into it from a gleaming dipper.

'That's a good pint and a dash for the cat!' he told me.

'Where is the cat?' I asked.

He shut one eye, laid his finger alongside his nose, and went off.

As I turned back, another man with an enormous basket on his arm pushed the little door open.

'Baker, missy!' he called, and set the basket on the path before me.

There were square loaves, round ones, the cottage loaves I liked so much, and little brown sticky buns.

'May I take what I please?' I asked.

The man laughed. He was a round, fat, jolly man, with little black, twinkling eyes, so I laughed too.

'Talk funny, don't yer?' he asked. 'You foreigners?'

My mother came out behind me.

'Look!' and I pointed. 'Here's wonderful bread, and we can have any of them.'

She smiled, picked up one of the twisted loaves and, to my delight, added three of the sticky buns.

'Nice mornin', missis!' said the man.

'It is indeed! Thanks be to God!' she agreed.

He looked very serious, touched his cap, and went away without another word.

After breakfast Patrick Henry went off to talk to Mr. Forbes and my mother unlocked the black chest. We hadn't really unpacked at all at the Cadogans, and it was amazing to see how much we had brought. Out of the black chest came a thick green rug which she laid down before the tiny fire-place in the sitting-room. There was just room on the mantelpiece for the black cabinet with the little drawers and their silver handles, closed in by doors decorated with raised gilded figures. On top of this, beside the silver candle snuffers, stood my speckled shell with the roar of the sea in it. The round mirror was hung on the wall opposite the window. Then out came the pictures and I knew we were at home. Patrick Henry had varnished and pasted them on cardboard with a frame painted round, so that they looked like real framed pictures, yet were light and easily packed.

When Patrick Henry came in he hammered nails into the wall and my mother hung them in a row—Wolfe Tone, young Emmet, Daniel O'Connell, Charles Stewart Parnell —and a smaller gaily coloured one of St. Patrick she placed underneath.

'Why didn't we have them at Fair Hill?' I asked.

'I was saving them for when your father came back and we made a home together,' my mother told me.

'Tricia! Help me bring in some more wood!' called my brother.

I went eagerly with him away from the house to a heap of odd bits of wood. He carried a bucket, but instead of filling it he turned to me, and he looked very serious.

'Now, Tricia, and don't forget,' he said. 'You mustn't be always asking her questions. If there's anything you don't understand, ask me when we're alone.'

I was puzzled.

'You see,' he explained, 'our father is dead. If mamma thinks about him it makes her sad and you keep reminding her. You shouldn't do that!'

'Why is he dead?' I asked.

Patrick Henry shook his head.

'I don't know. Everybody dies some time. But he should have come home first. If we'd all been together like other people, his dying would still be sad, but we wouldn't be so different. You do understand, don't you?'

I nodded.

'And you won't ask questions?'

I shook my head.   We filled the bucket with small pieces and, carrying the larger wood in our arms, went back loaded.

While we were working a stew had been simmering on the stove, and now we had our dinner.   We were eating bread and strawberry jam and drinking tea, when someone tapped at the door.

'Come in!' called my mother.

A short, stout man with a pale face and sandy hair plastered down pushed the door and stood looking at us severely.

'Sorry to interrupt ye, ma'am,' he said.   'But I 'm a busy man with little time to spare, and there 's a matter connected with this boy I 'd like to settle now.'

He spoke fiercely and looked so stern I was frightened, but my mother seemed delighted with him.

'Sit down, Mr. Forbes, and I 'll pour you a cup of tea.'

'Thank ye, ma'am, but I never take tea after me dinner,' said Mr. Forbes.   'I 'll take a seat.'

He pulled a chair up beside me and my mother looked very bewildered.

'Not drink tea after dinner!' she said.   'Isn't that very queer now?'

'Maybe, ma'am, maybe!   But I 've come to tell ye I 've never seen such a head for figures as this boy's.   I 've had my life made miserable with fules who call themselves book-keepers, but can't add two and two without a ready reckoner.   Now I gave your son a page of accounts.   He ran his pencil down the lines once and wrote out the totals, and when I said: "Will ye go up the lines for a check?" sez he: "I will not: my figures are correct!"   I gave him a month's bills of lading.   He turned them over once, and wrote down the amounts.   I 've been working on them since and there 's not one figure wrong.'

'Patrick Henry never had a figure wrong in his life!' exclaimed my mother proudly.

'I'd like him to do the figuring for this firm, ma'am,' went on Mr. Forbes. 'He can try it for a month and ye can live here rent free. If I'm satisfied and he is, at the end of a month we'll start him on a pound a week.'

'As well as the house?' asked my mother.

'As well as the house!'

Patrick Henry wasn't smiling, but his eyes were dancing. My mother looked thoughtful.

'That would mean we'd have to stay here,' she objected.

'But, ma'am! Aren't ye satisfied? I'll have gas put in if ye like. It might make things easier.'

They looked at one another.

'You're very kind, Mr. Forbes,' said my mother.

The stout little Scotsman gave his head a sideways jerk.

'On one condition, ma'am!'

'Oh!' cried Patrick Henry.

'Indeed!' said my mother, looking very proud and indignant.

'The lad's good at figures!' said Mr. Forbes. 'But if he's to get anywhere, he must pass exams. He should become an accountant, not be just a book-keeper, earning a couple of pounds a week.'

'I'll pass any exams you like!' said Patrick Henry.

Mr. Forbes stood up.

'Good lad! And while I'm here, I'll say I never saw such beautiful handwriting in my life! Ye'll never need a typewriting machine, I can tell ye that! And this is the little girl! She'll have a good time here. Good day, ma'am!'

He marched out. My mother leaned back in her chair.

'Oh, Patrick Henry, I'm proud of you! You've hardly left school and here you are, earning money and giving us a home. I'll make another pot of tea!'

## 21. THE SHINING CORRIDOR

I FOUND caves among the planks and built houses with blocks of wood. There were piles of sawdust like very dry sand, and I carried buckets of it into the smallest cave I could find. I brought the rag doll and my toys there, and, hidden safely, watched men lifting planks and stowing them on barges and lorries. When Saturday came a barge was tied to the bank and I explored it, seeing as I climbed back little green-and-white lizards sliding in the mud. The path went along the bank and I followed it, but I had promised my mother I wouldn't go away from the yard, so when I looked back and found that the plank hills were out of sight I returned. I made up my mind, however, to coax my mother and Patrick Henry along there so that we could go on and on.

The next day we went to Mass in a strange chapel, where there were dark men in thin blue clothes, sailors with tattooed arms, women in shawls with babies tucked inside, just as I had seen them in Cork. Small yellow men with darting eyes, and big yellow men whose eyes slanted, stood side by side. I looked for the Cadogans, but they weren't there, and I didn't want the Cronins.

Afterwards my mother went into the sacristy while Patrick Henry and I waited outside the porch.   At the gate a man was selling newspapers as the congregation crowded out.
'*Irish Independent!*' he shouted.   '*Irish Independent!* Support our own paper!'

'That belongs to home!' Patrick Henry told me, and he bought one.

I was tired and wondering about dinner before my mother joined us.

'I found out all about St. Winifred's Convent School for Tricia,' she said.   'It's where Cousin Kate used to stay on her way to France.   You'll learn everything there and there are other Irish children, so you won't be lonesome. We'll go along to-morrow.'

I almost forgot the barge and the canal.   But after dinner, as my mother put down her cup, she pushed back her chair.

'We'll go for a walk!' she said.

'Along the canal!' I cried.   'And look at the barge!'

Patrick Henry didn't mind where we walked, so we went through the gap in the little fence around our house, between the walls of wood, and came out by the barge. I scrambled on board and stood back for them to join me.

'A dirty old barge!' exclaimed my mother.   'Suppose you fell into that slimy water!   Oh, Tricia!   You promised to be careful!'

'I was careful!' I retorted indignantly.   'It's a lovely boat!   Just look at the colours in the water and the little fellas in the mud!   Now, aren't they dotes?'

My mother looked with horror at the glistening water, at the green-and-white lizards; she could see nothing beautiful in them.   I glanced at my brother.   He was laughing, but he shook his head at me.

'You don't like them,' I said mournfully.

I was so disappointed that they went along the path to please me.   There wasn't much room, for the walls of the yard rose on one side and the waters of the canal touched the other.

'If you 'd slipped!' groaned my mother. 'You 're a desperate child, Tricia! It 's time you went to school.'

Beyond the wood yard we came to a bridge—a narrow bridge which could swing back to let the barges pass—and beyond this again lay a stretch of waste land. I tried to coax them over the bridge, but my mother was determined.

'You 're as bad as your Aunt Hannah!' she told me.

So we went back, not indoors but on to the road where the trams sped by, and we climbed on top of one and rode all the way to the city. Though the shops were closed my mother was happy again, for the crowds of the world were there and, though we walked as slowly as any one, we were pushed at every step. I thought of the canal, the barge, the green-and-white lizards.

'Tricia doesn't like this!' declared Patrick Henry. 'But I know what she will like!'

He whispered to my mother. She smiled.

'This once,' she said. 'Because she 's going to a real school to-morrow!'

We went into a gay, bright shop with little tables in rows. At one end men were making music; one had a fiddle, though he couldn't play it nearly as well as Francis Joseph; another sat at a queer flat piano, and a third had a fiddle so big he rested it on the floor. We had coffee in big thick cups, and round tarts with black-currant jam in them.

'Now isn't this lovely!' said my mother.

I was glad when we were back on the tram and I saw the straight long road which led homeward. Tea in our own little house was much nicer than the coffee in the shop, and the seedy cake my mother cut in thick fingers tasted better than the jam tarts. After tea my mother told us a story about Maeve, the Warrior Queen—that was for me—and how Wolfe Tone came to Bantry Bay with the French at Christmas long ago—that was for Patrick Henry. Then it was time for bed. The night passed and there was I walking with my mother through a big iron gate, along a gravelled path, between beds of flowers, and up wide steps into a big stone building.

'Now don't interrupt!' she warned me. 'And don't ask questions, or the nuns will wonder what kind of a woman I am at all!'

'Why?' I asked.

'Now don't disgrace me!' said my mother.

While she rang the bell I looked back at the flowers. They were in lines—bright red geraniums, bordered with circles of blue lobelias, and I thought they didn't look like flowers at all. There wasn't one daisy in the wide stretches of grass, and I hated gravel. The door opened, and a nun in black and white motioned us in. We walked down a long corridor filled with sunshine. The floor glowed golden brown and my feet slipped along easily. All down one side were high, open, uncurtained windows. From one I looked out on a playground with two swings and a grand seesaw, not a bit like the one Uncle Liam had made. I wanted to stop and watch the many little girls and the boys who played there. But on we walked. We passed another playground, and here big girls were playing with balls and sticks. I remembered my grandfather was a champion hurler of Munster, and I wondered if Patrick Henry would play hurley here in London. There were trees pressing against the next window and the light was pale green, but the branches had lost most of their leaves. I didn't look through the other windows, for at the end of the corridor was a big white-and-blue statue of Our Lady. It was the biggest I had seen and the flowers banked round it had a wonderful scent. The noise from the playgrounds seemed distant, and I could hear the petals of the white and crimson roses falling on the polished floor. I saw corridors running right and left, but these were dim and quiet. The nun opened the door of a room, we entered and were alone.

'I don't like that one!' said my mother quickly. 'You needn't come here if you don't like, Tricia! I'll make an excuse!'

'I do like!' I whispered back. 'It's grand! Mammy! Does Patrick Henry play hurley?'

'Sh!'

The door opened and a very tall nun came in. She looked at my mother and never glanced my way. But she knew I came from Cork, my name, Patricia Nora, and how I wanted to go back again—I was sure of that! Indeed I wanted to be back in the wood yard, yet I wanted, too, to come to school in this convent.

'Your Cousin Kate is an old friend of St. Winifred's. She often visits us,' said the nun.

'That's why I wanted Tricia to come here, Reverend Mother!'

My mother was talking away, laughing and happy. I tiptoed to the window. A little boy passed by, reminding me of Dinny. He carried a huge ball, coloured in quarters He flung it from him, away out of sight.

'You'll be in the First Communion class, under Sister Damien,' said Reverend Mother. 'We have two other little Irish girls, and you'll make friends with them.'

'She isn't six yet,' my mother murmured doubtfully.

'The younger the better!' declared Reverend Mother. 'Why not leave her with us now?'

My mother clutched my hand.

'Do you want to stay?' she asked.

I nodded. The three of us went down the shining corridor to the front door, and there my mother kissed me as if we were parting for years.

As I walked back with Reverend Mother I kept looking up at her. She never once looked at me; her eyes gazed straight ahead, her hands were clasped in the loose folds of her long black sleeves, her feet made no sound on the polished boards.   Beside her I went softly, terrified of the noise I made.

She pushed a door and I faced rows and rows of eyes, eyes, eyes!   A nun stood beside a desk on a platform.   On the wall was a blackboard, and in her hand she held a long shiny stick.   The children stood up.

'Good morning, Reverend Mother!' they chanted.

I wanted to run, yet I couldn't move, for the eyes were watching, so I shut mine.   But I couldn't keep them shut, I opened one—a little bit—and I discovered that Reverend Mother had gone, the children were sitting, their eyes cast downwards, and I was forgotten.   The class was at lessons. One little girl in the back row still watched.   She smiled, and her eyes were blue and her hair a crown of short brown curls, tied back with a blue ribbon.   I smiled back.

The nun with the stick was studying me, her head on one side.

'Are you sleepy?' she asked.

I shook my head and she laughed.

'By to-morrow you'll be the biggest chatterbox in class. Sit at the back there, beside Cassie Driscoll.   She's a countrywoman of yours.'

Cassie Driscoll was the little girl with blue eyes and curly hair.   She made room for me on the bench.

'What's your name?' she whispered.

I told her.

'You'll share Cassie's books to-day,' said Sister Damien, over our heads.   'To-morrow you must have your own. Now all spell together!'

The class shouted bigger words than I had learned before: 'A—n an, i i, m—a—l mal, animal; a—n an, x—i—o—u—s shus, anxious!'   Cassie and I whispered.

'Next you—that's Mary Bernadette O'Kelly!   She's

the biggest in the class. She 's nearly twelve and she doesn't mind!'

I glanced sideways and met Mary Bernadette's lazy smile. I admired her long brown hair with little curls at the ends, and her large, calm, brown eyes; her blue velvet frock and white lace collar reminded me of Cousin Kate. She didn't try to spell, and when the others shouted ANIMAL she murmured 'animal' so gently I could scarcely hear. But while they built up the word she looked down at her buckled shoes and was silent.

'And she doesn't mind being a dunce!' I thought.

Every day I grew fonder of Cassie, and every day I admired Mary Bernadette more and more. The Driscolls kept open house; the front door was closed only at night and every one of the six children, except Peter, the baby, brought home their friends as often as they chose. Their teapot was so large Mrs. Driscoll said it destroyed her wrist to lift it, and Mr. Driscoll poured out. They had plum cake ready cut, and four kinds of sandwiches at tea, as well as toast and bread and jam. Someone was always playing the piano and Mrs. Driscoll thought dancing far more important than spelling or arithmetic.

My mother seldom went visiting, she hadn't the time, but Mrs. Driscoll sent her notes, came round herself and coaxed, so that often on Sunday the three of us set off for the Driscolls after dinner, and when we did go there the week-end was a happy one.

'She 's a lovely woman, no doubt of that!' declared my mother. 'And he 's flahooil to the backbone. They 're real old stock!'

Mr. Miles liked hearing about them, so did the Cadogans, but Mrs. Cronin closed her eyes and sighed.

'I 've seen their like before, but never one that didn't come to a bad end! Extravagant and foolish!'

'That Mrs. Cronin is nothing better than an angashore!'

exclaimed my mother, when the three of us were alone. I don't know how I put up with her!'

'We 'll be like the Driscolls one day,' said Patrick Henry. 'We 'll have a big house and servants, and the front door always open.   Only our house will be on Monte Notte.'

'Sundays Well!' my mother decided.

'Won't we go back to Fair Hill?' I asked.  'I want Dinny to come to tea!'

'So you haven't forgotten Dinny?' asked my mother. 'I 'm glad of that, Tricia!'

'I 'll never forget Dinny!' I cried.

Mary Bernadette's house was grander than the Driscolls'. The gate in the high wall was closed but opened by itself when you rang the bell.   The hall door was up a flight of steps as big as those at St. Winifred's, and a man stood there holding it back.   The hall was lofty and long, with dark oil-paintings on the walls, and the servants moved without a sound.   At the Driscolls' they were always rushing with trays, or pots of tea, or jugs of hot water.   Mrs. Doran took care of the house, managed the servants, and ordered the food from shops.   She had been Mary Bernadette's nurse and called her Miss Mary.   Even now, when Mary Bernadette was twelve, she had a maid to comb her hair, mend her stockings, and hang up her clothes.   Sometimes I thought that wonderful.   But mostly I liked the Driscolls' ways best.   Mary Bernadette had to ask permission to bring home a friend.   Luckily, however, her grand-uncle liked me and he liked Cassie, but he liked us best one at a time.   The rooms and fire-places were so large and the table so long, I felt smaller every time I went there.

I soon discovered Mary Bernadette wasn't a dunce at all. She had travelled over Europe, and could find the places she had been to on the map in the classroom.   She could speak to Josephine Rossignal in French, to Rosa Schwarz in German, and to the Gattis in Italian.   Mr. O'Kelly brought

Mary Bernadette to school every morning in a cab which carried him on to his office. He took off his hat and handed her out as if she were a grown-up lady. On Friday Mary Bernadette always had a big box of chocolates tied with ribbon. After dinner this was passed round and round the table, where we sat in the big refectory, until it was empty. Mary Bernadette gave the ribbon to a different girl every week, and sometimes she had only one chocolate out of all those in the box.

There were no lessons on Friday afternoon. We gathered in the big hall, which had a platform for concerts and plays. The small children sat in front, the biggest girls at the back, and Reverend Mother was in the middle of the platform in a great arm-chair like a throne. Those who could sing went up the steps at the side, bowed to Reverend Mother, sang, listened to her praise, bowed again, and went back to their seats. Then came the musicians, playing on the piano and their own fiddles.

'Very good, my little one!' said Reverend Mother to each performer.

Rosa Schwarz and her brother Karl, holding hands, sang in German. Rosa had two long fair pigtails, very big blue eyes, and prominent teeth with a gold band across them. Her father made watches so well that Rosa and Karl, too, had every extra. Their mother was always buying them new clothes and wonderful toys, yet they were homesick for the Black Forest where their grandmother lived. They had been very poor in Germany, with little to eat but black rye bread and sausage. The grandmother told them a different story every night when they were in bed, and their grandfather made them wooden toys which they liked far better than the expensive London ones. As they sang tears came into Rosa's eyes, and I knew they had been singing about the forest and its people. I was feeling sad when Sister Remi came along and bent over me.

'Patricia! You can recite. Go up now—speak slowly and clearly!'

Sister Remi gave us lectures on manners and why we came to school. She spoke very softly, but even the biggest girls were afraid of her.

I climbed the two steps. I longed to try *Fontenoy*, but I couldn't remember the first line and my mother had warned me not to shame her by saying *Paddy Heggarty*, so I decided on *The Irish Widow's Message to her Son in America*. I had never recited from a platform, and I didn't like having to stand where Reverend Mother could see me and I couldn't see her, but Mary Bernadette looked up at me and smiled, while Cassie made an encouraging face. I forgot Sister Remi and the way I should speak, I thought only of the Irish widow and was sorry for her with her son so far away. With every verse I felt sadder and sadder. Mary Bernadette brought out her lace-edged handkerchief and cried into it, Cassie was looking so mournful I was thankful I had only one verse more. But when I folded my hands and bowed Mary Bernadette and Cassie clapped their hardest, the six boys in our class stamped their feet, and suddenly the big girls at the back clapped too. I was terribly proud as I turned to Reverend Mother. I'd have something to tell my mother and Patrick Henry at tea time! Reverend Mother beckoned me to come closer.

'Very good, my little one!' she said. 'You'll be quite a nice little reciter when you lose your strange accent.'

Puzzled and ashamed, I stumbled down the steps and squeezed in between Cassie and Mary Bernadette. Guido Gatti was playing the fiddle. He was only a small boy, but very clever and we liked him, yet we didn't listen to a note.

'What did she say?' asked Mary Bernadette, who never whispered.

Cassie was too excited to sit still. I told them.

'Don't I speak nicely?' I asked.

'Of course you do!' whispered Cassie. 'Didn't every one clap? Every one, mind you! Even those big ones at the back!'

'They say that to every one, Tricia,' said Mary Bernadette. 'Rosa Schwarz talks too deeply, Josephine talks too fast, Clothilde and Guido don't end their words properly, Cassie used to drop her voice. There's only one girl in the Communion class who talks properly, according to them!'

There was great scorn in her voice.

'You?' I asked, feeling comforted. I didn't mind Mary Bernadette.

Mary Bernadette tossed her head.

'Indeed, no! Though they never find fault with me. If they did grand-uncle would take me away. It's Carmel Butterworth they really like, and they want us all to copy her.'

'Sh! sh!' hissed Sister Remi.

I was horrified. Carmel Butterworth! She sat behind me in class and pulled my hair, she put her feet up so that I had to sit on the edge of the seat, she joggled my elbow when I was writing a copy. She had sandy curls, she had thin legs, and she was the most unpopular girl in the class. I didn't want to talk like Carmel Butterworth.

I boasted at home about the recitation, but I said nothing of Reverend Mother's criticism of my accent. It would make my mother angry. I knew that and I was too happy to bother. I was learning French and drawing, dancing, everything but singing, for I had no voice at all though I liked singing to myself in the wood yard.

I came to the use of reason and made my First Communion. Mrs. Cadogan made the white frock, Miss Tilly the wreath, Aunt Kattie sent over the veil my O'Neill grandmother had brought out of the castle with her, and Cousin Kate sent me a pearl rosary in a lovely little case as well as a prayer book with a white leather cover and coloured pictures. Best of all, Mary Bernadette's grand-uncle gave each of us a brooch—a spray of daisies in mother-of-pearl with diamond centres.

'I can't let you take such a grand present!' protested my mother.

I coaxed, Patrick Henry coaxed, and I was allowed to keep it.

For a week we tried to be very good. Now we had made our First Communion we were almost grown up. We were very serious and forgave our enemies; we studied our catechism and said our prayers properly. Then I had a seventh birthday party. My mother made a big cake, the Cadogans came over, and Mr. Miles, with a book, *Alice in Wonderland*, for me under his arm. The Driscolls came too, and Rosa Schwarz and her brother were there. Of course Mary Bernadette came, and later in the evening her grand-uncle arrived with such a huge box of chocolates I couldn't hold it.

Miss Tilly and Bert came along by the canal. Only Harry Crouchman stayed away, and I had been to the shop to ask him specially! Mr. Forbes put fairy lamps all over the wood yard, and when it was dark we played hide and seek among the piles of timber. When it was ended and the last visitor, Mr. Miles, had gone, I wished I could be seven all over again.

## 22. ST. PATRICK'S DAY

WE were in the senior school now and had separate desks with lids, but Mary Bernadette, Cassie, and I were ſtill together. There were no boys in our class and we had home work every evening. Patrick Henry helped me and my mother watched us proudly. He was beſt at figures, while they were a great puzzle to me, and I had no memory for spelling at all.

My mother was very scornful of the poetry we were taught at St. Winifred's, and gave me a penny for any poem of her choice when I had learned it without one miſtake. On Saturday I went to a children's class for Irish in a room behind the chapel the Cadogans attended, and she gave me another penny for every page I could read or liſt of words I had by heart from O'Growney's firſt book. By St. Patrick's Day I knew *The Battle of Fontenoy* without a single miſtake, though it was a very long poem. I said it again and again to my mother, and she never grew tired of hearing it. The weekly concert at school was to be held on the 17th and we could invite our relations. Patrick Henry sat up the night before, making three harps. He cut them from cardboard, covered the cardboard with silver tinsel, and gave each three strings like the harp in the legend of the Red Dwarf—one for sleep, one for laughter, one for sorrow.   Mine glittered splendidly on my white Communion frock, and I carried the others to school wrapped in a cardboard box.   I was very proud of those harps, but when I saw the grandeur of Mary Berna-dette and Cassie I nearly lost the box.   Mr. O'Kelly's cab drove up to the school entrance as I came running along, and Mary Bernadette stepped out looking like a fairy princess.   She wore a white silk frock, embroidered in green with four-leaf shamrocks; her hair was caught back with shamrock clasps, and I thought her so lovely I nearly curtsied, as if she were Reverend Mother, while her grand-uncle bowed so low it was a wonder his hat didn't touch the ground.   Cassie was in green—green frock, green shoes, green socks, and green bows in her curls.   They were both as pleased with my brother's harps as if they 'd made them themselves, and I longed for the afternoon so that he could see us wearing them.

Every one wore shamrock in honour of the day.   We had chicken and trifle for dinner, and then came the con-cert.   Cassie sang *The Harp that Once*, I recited *Fontenoy*, and I could see my mother and Patrick Henry looking very pleased.   Mary Bernadette just clapped.

'I 'm sure I shall never be so happy again!' I told my friends.

'There 's more to come!' declared Mary Bernadette.

'It won't make me happy!' said Cassie.   'And it won't make Tricia happy either.'

'It 's a party!' explained Mary Bernadette.   'My grand-uncle is giving it.   Your mother and brother are coming, all the Driscolls except Peter, and everybody!'

'A party!' I cried.   'But that 's lovely!'

Cassie looked tearful.

'A good-bye party,' she told me. 'Mary Bernadette's going away!'

'Going away!' I repeated. 'Oh, Mary Bernadette, you can't go away! I thought we were going to be together for years and years. And then I thought we'd be together!'

Mary Bernadette put an arm around each of our necks. 'I'm a great deal older than you are,' she explained. 'I'm going away to boarding school. When we meet again I'll be grown up. But you're the dearest friends I shall ever have and I'll never forget you, I promise!'

We couldn't cry on Patrick's Day, but we came very near it. My mother knew Mary Bernadette was going away and she understood how I felt.

'She's a lovely girl!' she said. 'You're lucky to have such friends. Even if they do go away, Tricia, you never lose them. You can't lose anything you've once had, nothing worth while.'

That comforted me. But I did wish Mary Bernadette's grand-uncle would change his mind and not take Mary Bernadette away.

The party was the best I remember. People played the piano and sang songs, and in one of the rooms a long table had dishes of sandwiches, iced cakes, and chocolates, and little glass saucers with jelly and blancmange on them. Three servants stood behind the table, handing out cups of tea and coffee and opening bottles. My mother and Mrs. Driscoll had a great time telling one another about their old homes. Patrick Henry and Chris Driscoll talked of what they were going to be. Patrick Henry was sure he was going to become a rich man. Chris wanted to ride horses all day long.

Mr. Driscoll enjoyed himself more than any one else. He borrowed my harp to look at, then lost it and, after a long time, found it fastened in Mrs. Driscoll's lace collar. He stood the coal scuttle on the table, put a jug and tumbler beside it, and poured out any drink we asked for. I had milk, my mother and Mrs. Driscoll had tea, the grand-uncle asked for a glass of wine; mostly every one had tea or ginger beer, yet afterwards when I peeped into the scuttle it had only pieces of coal in it, so I knew Mr. Driscoll had worked real magic.

Cassie and I were lonely without Mary Bernadette though she sent us each a picture postcard from Paris. Mine showed the Eiffel Tower, soaring into the air over the city; Cassie's was of Notre-Dame. Then one day Charlie Pryor came to the convent. She was quite as old as Mary Bernadette, but she was dressed so babyishly that some of the girls poked one another and laughed behind their books. She wore a check frock with short puffed sleeves, white socks, and black strap shoes. Her straight dark hair was drawn back from her face with a ribbon, and she looked round at the class as if she felt too sad to care how much we laughed.

'Cassie!' I whispered. 'She 's Alice in Wonderland!'

'Chatterbox!' snapped Sister Batilda, our new teacher. 'Stand up and repeat what you said!'

I stood up. I was too excited to mind a bit.

'I told Cassie Driscoll the new girl is Alice in Wonderland, Sister Batilda!' I answered. 'Her picture is in my book!'

Every one in the class had seen my book and now they stared at the new girl, not laughing but envying her. I had *Alice in Wonderland* in my desk and I pulled it out.

'You 'd better sit next to Patricia, Charlotte!' said Sister Batilda. 'She seems to know you already.'

Charlotte sat beside me and under the desk she squeezed my hand.

'Thank you, Patricia,' she said.

We walked homeward together, for Charlotte lived farther along the canal. Her mother was dead, so she lived with her grandparents. Because *Alice in Wonderland* had been her mother's favourite book the old people dressed Charlotte like Alice.

'It's a beautiful story,' she said seriously. 'But everybody hasn't read it and—well—you know how the girls laughed!'

She was pleased when we called her Charlie and while she was in school she was happy, but she hated walking along the streets, and we discovered back lanes which no one but ourselves seemed to use. Often she came through the wood yard and took the path by the canal. My mother liked Charlie and talked to her as if she were grown up. She came in to tea and, though her grandmother dressed her like a baby, she let Charlie stay out as late as she liked.

Charlie hadn't been at St. Winifred's many weeks when she discovered my secret—I couldn't tell the time! Patrick Henry had taught me long ago when I was quite small, but he didn't know that I never learned anything but writing from him. Then I was ashamed to tell the nuns. Sister Damien was always sending girls in from the playground to look at the clock in the refectory, and because Carmel Butterworth loved running messages, she was usually chosen. But now Sister Batilda often asked me. Luckily the refectory was downstairs next to the kitchen and I could ask any lay sister I met in the passages. One day I couldn't find any one and I couldn't think what to do, when suddenly the angelus rang and I knew it was twelve o'clock. But sooner or later Sister Batilda was sure to find me out.

One day Charlie and I were sitting in my favourite cave, playing Indians with the rag doll. I had many dolls, for I never lost or broke them, but Poosie was the one I loved. She had known Fair Hill and Dinny and Captain O'Connell and Aunt Kattie. Rain was falling; Charlie loved rain, for she had a mackintosh cape which covered her Alice clothes and made her look like an ordinary girl. We had bows and arrows, and Charlie was shooting. Suddenly she dropped her bow.

'I'll teach you to tell the time,' she said, 'if you like.'

'Ch-Charlie!' I stammered, feeling my face go hot and red.

'You'll have to learn some time and I can teach anything I know.'

'How did you guess?' I asked.

'You always look bothered when Sister Batilda sends you for the time and you can't do clock sums. I'll teach you all about clocks.'

I felt such relief I wasn't the least bit ashamed. Charlie made a heap of sawdust, drew a circle in it with a bit of stick, and marked the hours. She used the stick as the hour hand, and a smaller piece was the minute hand. In ten minutes I understood.

'Charlie! I'll do anything in the world for you!' I declared.

That was the day my mother told me I must take my lunch to school instead of having dinner with Cassie and the others. Many of the girls brought sandwiches and bought milk or cocoa. I was dismayed, not because I was greedy, but taking my lunch meant going among strangers instead of sitting with my friends. When I had got over the excitement of learning the clock, I told Charlie my new trouble.

'My mother says we haven't any more money to spend,' I explained. 'And, mebbe, I won't be having extras. But I don't mind them.'

'If you're going to take your lunch I'll take mine,' said Charlie. 'I'll say I don't like the dinners.'

When Cassie heard this she insisted on joining us. We sat at tables in the big hall, unwrapped our sandwiches or meat pies, put them on plates, paid our pennies for milk, stuck our elbows on the table, and talked as much as we

liked.  Mrs. Driscoll gave Cassie a basket every day with
fruit and cake as well as her lunch, so that we never regretted
the dinners of our grand days.

I did miss the dancing and music, though it was the
violin I wanted to learn, not the piano.  Because I had
fewer lessons to prepare and I worked as hard, I learned
better.  From being in the first ten of the class I climbed
to the first four.  My reports pleased my mother, though
she didn't give me all the credit.

'Why wouldn't you learn well?' she asked.  'Look at
the clever father you had, and isn't your grandfather a
famous scholar!  And where would be the use of sending
you to a grand school if you were nothing better than a
numskull?'

When I realized that I was to be given three prizes at the
Christmas prize-giving as well as a present from the Christ-
mas tree, I thought she would at last be really proud of me.
But there was news from Mr. Blanchard, and she and
Patrick Henry could think of nothing else.

'Will I have a new frock?' I demanded.  'Cassie is
having a blue one, and even Charlie will have a proper
frock.  I want buckle shoes!'

'I'm ashamed of you!' cried my mother.  'Here's Mr.
Blanchard letting us have a share in a gold-mine that may
make us rich and all you think about is a new frock!  You
think too much of clothes!'

'Wear your best frock,' said Patrick Henry kindly.
'You'll look prettier than any of the other girls.  And
when they find the gold in the mine you shall have a new
dress every Sunday!'

'Me best is too short,' I told him.  'Sister Batilda says
I'm a disgrace and she'll send me back to the babies.'

But all they would talk about was Mr. Blanchard and
his gold-mine.

I had good strong winter boots, but my indoor shoes

were coming to pieces and my mother absent-mindedly mended them with white thread, the last ball of thread she had left over from her lace-making.

'I'm having three prizes!' I grumbled. 'There isn't another girl with three prizes and I'll be a show. You'll be sorry when you see their lovely frocks!'

Then I found out they weren't even coming to the prize giving!

'You're only a little girl,' said my mother. 'Next prize giving you'll be the best dressed of them all and we'l bring Mr. Blanchard to see you. Mind you win four prizes next time! And don't be fretting. You can bring Charlie Pryor back with you and I'll leave the key under the mat in case we won't be in.'

I forgot my shabby frock when I saw the convent all lit up. I thought how Sister Batilda said she was proud of me. But when I came into the cloak-room I remembered my clothes, for it was like fairyland and the fairies in bright-coloured silks and velvets were my schoolfellows. I opened the door of my locker and hung up my hat and coat; then stood watching, growing more unhappy every moment. Sister Batilda was sending the girls who were dressed out into the corridor to leave room for the others. She saw me standing there and clapped her hands impatiently.

'My dear child! Dress yourself! Where is your frock? I'll help you.'

'I haven't a party frock,' I told her. 'This is me best one.'

She looked at the frock, too tight and too short, at my shoes sewn with white cotton.

'I am sorry, Patricia!' she said. 'But you can't show yourself like that! I'll have to take your name off the list and give you your prizes upstairs.'

She hurried off. The other girls went away and I was left alone in the cloak-room. I sat on the floor and tried

to tell myself a story. The door was pushed open and
Cassie came running in.

'Tricia! Tricia! Where are you?'

She came over and knelt beside me.

'What's wrong? Why aren't you dressed? Why are
you crying?'

I told her.

'It's a shame!' she muttered. 'I'll tell mummy! She'll
know what to do!'

I loved Cassie for her friendship, but what could Mrs.
Driscoll do? If she had known before, she'd have given
me a frock, I knew she would. But would my mother let
me take it? I was considering this when Mrs. Driscoll
swept into the cloak-room, Cassie running behind her.
She lifted me to my feet and hugged me.

'Cassie! Take off your shoes. You can wear your
school ones. They're new and not too bad. Thanks be
I brought an extra pair of stockings in case you made holes
in those. Into them, Tricia, quick! Now, off with that
frock!'

She wore a wide cream lace scarf. She pulled it off,
draped it round me, and fixed the folds with safety-pins.
She had Cassie running out of the cloak-room and back
again, and presently Sister Batilda arrived with a green
silk sash.

'Now!' said Mrs. Driscoll. 'Is Tricia going to receive
her prizes in the cloak-room or is she to sit in the front row?'

'It'll have to be the front row,' replied Sister Batilda.
And she'll be the best dressed there!'

'There's not many women can beat me with a lace
scarf and a packet of pins!' bragged Mrs. Driscoll. 'Now,
children, run along and be happy!'

I was glad of the lovely lace frock, with its smell of
scent, the green sash, and Cassie's buckled shoes, but I
wished I had been dressed in them when I came from

home.   However, when I went up to take my prizes Mr.
Driscoll and Chris stamped as well as clapped and I had to
feel happy, and when I won the fairy doll from the top of
the tree I almost forgot those terrible shoes mended with
white thread!

'What are your prizes?' asked Cassie, when we hid ourselves behind one of the big curtains with a plate of cakes
and sandwiches and two big glasses of pink lemonade.

'I told Charlie where we 'd be,' she added, as I peeped out
I let her take my prizes into her hands.

'They 're books!' I told her proudly.

Cassie looked disappointed.

'Oh, Tricia!   And I thought they were boxes of chocolates!   Do you remember the ones Mary Bernadette's
grand-uncle used to give her?'

We were still talking of Mary Bernadette when Charlie,
bringing her plate and glass, slipped between the curtains
and sat on the window seat beside us.   She was dressed
in black velvet with a lace collar, and I thought her lovely
with her big solemn eyes and straight, dark hair.   She
carried her one prize for arithmetic—the hardest of all to
win—a wooden work-box with spools of coloured cottons,
needles, pins, and cards of silk.   Proudly I showed mine
for composition, history, geography—*Hans Andersen's Fairy
Tales*, *Robinson Crusoe*, *Arabian Nights*.

'You 'll never be able to read through them!' said
Cassie admiringly.

She hadn't even one prize.   I looked at her buckle shoes
which I was wearing.

'Have one of my books,' I suggested.   'I 'll still have
two.'

Cassie was tempted.   Then she shook her head.

'No, Tricia!   It wouldn't be fair!   Anyway, mummy
and daddy don't care what we do.   Your mother expects
you to win prizes.'

Charlie came home with me, and when we pushed open the green gate the little house shone with light and Patrick Henry was coming down the path to meet me. He went on with Charlie, for the night was dark, and I ran in to show my three prizes. My mother hugged me, but when I threw off my coat and she saw the lace frock Mrs. Driscoll had fixed, she wrung her hands.

'What kind of a mother am I at all! Who dressed you, Tricia? I'm ashamed!'

'Mrs. Driscoll. And it isn't really a frock. It's her scarf and Cassie's party shoes, and here's me prizes.'

'You poor child!' she cried. 'And will you look what came! I wrote to Cousin Kate you were winning three prizes and she sent you this party frock for a Christmas present. I've never seen anything lovelier! Patrick Henry would have taken it to St. Winifred's, only it came too late.'

I looked at the cardboard box which lay open on the table. My mother lifted out a frock of old gold silk, with long stockings and shoes to match. I wished it had come in time, but suddenly I knew the lovely frock didn't matter. My mother had cared, so had Cousin Kate, so had Mrs. Driscoll, and I had three prizes!

'You won't want me to be telling you any more stories,' said my mother. 'Now you'll be reading them to me.'

## 23. TROUBLE COMES TO THE DRISCOLLS

WRITING in our copy books—'Manners Maketh Man,'
'Good Wine Needs No Bush,' 'Look Before You Leap'—
was a great time for telling secrets or passing notes. If
we filled the page Sister Batilda was satisfied. She sat up
at her desk reading. A girl who whispered loudly or
passed too many notes might be called to show her copy,
but on a sunny day, when the windows were open and
out-of-door noises came lazily in, it was one of the pleasantest
half-hours in the week.

'Chris asked daddy to let him learn riding and he
wouldn't!' Cassie told us in an astonished whisper as I
carefully wrote 'Time Stays For No Man' for the sixth time.

'Was Chris bold or was your daddy cross?' I wanted
to know.

'Daddy wasn't a bit cross, but he says he's lost all his
money and we'll be beggars.'

Cassie looked as if she were going to cry. I thought
she was very foolish.

'You don't have to be beggars because your daddy loses
his money!' I told her. 'We're always losing ours.

We 've lost it now.   That 's why I 'm bringing my lunch and not having any extras.'

'What happens then?' asked Cassie.

'Patrick Henry earns some, or Mr. Blanchard sends my mother a letter.   I expect I 'll be having extras next term. It doesn't matter the least bit about losing money.'

Charlie never talked about money, but I knew she had more to spend than any one else in the school.

'Ask your brother if I can give you pocket money, Cassie,' she said.   'You can have all mine every week.'

I thought Cassie's troubles were settled then and told how my mother, Patrick Henry, and I were going back to Cork one day with a bag of gold.   Cassie had forgotten Cork and Charlie had never known it, so they liked to hear about the place and the people.

Next morning Charlie called for me and we had so much to talk about we were almost late.   I was at my desk getting back my breath before I realized that Cassie's seat was empty.   I made faces at Charlie and she nodded to show she had noticed too.   Then Carmel Butterworth pulled my hair and passed me a note.   Deciding to pull her sandy corkscrews when we were in the playground, I poked the note in my arithmetic book and read it as soon as I dared:

'Cassie Driscoll's father shot himself.   He is dead.   It is a mortal sin.   He will go to hell.'

I turned right round and stared at Carmel.   She was looking so pleased I hated her more than ever.

'Wait till we 're in the playground!' I thought.   'You wait!'

Charlie slipped into Cassie's seat and held out her hand for the note.   Sister Batilda must have known we were breaking rules but she went on writing a problem about two trains on the board and took no notice.   Charlie read the note, then she sat still without looking at me.   We both knew Carmel always told the truth. That was one of the reasons why she was so unpopular. We all tried to tell the truth, but she told it when there was no need to tell anything. I did no lessons, neither did Charlie. We sat wondering about Cassie. At dinner time I discovered I had forgotten to bring my lunch.

'Doesn't matter!' said Charlie. 'Share mine!'

She had cold meat pie and two apples, and we bought hot milk. There was no pleasure in the food, and the moment we had finished we ran out to the playground.

'We'll go straight to the Driscolls,' said Charlie. 'We'll have time.'

Following us came Carmel. I looked back and saw her grinning. I thought of my friend and ran at the enemy, and without a word I kicked those thin legs, I pulled her curls, I slapped her face. Then I was pulled away and Sister Batilda stood there looking very severe.

'That was very wrong, Tricia!' she said.

She had never called me Tricia before, so I knew she wasn't really angry, but Carmel Butterworth was screaming, threatening to tell her father and have me put in prison. Something had to be done.

'Carmel! Did you pass a note in class?' asked Sister Batilda. 'A very cruel, stupid note?'

'It's the truth!' screamed Carmel.

'Did you pass a note in class?' repeated Sister Batilda.

Her thin face was thinner than ever. Her pale eyes were flashing. I saw her hands clenched.

'Does she want to beat Carmel?' I wondered.

Carmel nodded and stopped screaming.

'Do you want to win the good conduct prize?' demanded Sister Batilda.

It was the only prize Carmel had any chance of winning, and her father was vexed because she hadn't won even that.

'Yes, Sister Batilda!' answered Carmel.

'Then tell Tricia you 're sorry!' ordered Sister Batilda.

Carmel's mouth fell open. I was surprised, too, and I began to be really fond of Sister Batilda.

'She kicked me!' screamed Carmel. 'She pulled my hair! She slapped my face!'

'How many times have you pulled her hair?' asked Sister Batilda.

'I 'm sorry!' mumbled Carmel at last.

She went slowly back into the school and slammed the door spitefully. Sister Batilda took us each by the hand.

'Cassie is upstairs,' she said. 'I needn't tell you to be kind to her. And pray for poor Mr. Driscoll.'

Cassie was in the blue room. There was the green room, the red room, as well. Boarders met their parents there and day girls scarcely ever entered them. At first we didn't see Cassie. She was sitting far back in a big arm-chair, blue like the rug, the curtains, the vases. Her face was white, her eyes big and frightened. We squeezed into the chair with her and we all cried together.

'We 're going away,' Cassie told us. 'I 'll be like Mary Bernadette. I 'll never see you again!'

'Where are you going?' I asked. 'Are you going home?'

Home to me was still Cork.

'I don't know,' said Cassie. 'I thought we were going to be happy for ever. Poor daddy!'

'We 'll pray for him every night!' promised Charlie.

'Cassie—I kicked Carmel Butterworth and I pulled her horrid curls and I slapped her face!' I said proudly.

Cassie dried her eyes.

'You didn't!' she said breathlessly.

'She did!' Charlie assured her. 'And Sister Batilda made Carmel apologize to Tricia for pulling her hair.'

I described the battle, and we grew so excited we laughed and thumped one another. Suddenly we became serious.

'Why did you kick Carmel?' asked Cassie, her soft little face growing hard and determined. I didn't answer.

'Tell me! You must!' urged Cassie.

I told her in a whisper.

'Oh!' cried Cassie. 'My daddy in hell! Oh, no!'

'I don't believe in hell!' said Charlie quietly.

Cassie and I looked at her in terror.

'You must!' protested Cassie.

'Well, I just don't!' declared Charlie.

Sister Batilda brought us glasses of hot milk and sat talking. She told Cassie she must be very good to her mother now and try to comfort her. Then Charlie and I walked home with Cassie as far as her gate; Sister Batilda had told us not to go in, so we said good-bye there.

## 24. GOLD-MINES AND THE BLACK BOX

I was reading the story of 'The Three Calendars and the Five Ladies of Baghdad' from my prize, *Arabian Nights*, when we heard a thumping at the door in the fence. Patrick Henry ran out and my mother looked over at me.

'Time you were in bed, Tricia! I'd forgotten you were still up!'

'Do let me finish!' I coaxed. 'I must know what happened!'

'Well, ten minutes. Not one more!'

We both stared as Patrick Henry staggered in, carrying a heavy parcel.

'What in the wide world is that?' cried my mother.

We loved opening parcels. I put my book away and, keeping very quiet so that my mother wouldn't remember bedtime, stood on tiptoe beside the table determined to see everything. The parcel was wrapped in brown paper, bound with cord and with blobs of red sealing-wax at every knot. My mother, too impatient to wait while Patrick Henry untied the string, cut it with the bread knife. Under the brown paper was a covering of canvas with a letter pinned on top. My mother opened the letter and a key fell out.

'Mr. Blanchard writes this is your father's. He kept his papers in it and they 're all here!'

When the canvas was stripped off there was a black leather box studded with brass nails, and I thought it must be the baby of the big black chest by the window. My mother's hands were trembling so that she couldn't fit the key in the lock; Patrick Henry took it from her and I was so excited I felt suffocated. Perhaps there 'd be a bag of gold, or jewels! The key clicked as he lifted the lid and I saw bundles of papers, a queer red cap with a black tassel, a wooden box packed with lovely white and red toys, a book, and papers, papers, papers, tied with string.

'They 're real ivory chess-men,' explained my mother. 'I must teach you both to play chess—when I have time.'

I curled up in the arm-chair, the fire was red and the cushions soft and warm. I forgot the Five Ladies and the Three Calendars.

'Title-deeds,' said my mother. 'Here 's tax papers. Those are gold-mine certificates! The one Mr. Blanchard told us about. I remember your father explaining them.'

'What 's this?' asked Patrick Henry, holding up the cap.

'A fez, they call it. All the men wear those in Egypt.'

'Egypt!' said my brother longingly. 'Why can't we go there?'

He opened the book. My mother looked at it with him

'His diary!' she murmured.

'There aren't any dates!' objected Patrick Henry. 'A proper diary has the date for every day.'

My mother laughed, but she was nearly crying.

'Sure, he never knew which day of the week it was, never mind the date. Ah, Patrick Henry, listen to this:

'"Sunday to-day. A young bear on board plays with the

captain's dog.   Arrived at Syra.   Overlooking the town.
Wednesday.   There on the top of the hill is the bishop's
palace and church in which 13 years ago I was confirmed,
and there in the harbour, lying at anchor is the very boat,
the Austrian steamer *Archduke Maximilian*, in which I came
from Athens to Syra on my way to Alexandria via Smyrna.
13 years.   Thursday.   On deck at 6 a.m.   We have just
passed Greece on the right.   We are now on the open
sea for the first time out of sight of land.   Mesina.   Remained 2 hours.   Took in coals and left for Palermo at
2 a.m.   Saturday.   Arrived at Palermo.   Went ashore.
Left for Marseilles at 5 p.m.   Why did the French steamer
break down?   Why did I miss the Russian boat?   Landlord at Port Said said he did not think I would go in the
Russian boat.   'Why man, I would go in a nut-shell!'
That tickled him.   'Monsieur est pressé?'"'

'Syra, Athens, Smyrna, Palermo!' sighed Patrick Henry.
'Will I ever see them?'

'If these papers mean anything,' said my mother, 'you
shall see the whole wide world, every bit of it!'   She sighed.
'To think of him writing in this book—day after day!'

I was half asleep.   I sat up blinking.

'Will we go back home?'   I yawned as I spoke.

'God bless my soul, Tricia!   Are you still there?' cried
my mother.   'You're a terrible child!   You never want
to go to bed and you never want to get up.   Off with you!'

I lay in bed listening to their voices and thinking.   The
Driscolls had gone away; no one knew where they had
gone.   Charlie and I had wandered through their garden,
peeping in at the windows of the empty house and wondering
where Cassie was now.

'I know!' I declared suddenly.   'She's gone to America.
I'm sure of it.   Everybody goes there!'

'You came to England,' said Charlie doubtfully.

'That's because of Mr. Blanchard. Only for him I expect we'd be in America.'

The thought that Cassie was in a real place made me happier about her; almost as if she had written us a letter. Sometimes I wondered why she didn't. I had been very fond of Cassie—fonder of her even than of Charlie or of Mary Bernadette, and now I might go to America and find Cassie. The little black box was surely a treasure chest! But my mother had no wish at all for America; it wasn't a place she had any regard for, though she liked talking about American history. She gave me a threepenny piece for learning *Paul Revere's Ride* without being told. We were going home—first to Manchester to see Mr. Blanchard, then home!

Suddenly we were packing. I was leaving St. Winifred's —leaving Charlie—that was the sad part of it—and then for the first time I went to her home. The wood yard had been on her way from school, so it was natural for her to come in with me, and besides, my mother loved visitors and was always ready to make tea, cut thin bread and butter, and mix pancakes or potato cakes. But Charlie's grandparents were old and easily bothered.

'It's the one chance you'll have of seeing where I live,' said Charlie. 'I'd like you to remember me as long as you can!'

'I'll never forget you, Charlie!' I declared. 'Never! never!'

I looked at her. This term all the girls had to dress alike in uniform—a blue tunic, white blouse, long black stockings. Most of us liked the change and Charlie was so happy she danced, but I always thought of her as the Alice in Wonderland she had been.

'You look like orphans!' said my mother scornfully. 'Can you imagine Mary Bernadette in uniform—or Cousin Kate?'

We went by the canal path, over the little bridge, across the waste land to a street where each house stood separate in its own garden. Charlie's house had a big porch, and an old man wearing a velvet cap and slippers sat reading in a rocking-chair.

'That's grandfather!' said Charlie. 'You'll have to shout. He's very deaf and he's rude. Don't mind what he says.'

'Here's Patricia Lynch!' shouted Charlie.

The old man looked at me over his book. He wore glasses and they had slipped to the end of his nose, so he looked over them too.

'Hm, not bad!' he said. 'Not bad! Though I never did like the Irish! Worse than Jews! And there's too many girls in the world, far too many!'

'You're a rude old man!' I cried at the top of my voice. 'You don't deserve to be Charlie's grandfather! My grand-father is a great scholar and he's writing a history!'

To my amazement he put his book on his knee and smiled. Then he rubbed his hands.

'Spirit!' he chuckled. 'That's what I always did like. Spirit! Good fighters—the Irish! Go in and have some seed cake. Sticks in your teeth.'

We went into a hall so dark I kept close to Charlie. As I began to see properly I discovered a clock, so tall it reached the ceiling.

'That's a grandfather's clock!' said Charlie proudly.

'When you go travelling how can you pack it?' I asked

'We never travel,' replied Charlie.

At the end of the hall was another porch and we came through this into a garden with a pool and a stone seat half-way round it.

'That's grandmother,' said Charlie.

I didn't see her at first. Then I discovered an old lady sitting in the bend of the seat, leaning on a black stick and peering into the pool. The water was so smooth I could see the reflection of her white lace cap and the big brooch in her frock. A goldfish lay in the middle of the reflection as if he were a brooch too. We stepped softly and the old lady saw our reflection before she heard us.

'That's lucky!' she said, thumping the ground with her stick. 'But who for? Sit down, little girl. We'll have the seed cake and lemonade out here, or would you prefer tea?'

'I'd prefer tea, ma'am, if it's all the same to you,' I said, feeling very shy as I sat beside her.

Charlie went back to the house.

'I can't bear to look at Charlotte,' sighed the old lady. 'I've lost my child. When I used to look at her dressed like Alice, she was my own daughter all over again. Now she is like a hundred other girls.'

'Charlie doesn't look like any other girl in the school!' I protested. 'She's the prettiest and best of them all!'

The old lady held up her hand.

'My dear child, you mustn't contradict! I do hope you won't teach Charlotte bad manners. Now tell me about your parents and where you belong.'

I was thankful when Charlie came back with the tray. There were two cups on it, no saucers, and a tumbler as well as a small plate of seed cake cut in fingers. I tried to be very polite and not disgrace my mother, but the tea was weak, too milky, and half cold, the cake was very dry and I could eat only two fingers. At that moment my mother and Patrick Henry would be having tea, and perhaps Mr. Forbes would be there, for he was terribly sorry we were going away. There'd be a big pot of hot strong tea, thin bread and butter, strawberry jam, bananas, and a plum cake.

'You are leaving this district, I believe?' asked the grandmother.

'We ate, ma'am.'

'And where are you going?'

'We 're going home!'

'And where is home, may I ask?'

'Fair Hill! It 's the loveliest place in the world and I was afraid I 'd never be there again.'

We gave the cake crumbs to the goldfish. There were seven, and though they all looked alike to me, the old lady knew them and their names. I remember one was called Alphonse. When I was putting on my hat and coat she took my hand in hers, which were so smooth I fancied she must be wearing silk gloves.

'Promise me, my dear, that you will never keep goldfish in a small glass bowl.'

I promised and went back through the house with Charlie. The rocking-chair was still in the porch, but it was empty. I would have liked to rock in it, but now I was shy of Charlie and did not like to ask. We walked slowly across the waste land to the bridge. Patrick Henry was waiting at the other side.

'Come back with us for a little while, Charlie!' he called.

I could see she wanted to, but she shook her head.

'To-morrow!' she called back.

'Did you have a good time?' asked my brother, as I followed him along the path.

'A lovely time!' I answered. 'There was a pond with seven goldfish in it. We fed them with cake crumbs.'

My mother had kept two bananas and a thick slice of plum cake for me, and she made a fresh pot of tea. We were drinking it when a great knock sounded on the door in the fence. My brother rushed out and returned with an envelope in his hand.

'The post?' cried my mother.

'A telegram!' replied Patrick Henry.

She wouldn't touch it.

'Bad news!' she said.  'I know it's bad news.  I thought I saw my father in the street yesterday and I dreamed of him all night.  Why didn't we go home before?  Why did we ever come away?'

Patrick Henry opened the telegram.  It was from Uncle Cathal.  Grandfather was dead.

## 25. LIKE THREE TINKERS

WE did no more packing. My mother wept all night. Every time I woke I heard her. I wanted to comfort her, but I knew there was no comfort. In the morning she could not lift her head from the pillow, or even drink the hot tea my brother made. He was frightened and went for Mr. Forbes, who brought a doctor, and when the doctor came he was from Cork and knew grandfather! He knew all about us!

The Cadogans and the Cronins, Mr. Miles, and Miss Tilly, with Bert, came to sympathize.

'You'll be going to Cork on the boat,' said Tomas Cadogan. 'But I must wait for the messenger.'

'We're not going back,' my mother told him. 'I couldn't bear it now. Cathal is on his way to America. Kattie and Liam are going as soon as I send the passage money. Oh, why didn't I go home while it was home!'

'Aren't ye very foolish to be handing out money the way ye do?' snapped Mrs. Cronin. 'Don't I know well ye've been sending and sending ever since ye came over, and now ye're not done! An' ye to be talking of making

Patrick Henry a rich man!   Ye 're like yer father, Nora—
never able to say "No" to a beggar!'

'When ye 're in Liverpool,' little Mrs. Cadogan whispered
to me, "'twill be easy to slip down and have a look at the
Dublin boat—North Wall is where it makes for.   Ye 'll
watch out, where the ships are, for the finest, grandest boat
on the river, an' that will be the Irish steamer!'

This was the first time I heard we were going to Liverpool
Charlie envied me, even though I was leaving the little
wooden house and St. Winifred's.   She came to the station,
and it was her face I saw when the others had grown dim.
Mr. Forbes was there too, looking very cross.   He couldn't
understand why we didn't stay with him if we weren't
going back home.

In the train I discovered I had left my rag doll behind

'Will Mr. Forbes send her?' I asked anxiously.   'I know
where she is—in the little cave as you go down to the
canal.'

'The man would think me quite mad if I wrote wanting
him to go hunting for a rag doll,' said my mother.   'I 'll
buy you a sleeping doll with real hair, when we get to
Liverpool.   I 'm terribly sorry about Mr. Forbes.   He was
a good friend.   But why won't he understand we couldn't
settle down in a wood yard?   It wouldn't be fair to you,
Patrick Henry.'

My brother nodded; he was looking very serious, and
I knew he was unhappy at leaving Mr. Forbes.

We all liked travelling.   We had a carriage to ourselves,
and my mother had packed a meat pie and egg sandwiches
and had bought a basket with a filled teapot and cups and
saucers in it.   She brought out the chess-men and taught us
the moves, though we hadn't a board.   Then we leaned back
and she told me about Tuan who, when he was very, very
old, turned into a stag, then into a wild boar, after that
an eagle, and, at last, he became a man again.   It was a

long journey and I was wondering if we could have passed Liverpool when we came into a noisy, crowded station where men shouted: 'Livpool! Livpool!' I hadn't time to look at the place for, as I put my head out of the window, there laughing up at me was Aunt Kattie! Aunt Kattie in the black cloak with the crimson lining and the hood to pull over her head that she had talked about so long ago.

'Aunt Kattie!' I cried. 'It's Aunt Kattie, and she has her American cloak!'

'Aunt Kattie!' said Patrick Henry behind me. 'Isn't this grand!'

He was about to jump out, but my mother was first, and she and Aunt Kattie stood with their arms around one another in that crowded station and cried without caring who saw them.

'So you've found them, Kattie? Now, where's the use of crying?' asked a tall, grandly dressed man who had been pushing and dodging to reach us. 'Will it bring himself back? Will it do any good at all?'

'Uncle Liam!' said Patrick Henry. 'I am glad we're all together again. It's been so lonely!'

'Didn't you know we'd be here?' asked Uncle Liam. 'I understand. Nora wanted to surprise you! How'd you like to come with us, Patrick Henry?'

'To America?' asked my brother. His eyes grew bigger and bigger, his face became red. It was queer how old he seemed when the three of us were alone, and when we were with other people he grew young again.

Uncle Liam slipped one arm through my mother's, the other through Aunt Kattie's.

'Now we'll go to the hotel. I'll settle your business for you to-morrow, Nora, and we'll all be off to America on the same boat.'

My mother wiped away her tears.

'Don't be foolish, Liam! You'll not interfere in my

affairs and we 're not going to America! If you want to help, find our luggage.'

We had two crowded noisy days with Uncle Liam and Aunt Kattie in Liverpool. Then we saw them off on the ship to America. I spent a whole day alone in the hotel, for my mother and Patrick Henry went out after breakfast, telling me to read a story book until they came back to dinner, but I did not see them until late that night. I sat at the window with a new doll Uncle Liam had bought me, reading *The Snow Queen* and watching a few snowflakes drift past. A maid came in and tidied the room, but she did not speak to me; she didn't appear to see me. I grew cold and hungry. I took out the chess-men and played with them. When I had packed them away carefully I ventured out on the corridor. The shadows and the rows of shut doors frightened me, so I ran back. I clambered on the bed and cried myself to sleep. When I woke it was dark and I was still alone. I said my prayers. I recited all the poems I knew and, at first, the sound of my voice was company. Soon it seemed as if it belonged to someone else and I lay quiet, shivering with terror. At last I heard footsteps outside the door and an angry voice protesting: 'How was I to know you 'd go out and leave a child alone all day!'

My mother rushed in, my brother was stroking my hair, and there I was sitting up in bed, eating hot bread and milk with brown sugar on it, listening to a fat man saying he had a young child of his own, and a girl in a white cap and apron declaring she had been in and hadn't seen a glimpse of the little girl.

'I 'll never leave you alone again,' promised my mother. 'It 's all Blanchard's fault! But he 'll not cheat me! I 'll follow him to the end of the world. I 'll have my children's money if I have to fight for it!'

I was delighted. Never to be left again in a horrid

bedroom! Never to be frightened! To travel all over
the world in search of the man with the bag of money.
I fell asleep laughing, while my mother was telling me
about Iubdan, King of the Tiny Folk of Faylinn, and his
wife Bebo, coming to the court of King Fergus and falling
into the porridge pot.

We spent Christmas in Manchester, a dark, wet town.
We didn't live in an hotel this time, but at a house where
the people who were acting in the pantomime stayed. We
had two rooms over the front door, but we lived in the
big sitting-room downstairs. My mother helped to sew
dresses, my brother painted old shoes with gold or silver
paint and made them beautiful. The players were always
practising songs and dances. They didn't mind me watching
them; indeed they asked my opinion and listened to everything I said. On Christmas Day we all had dinner together.
We sang carols and my mother gave them her best songs.
On St. Stephen's Day we saw the pantomime from a box,
and it was wonderful to find our friends turned into
Cinderella and the Ugly Sisters, the Prince, the Fairy Queen,
and the gaily dressed dancers and singers.

My mother and Patrick Henry saw Mr. Blanchard several
times. Sometimes he made them feel sure we would be
rich in a week; then my mother said she didn't believe a
word he told her, but what could she do? We left the
pantomime people and went to a smaller, darker house,
where the tea was weak, the bread stale and thick, and the
fire always smoking. Yet my mother told her best stories
in that house.

One night we sat at supper, silent and unhappy.

'Why wouldn't I write to Mr. Forbes and ask would he
have us back?' asked my brother suddenly.

'And give him the laugh of us?' demanded my mother.

'He'd never laugh. He'd be too glad!' persisted
Patrick Henry.

My mother set her lips obstinately.

'Where's the use in talking that way? Do you suppose his books are waiting and the little house standing empty there for our return? Have sense!'

I thought of the wood yard and my rag doll, the little house with all our treasures spread out, making it friendly, and Charlie coming along the canal path. Thinking of Charlie made me remember another friend, the earliest one of all, and I burst out crying.

'I never thought to ask Aunt Kattie about Dinny!' I lamented. 'And now I'll never know. He'll think I've forgotten him!'

My mother put her arms round me.

'Dear Tricia, I couldn't bear to tell you before. Dinny is dead. His father sent for him and his mother, and he died on the way to America; God rest his soul!'

I looked up and through my tears saw her and Patrick Henry gazing very sadly at me. But death didn't trouble me as it did them.

'Was he on a ship?' I asked.

My mother nodded.

'Then he won't be lonely on Fair Hill without me,' I said thankfully.

We were still talking about Dinny when the landlady came in with a letter.

'Came this morning,' she told us. 'Stuck it up on the mantelpiece and clean forgot!'

My mother always studied the envelope of a letter carefully, the postmark, and the writing. She shook her head. Patrick Henry gave one glance and smiled.

'Mr. Forbes!' he said. 'I am thankful to see his writing!'

He was right. Mr. Forbes didn't ask us to come back, but he offered to recommend my brother to firms in Liverpool and in other cities who wanted accounts checked but did not employ a regular book-keeper. He would earn more money this way, but he might have to travel continually.

'If we 'd prayed we couldn't have asked more!' exclaimed my mother. 'We 'll leave this horrible place to-morrow.'

We went back to Liverpool and from there to Chester We stayed in Nottingham and we lived in a cottage in Rottingdean. Patrick Henry and I walked into Brighton every day—he to do accounts in offices and I to a convent school with big iron gates set in a high wall. The wind from the sea blew through the classrooms. For the first time I hated lessons and longed for the slamming of desks and wild scamperings along the corridors, across the gravelled playground.

My mother met me as I came out of the gates and I went shopping with her. I carried a basket and she had the string bag. We bought bunches of little black grapes, thin slices of cooked ham, and Cambridge sausages in the lovely Brighton shops. We walked along the cliff road with the blue, white-edged waves dancing off to Ireland and foreign parts. We passed Blackrock, which wasn't the least bit like Blackrock at home.

'Do you remember?' my mother would begin, for she was afraid I 'd forget home and Ireland, but before she could come to the sad part I 'd coax: 'Tell me a story now.'

Sometimes she wouldn't want to tell a story but a poem, or even sing a song. Then I 'd have to watch out, for she didn't like strangers to hear her singing out of doors.

On Saturdays we went down the stone steps to the Aquarium and saw herrings swimming towards us in a gleaming shoal, a disappointing octopus, and a greeny-black lobster, which horrified my mother so that she wouldn't buy a tin of lobster for weeks, and lovely little sea-horses with their tails curled about seaweed stalks. When we came up from that damp cavern Patrick Henry would be waiting for us, a book under his arm, his face brown, his large eyes sparkling. He had so much to tell that we wandered from the path and came so close to the dangerous parts of the cliff it was a wonder we didn't walk on into space.

We were always hungry. Mrs. Greenside, our landlady, big and silent, couldn't make a decent cup of tea, but she baked large potatoes, scooped out the inside, mashed it with pepper, salt, and butter, minced beef, or kippers, or maybe cheese. All went back inside the crisp skins and sat on the fender in a dish, ready for us, and we never knew what would be inside until we began to eat. She made a marvellous fruit pie with plums preserved in syrup. She never minded us coming home late from a play on the pier, or a concert or a lecture at the Pavilion. We left behind the lights and music of Brighton, around us was darkness, the roar of the waves below, tossing lights far out on the sea, and Mrs. Greenside's lamp in the window, with the fire-glow on the blinds.

We went by bus only on Sunday, to make sure of Mass Other times we toiled along the cliff road in downpours of rain, storms of wind and snow, or when the moon made a world of ebony and silver.

Then we went back to dingy towns and lodgings which would have shocked Mrs. Greenside, to houses without gardens, to streets without a tree in them, and rooms with such ugly furniture and wall-paper I had nightmares instead of dreams. My mother put them into the stories she told me, turning them into castles of enchantment whose inhabitants were under a spell, but that made me hate them even more. We would go into the ugly rooms and out of the big black chest would come our treasures. My mother worked quickly, taking down torn lace curtains, putting up gay cretonnes, lifting down the queer pictures and carefully setting Wolfe Tone, Emmet, Parnell, and St. Patrick on the nails, the green rug before the fire-place, the cabinet, the brass coffee-pot, and my speckled shell on the mantelpiece, over it the round mirror and, opposite, the rich colours of the Holy Family, so that Patrick Henry, coming anxiously into a strange house, would climb the stairs, open a door, and there was home.

But in some places my mother wouldn't even unlock the black chest.

'Insult my pictures and the lovely rug by putting them out in such rooms!' she'd cry. 'I'll not dream of it! We must spend less and live more cheaply so that we can always live in clean, decent rooms.'

Then we met the MacGarrys, who taught her how to live on Scotch oatmeal. My mother bought a little sack of it and a black iron saucepan. The porridge was so thick it had to be stirred and stirred. If I ate my saucerful without a fuss she would tell me an extra story. Indeed she told some of her best stories on Scotch oatmeal.

'Remember the MacGarrys!' she said. 'Tall and strong, and buying back the castle of their ancestors!'

Yet all she saved went into Mr. Blanchard's gold-mine, and it wasn't always the same mine.

There was a Miss Friend who wouldn't take encumbrances. She and her brother lived at the sea end of a row of ramshackle houses outside Dover. There was a balcony with red roses climbing up to it, and the gay defiant crowing of a cock sounded over the wall. A card hung in the window, 'Apartments to Let,' and, as my mother pushed the garden gate, Miss Friend opened the door. She was tall and thin, and so fair she seemed bleached, though her long nose was red. Her hair was fixed in steel curlers and she shook a duster at me as if I were a chicken.

'Sorry, ma'am,' she said. 'You look respectable, but I can't take encumbrances.'

'Can't take which?' asked my mother, who didn't understand Miss Friend's accent.

'The child!' explained Miss Friend, flapping the duster at me. 'You see, there's the garden and the chickens.'

'Oh!' said my mother.

'I won't be bold!' I pleaded, longing for the garden and the chickens. 'I'll be very good. I will, indeed!'

A big black-and-white cat pushed by her, stalked up to me, rubbed against my legs, and purred.

'If Bumper likes the little girl, of course that's different,' said Miss Friend, retreating.

We went in quickly. Mr. Friend was in the passage, listening. My mother smiled at him and began to tell her troubles. Before she had finished we were having tea and hot fruit cake in the kitchen, and when Patrick Henry arrived tea started all over again.

Once, at the end of a long dusty road, we came to a house with 'Sarsfield Lodge' in dim gold letters on the gate.

'Sarsfield was the best fighter Ireland had!' my mother told me. 'Wouldn't you be proud to live in a house with his name on it?'

'Maybe we wouldn't be let,' I answered, for this was a big house, almost a mansion, though the windows were dirty and the front garden was a jungle of weeds. We lived there for three whole months with two sisters who used three rooms out of nine, never went out, and had twenty-seven cats.

Another house attracted my mother because of the monkey-puzzle tree growing before the door.

'That's the queerest tree I ever set eyes on!' said my mother. 'I'd like to see the inside of that place!'

It was the blackbeetles drove us away from the monkey puzzle house. We liked cats, and we didn't mind mice if there weren't too many, but we dreaded the beetles!

At the opposite corner was a lamp-post and, when school was over, some children flung a rope across the iron bar which stuck out from the lamp and made a swing.

They were always the same children; most of them in torn clothes and broken boots. The one who owned the rope wore a clean pinafore and her golden hair was coiled round her head. When the window was open I could hear all they said and I learned their names. I saw how Lizzie Bragg tied the rope, folding a shawl to make a seat, and I determined to be friends with her. Although it was her rope she was the last to swing. She put the youngest on first, and she fought the big boys who tried to take away the rope.

I had been indoors all day, and now I was alone looking out at the empty street. Rain poured straight down, making the dingy houses glimmer mysteriously. Over the dripping roofs came a sudden ray of sunlight turning the overflowing gutter into a golden stream.

'They won't come to-night!' I thought.

I drew a picture of the lamp-post with Lizzie swinging from it, the rope out stiff and straight. The rain stopped, the lamp-post glittered, and round the corner came Lizzie Bragg. The others followed, skipping with the rope. I rolled up my drawing and tiptoed from the room, down the dark stairs, into the darker hall, and groped my way to the door. It wasn't quite shut and I slipped out past the monkey-puzzle tree. Lizzie and her companions watched as I stepped over the gutter with its fleet of straws and crumpled paper.

'This is for you!' I said, holding out the drawing.

Lizzie put her hands behind her and stared suspiciously as I unfolded the sheet of paper.

'Hi, kids!' she exclaimed. 'Will yer look at this!'

They crowded forward, pushing me into the roadway.

'It's me!' said Lizzie proudly. 'See me 'air all piled up. An' there's me name, only it's spelt wrong! Us Bragges 'as an "e" on our name.'

They were excited. So was I.

'I mustn't play in the street,' I explained. 'I do my

lessons up at that window and I watch you. I thought maybe you 'd let me be friends.'

'You bet I will!' replied Lizzie. 'Say! Did you do this by yerself?'

I nodded.

'She 's a n'artis'!' declared one of the boys.

'Not 'arf she ain't!' agreed Lizzie. 'I 'll let 'er look at me 'air. Now wait!'

She pulled out the pins. Slowly the shining coil unwound until it hung over her shoulder below her waist.

'Nearly ready fer cutting!' announced Lizzie. 'The 'airdresser gives me mother five shillings for it. 'E calls it a switch! Then I start growing another.'

She twisted her hair up again and pinned it securely.

'Now we 'll swing,' said Lizzie.

She flung one end of the rope over the bar, tied a double knot, and fixed the shawl.

'You 'ave first go,' she told me. 'Case yer mother comes back an' catches yer. Young Sam, watch out!'

I sat on the folded shawl and clutched the rope.

'I 've never been on this kind of swing before,' I said.

''Old tight! I 'll swing yer!' Lizzie reassured me.

She bent closer.

'Can I 'ave that picture fer keeps?'

'I did it for you,' I told her.

Lizzie seized the rope above my head, running round and round until I swung out. I shut my eyes. I promised if I ever sat safely again at the window I would never be bold! Never! never! I was flying. I opened my eyes. I sailed round the lamp-post, I wanted to go on swinging, slower, slower.

'Die, baby, die!'

chanted Lizzie.

'Open yer mouth
An' shut yer eye.'

My feet touched earth again.   I kicked the lamp-post.

'Better 'op it!' said Lizzie.   'You don't want ter be copped.   Say, watcher name?'

I told her and ran.

'Termorrer night!' called Lizzie.

I waved my hand. The door was as I had left it, the passage was dark, the stairs dark, even the room above was dark. But when I reached the window, the street lamp was alight and another girl flew through the air.

## 26. GOOSE GREEN

THE wind made me cough. I wouldn't eat porridge. I turned away even from bread and milk. When my mother turned down the gas and left me in bed at night the leaves on the wall-paper began to quiver and ruſtle. Now I looked into a foreſt—a foreſt of withered leaves, no branches, no trunks. Suddenly the leaves turned to faces, thin, angry faces. From all sides of the room they threatened me, coming nearer and nearer until I screamed for help.

'Maybe you should ſtay in one place with Tricia,' suggeſted Patrick Henry to my mother. 'It isn't fair for both of you to be wandering like tinkers. And it won't be for long!'

Before they decided, a letter came from Mr. Blanchard in Paris. They muſt come at once, he wrote. He had money and good news.

'Would you like to go to a boarding school while we fix things?' asked my mother.

I was horrified. Hadn't she always told me they were prisons, except the one in France where she went with Cousin Kate?

'Now why wouldn't I write to Mr. Forbes?' she suggested.

'Would you stay on a farm without us?' she asked, when his answer came.

I shook my head.

'You promised you 'd never leave me. You promised!'

'But a farm,' she coaxed. 'You know—pigs and cows. Mr. Forbes knows the man. And there 's a little girl your own age.'

'And trees?' I asked. 'And a cat and a dog, and chickens and ducks?'

She laughed.

'Sure, 'tis a zoo you 're wanting. But you 'd grow big and strong so that we 'd all be together again, and maybe we 'd take you to Paris next time. You 'd love Paris!'

'You won't forget me?'

'Forget you!' cried my mother. 'You don't know all you mean to me. You and Patrick Henry are my world!'

So I went to Goose Green.

My mother and Patrick Henry came with me as far as Canterbury. From there I went on the train by myself to Ashford. I had my ticket in the pocket of my coat, and my clothes, my books, my toys were in the tin box.

'Maybe one day you 'll have a real travelling chest,' said my mother.

I couldn't believe she would let me go until her face and Patrick Henry's had become faint blurs. I expected to feel miserable, but there was so much to look at, inside the carriage and out, that I had no time for sorrow. They were going to Paris where Mary Bernadette's Eiffel Tower and Notre-Dame belonged. But I was going to Goose Green where the Martins lived with all their animals. My fellow travellers were friendly. They asked where I was bound, and I had scarcely told them when the guard came along and opened the door.

'Here's a gentleman with a horse and chariot asking for the lady for Goose Green,' he said.

'That's me!' I cried, for I knew none of the other passengers were going there. I had never been called a lady before, so instead of jumping, I tried to step out properly. But a man in the carriage lifted me down to the guard. I thanked them both, but I would have been better pleased if they had left me to myself.

'Here she is!' shouted the guard. 'Here's the little gel from Lunnon!'

'Me box!' I called. 'Me tin box!'

I stubbed my toe against it, for it was on the platform beside me; a brown tin box, with a rope corded crosswise round it, for my mother never trusted locks, and a label on each handle:

PATRICIA NORA LYNCH,
Passenger to GOOSE GREEN

The guard was leaning from the last door. I waved to him, but I was looking at a big red-faced man with very fair hair, wearing a bright blue coat, and carrying a whip over his shoulder, who was coming down the steps of the bridge.

'Hallo, missy!' he said. 'I'm the carrier!'

He caught up the tin box and marched before me. I was delayed because I couldn't find my ticket. At last the ticket collector discovered it in the little pocket of my new reefer jacket. By that time the carrier, my box on his shoulder, had crossed the bridge and was going down the steps at the other side, so I had to run my hardest. Even then he was through the gate and poking the tin box in at the back of a tilt cart before I caught up. The tilt was as white as if it had just been washed. The cart was painted yellow and, on the side, in white letters, I read:

LUKE JUKE, Carrier

The grey horse was fat and well groomed, the brown harness dark with polish, and even the nosebag, which Mr. Juke was slipping off, was neat and well stitched. The horse rubbed its nose against the carrier's shoulder.

'Up to front!' said Mr. Juke.

I was determined not to be lifted and swung about. I scrambled quickly over the wheel, but before I was safely on the seat, the grey horse gave a tug. I tumbled forward, but Mr. Juke caught my arm and settled me on the seat beside him. The cart bumped and swayed across the station yard. Two boys were hopping over the cobbles, a little girl pushed a box on wheels along the gutter. Pigeons strutted around the wheels and a black dog lay stretched in the gateway, its long ears spread on the ground. The grey horse slipped. Mr. Juke cracked his whip and the pigeons fluttered up, their wings grazing the tilt. The hopping boys stood still, the little girl backed against the wall, but the dog did not move until I was sure a lifted hoof would descend on him. Then he leaped suddenly, swung round, and was on the cart beside me, his quivering tongue lolling out, his tail thumping.

'Hey, Bobbit, ye rogue!' said the carrier.

The cart lurched into a wide sunny street of bow-windowed shops. Then came small houses with polished knockers and whitened steps. We stopped at an inn with a newly painted sign. Mr. Juke thrust the reins into my hands, jumped down, and ran into the courtyard at the side. A man, chewing a long straw, threw a bucket of soapy water over the stones and brushed them with a stiff yard broom. A white cat stepped carefully across the damp cobbles and would not hurry even when Mr. Juke came running, his arms piled with parcels. He tucked them away at the back and I looked over my shoulder to see baskets and packets, tins, bottles, boxes, a barrel, all fixed with wads of straw so that they could not move.

We swept by a pond, green and smooth, with a tree drooping over it, and a broken ladder stretched half-way across, then out on a white road with high hedges. There were gates in the hedges and at almost every gate some-one waited to give Mr. Juke a parcel, take one from him, or ride a little way with us. People sat on banks at the ends of lanes which began winding as soon as they left the road. Often they stood talking to Mr. Juke while the dog slept and the horse rattled its harness. I could see farm-houses and, beside them, queer little houses with big sloping chimneys which Mr. Juke called 'oast-houses.' There were no streets, no crowded pavements, only the pleasant sounds of birds and bees, and the horse's hoofs on the dusty road. On each side I saw vines climbing poles, set closely together in rows, and a pungent smell filled the air.

'Them's hops!' said Mr. Juke. 'Picking starts ter-morrer!'

'Better than Lunnon?' he asked suddenly.

'I'm not from London!' I exclaimed indignantly. 'I'm from Cork! At least I was in the beginning and we're going back—one day!'

'Tell the whole story,' suggested Mr. Juke. ''Twill pass time!'

I told him and, as I spoke, the neat green hedges and quiet lanes, the rows of hops, the secluded farmhouses with whitewashed trees growing around them vanished. I saw the stone walls, the whitewashed cabins, the mountains closing in on one another. I rode in Peadar Keeley's turf cart with Mrs. Hennessy and there was Yalla Hankercher in his battered cart with the tattered tilt and Dinny was with me all the way.

'Goose Green!' said Mr. Juke, though there wasn't a goose in sight.

The road cut the green in two. On one side were tiny

houses with long gardens, packed with flowers, on the other
a row of shops with a grass walk and seats in front.

As we came towards the green the village was deserted,
but at the sound of the grey horse's hoofs, from every house
children came running, old men hobbling, women with
their sleeves rolled up hurried out. They came even from
the shops. Once more I held the reins while Mr. Juke
handed out a bundle of papers, boxes of sweets and biscuits, the barrel, packets and bundles until the cart was
almost empty.

On went the grey horse, past a red square church on one
side and an inn with a table and bench before the low,
wide window. An old man, with a long white beard and
a crumpled top hat, sat there with his legs stretched out,
and a sign with a white goose on it swung overhead. We
stopped where a little girl in a pink frock was swinging on
a white gate. She stepped off and stood staring up at me,
her hands behind her back. To my amazement Mr. Juke
lifted me down with one hand and my tin box with the other.

'Here's the little gel from Lunnon, Rosalie,' said Mr.
Juke. 'Give her a kiss an' say how do 'ee do? Where's
Martin?'

'Up along, milking,' said Rosalie.

She looked me over, stepped forward, and kissed me.

The ground rose inside the gate and, both carrying
parcels, we followed Mr. Juke up a path of stone steps.
I was tired now and hungry, and very lonely. I kept
looking at Rosalie, hoping we would be friends. She was
indeed pretty, like a doll, blue eyes, tight yellow curls, pink
cheeks, and small, even teeth. She never stopped asking
questions, and gave me no chance to answer.

'Are there many girls in Lunnon called Patricia? Do
they call 'ee Pat or Patty? Is Lunnon big? Is it bigger
than Canterbury? Is it true there beant any horses there
at all? Be 'ee good at lessons? Do 'ee know any stories?'

We climbed steadily. Above us rose a square stone house, grim and bare. There were no flowers round it, no curtains to the windows. We came to a path that went round to the back of the house. Across a yard were sheds, and I heard the pleasant lowing of cows and the sharper voices of calves. Farther away a pig grunted comfortably and a piercing crow rose above the clucking of hens. A gaunt cat slunk into one of the sheds and I heard the rattle of a chain, as a thin, vicious dog stepped away from the barrel which was its kennel and snarled.

'Here she be, mother!' called Rosalie. 'Here's the little gel from Lunnon!'

I was tired of being 'the little gel from Lunnon.'

'I belong to Cork!' I interrupted. 'I came from there and I'm going back one day!'

As I spoke Mrs. Martin came out from the house. She was thin, but she wore such a number of petticoats that her clothes stood out all round. Her dress was black and reached her ankles, and over it she wore a gathered white apron with a bib. Her hair was drawn back so tightly it seemed to be tugging at her eyes. Her lips were thin and she poked them out as she stared at me. Suddenly she seized my arm and felt it and, stooping, she pinched my legs.

'Mr. Forbes said 'ee was poorly and mother thought 'ee needed country air. I think ye're a big fat gel. Look at Rosalie! She's a year older and much thinner!'

I hated being called a big fat girl. I frowned at Mrs. Martin, but she was taking the parcels from Rosalie. I put mine on the ground.

'Pick them up, me lady, and don't start sulks! They don't pay here! Juke, take that box up to Rosalie's room!'

Mr. Juke put my box down with a clatter on the stones.

'No, Mrs. Martin! I won't take the little gel's box up! I'm a carrier, not a handyman.'

'Ye'll be sorry, Juke, when we have a decent engine van

on the roads instead of a Noah's Ark.  It 's coming, I tell
'ee!  It pays to be obliging, don't 'ee forget!'

Mr. Juke was marching off, very indignant, when a tall,
round-faced man, with smiling blue eyes, came through
a door in the wall beyond the house, wiping his hands on
a wisp of hay.

'Why, here 's the little gel from Lunnon!' he cried.
'I bet Rosalie 's been telling 'ee how pleased we all do be.
Hallo, Luke, come in and have cup of tea.  Kettle 's on
boil.  And little gel sort of knows you by now.  Let 's
all sit down to tea.  Here 's mother!'

'Won't stay!  Can't!' growled Mr. Juke.  'But thanks,
Martin, and I 'll take up the box.'

'That 'ee won't!' declared Mr. Martin.  'Ye 're a carrier,
not a handyman.  See 'ee Satdy?'

'Satdy!'

Mr. Juke did go this time, taking off his hat to a tiny
little woman who tripped round the corner of the house
and stood smiling at me.

'What a nice little gel!' she said, and kissed me twice.
'My, Rosalie, beant 'ee lucky to have such a friend!'

She was so small she didn't reach Mrs. Martin's shoulder,
and though she was old, she was like Rosalie.  Her curls
were grey, not fair, but her eyes were as blue and her
cheeks as rosy as her grand-daughter's.  I felt happy at
once.

'Ye shall have pancakes to tea, little gel,' she told me.
'As many as 'ee can eat!  I do love making pancakes, and
I beat up the batter, I did, afore I went down to the village.'

She trotted into the house and we all followed her.

There was a long table in the kitchen, with forms at
each side.  Old Mrs. Martin made tea at a range which was
red with rust.  The knives were rusty, so were the spoons.
The table was set with enamel mugs and plates.  We had
no saucers and the tea was the weakest I had ever tasted,

but old Mrs. Martin's pancakes were light and golden brown.  She turned them out six at a time from an enormous rusty frying-pan and ate her own sitting by the stove. We had thick home-made plum jam with the stones taken out. I ate and ate but stopped with my mouth full, for between two sheds I saw a wonderful sight.  I had been seeing it all the time without understanding.  Now I knew that the purple flowers on some trees, the rose-coloured flowers on others, weren't flowers at all, but plums!

'Look!' I cried, pointing.  'They 're surely plums!'

Mr. Martin showed all his teeth in a friendly smile.

'Plums they be,' he said.  'Purple Pershores and Victorias. Behind them 's pears—Ladies' Thighs!  They be the best eaters in the market.  Be 'ee a good picker, Patty?'

'Me name 's Patricia Nora!' I said firmly.  'Me friends call me Tricia and I don't come from London.  I come from Cork!'

'None of that sauce, me lady!' cried Mrs. Martin.

Rosalie licked her knife.  But her mother saw and gave her a slap.

'I 'll larn 'ee manners if I knock yer head off!' she said fiercely.  'Go off now and shut in the hens and fetch the sticks.'

'May I go too?' I asked.

''Ee won't be so willing in a week's time!' was Mrs. Martin's answer, so I ran after Rosalie.

'Are all those plum-trees really yours?' I wanted to know.

'Don't talk so much about plums!' whispered Rosalie. 'I 'll see 'ee get plenty.  First we 'll shut up they hateful hens.'

We coaxed the hens into the barn and I was sorry to shut the door on the handsome cock.  He looked up into my face and crowed softly as if saying good night.

'Now we 'll fetch the sticks!' said Rosalie, at the top of her voice.  'There 's heaps!' and she showed me a stock of small dry branches covered over at the back of the cow shed. 'Father gets them for me. He wants me to have hands like a lady! Be 'ee a good runner?'

Rosalie didn't wait for an answer but hopped and skipped along by the sheds until we came opposite the plum-trees. We could see them, but we couldn't touch them, for between were two fences, and between the fences a strip of muddy ground and at one end a pigsty. Lying before the sty, peaceful and content, was a huge sow.

'Now, listen,' said Rosalie. 'That's Clementine! She's here to keep every one who wants plums away from 'em. I'll climb the fence at this end. Clem will rush after me. Then do 'ee climb at t' other end and we'll both be over.'

I looked at Clementine. She must have been the biggest sow in the world. She heard us talking and, lifting her head, blinked her little red eyes.

'Ye're not scared, are 'ee?' demanded Rosalie. 'Young Sammy Pryde does it when 'ee's up along cleaning the stables. Us could do it every day!'

'I'll try!' I said.

''Tis no use trying!' declared Rosalie. ''Ee must do it! Clem's fierce. Her mustn't catch 'ee!'

'I won't let her!' I promised.

I went to the end of the fence by the sty. Clem grunted. Rosalie climbed at the far end, and as she jumped down Clem stood up, then, grunting angrily, charged down the trampled and muddy strip. I stood watching in terror.

'Run!' screamed Rosalie. 'Run!'

I scrambled over the fence and stumbled across. As I pulled myself up into the shadow of the plum-trees Clem came pounding back.

'Us must hurry,' said Rosalie. ''Tis growing dark. Us'll fill this basket.'

A ladder lay in the grass. Between us we managed to lift this against a Pershore tree. Rosalie went up first with the basket.

'Do 'ee hold it,' she told me. 'I'll pick best. But 'ee 'll soon learn!'

We went on to a Victoria plum. When the basket was so heavy we could scarcely lift it, Rosalie insisted on picking pears.

'Can't we leave some?' I asked. 'We can get more to-morrow!'

'Rain to-morrow!' declared Rosalie. 'Look at the swallows flying low and listen to the old rooks! When the moon rises 'twill be a watery moon. And I never have enough plums!'

We heard voices.

'Sh!' whispered Rosalie.

She looked so frightened I was frightened too.

''Tis mother come down to look at Clem,' she told me, her face close to mine. 'Granny's with her! What shall us do?'

I could see a wall beyond the trees.

'Can we climb the wall?' I asked, speaking as softly as I could.

She shook her head.

'The ladder?'

Rosalie nodded.

We couldn't carry both ladder and basket. So, resting the basket in the long grass, we carried the ladder between the trees to the foot of the wall. Carefully we propped it up, though its weight made us pant and tremble. We returned for the basket and I urged we should half empty it. But Rosalie wouldn't sacrifice a single plum or pear. Darkness came as we climbed the ladder. I went first this time, for Rosalie wouldn't trust me with the basket. When I reached the top I looked back at her.

'How can we get down?'

'Drop! 'Tis easy! The ground's high and the grass thick!'

I scraped my knees but I was over the wall.

'Basket's coming!' warned Rosalie. 'Catch it!'

I stood on tiptoe. The basket landed on my head. I staggered, but Rosalie was beside me and the fruit was saved. We were on a road, and though I thought Rosalie greedy, I giggled with her as we dragged the basket along by the wall, on the edge of the ditch, and finally reached the big white gate at the front of the farmhouse.

## 27. WE GO TO THE CIRCUS

RAIN began while I was pulling on my stockings and I stopped to watch it beating on the window. The walls of the farmhouse dripped inside as well as out. The dog whined in his kennel; the cat sat in the doorway of the shed opposite the kitchen and looked mournful.

'Lucky we picked plums!' whispered Rosalie.

The kitchen window was open and the rain swept past on the driving wind. The table and chairs were damp, the floor muddy. Now I understood why the range, the saucepans, the frying-pan, were rusty.

We had thick rashers for breakfast. I ate the lean and mopped the gravy with my bread. Then I chopped the fat in small pieces and called:

'Puss! puss! Breakfast!'

'Are 'ee daft?' cried Mrs. Martin. 'Let the beast catch rats if 'tis hungry. Good bacon, indeed!'

I clutched the plate with both hands.

'It's my breakfast, Mrs. Martin, and I want the pussy to have some!'

They all stopped eating. Mrs. Martin stared at me and I stared back.

''Ee 'll want Tiddles to have milk in a dish next, I suppose?' she jeered.

'Indeed I do!' I declared. 'He 's the thinnest pussy I 've ever seen.'

While we argued, Tiddles rushed through the rain, leaped across the window sill, and came to me, tail up, eyes pleading but suspicious. I put down the plate and Tiddles ate, growling with satisfaction. He licked the plate until it was polished, then gazed in bewilderment at the dish of milk the old granny put on the floor. He gulped uneasily, glared round, his ears flattened back, settled down, and gurgled happily until the last drop disappeared, then blinked up at our intent faces and, stalking over to the fender, sat there purring.

'The cat sits by the fire!' I chanted.

'Time a bit of work was done!' snapped Mrs. Martin. 'Watching cats eat good food!'

'I 'll wash up!' I announced. 'Rosalie can dry.'

I enjoyed washing up in hot soapy water, but Rosalie hated work. I wanted to please Mrs. Martin, for I was longing to make Tiddles a sleek, contented cat who would do tricks. I even hoped to make Pincher, the dog, friendly, though that wouldn't be easy. So I dried as well as washed up and arranged the crocks neatly on the dresser.

'Now go and swing in the barn!' Mrs. Martin told us. 'I 'll not have two children under my feet.'

We put our heads under our coats and ran. The barn was big, with hay piled at one side. There were logs, one with a big saw stuck in it. Rakes, forks, and spades stood in a corner, and a swing, with a low, wide seat, was hanging from the rafters.

'You can swing and tell me about Lunnon,' said Rosalie. 'I'll lie in the hay and eat plums.'

I told Rosalie about London. She liked St. Winifred's best and just yawned when I told her of the Cadogans and the people around the courtyard.

'I'm going to boarding school when I'm fourteen!' she boasted. 'I'll stay till I'm sixteen. Then I'll run away and be a bare-back rider in a circus. If only my hair would grow long!'

'Shall I draw a picture of you with long hair?' I asked.

Rosalie stopped biting a red plum. I pulled a Pershore from my pocket and began to nibble it.

''Ee can't draw pictures!' said Rosalie.

'I can! And I can recite poetry and I know stories and stories and stories!'

'Begin with a story,' ordered Rosalie. 'One about a girl with long golden hair who runs away from school and joins circus.'

'I don't know one!' I objected.

'Make it up, silly! Make it up! If 'ee can draw pictures, 'ee can make up stories. And it needn't be made up! Here I be. The circus will be coming and I be going to boarding school.'

Swinging slowly and eating plums, I began the story of Goldilocks and her white horse. If I put in anything Rosalie didn't like she grumbled until I took it out again. And she wouldn't let me finish it.

'I'm going on for years and years! Let the story go on too!' said Rosalie.

At dinner I saved my bones and fat for Pincher, who growled and snapped but ate every bit. We were all hungry after dinner, for Mrs. Martin was very mean about food. When the granny did the cooking, we feasted. Though she was old she went out nursing, and even Mrs. Martin thought her cleverer than a doctor; and to-day she was away nursing. After dinner we went back to the barn. Mrs. Martin gave Rosalie a basket of mending. Rosalie poked it in the hay and sprawled comfortably eating plums, while I went on with her story. Tiddles sat with us, washing and purring, and presently the hens came scuttling in, with the cock following. Mrs. Martin went out visiting and the granny came back in time for tea, so we had hot plum pie and a jug of thick cream. Then we went with Mr. Martin up to the big attic to help him rummage round.

I slept with Rosalie in the little attic, which had a ladder of its own, fixed securely. Mr. Martin had to carry up a ladder for us to reach the big attic. It was far too short, so he lifted first Rosalie, then me, and poked us through the trap-door. The window in the roof could not be opened and it was coated with dirt. But there were several missing slates, so that the attic was well lighted and rain dripped in.

'There's a chest of books I bought at auction last spring,' said Mr. Martin. ''Ee might like a look at 'em, Tricia? I heard 'ee telling Rosalie a story in the barn. That reminds me, Rosalie. How are us agoing to get to the circus this year? Mother's dead set against it.'

'How much does it cost?' I asked.

'Us 'd get in half-price, sixpence,' said Rosalie. 'Father 'd be a shilling!'

'Then there's the carrier,' added Mr. Martin, sitting on a broken chair and stretching his legs.

'Luke Juke would take us for nothing, ye know 'e would,' urged Rosalie. 'Juke's always giving people lifts.'

'Luke Juke has a living to earn, same as me,' objected Mr. Martin. 'He don't ask for free milk or butter. I'll not ask for lifts.'

'I'll ask granny!' said Rosalie.

'Let granny be!' exclaimed Mr. Martin. 'Her's little enough for her few pleasures. No, Rosalie, us'll have to think of some other way.'

'I can pay for myself!' I told them proudly. 'I'm to have sixpence a week pocket money!'

'Sixpence!' screamed Rosalie. 'That's not fair! I'm stuck with threepence!'

'Patty's mother be a rich lady!' Mr. Martin told her. 'You'm a farmer's daughter.'

'Sixpence a week!' grumbled Rosalie, looking at me enviously.

I was so pleased to hear my mother called a rich lady that I sat down on a pile of newspapers and didn't say another word. Maybe she would be a rich lady one day, when the gold came out of Mr. Blanchard's mine.

'I ought to be paid for picking fruit!' said Rosalie. 'Can't 'ee ask mother to pay me?'

'Ask her yourself,' said Mr. Martin. 'I'm all for a quiet life. Patty—that's the chest of books!'

The chest was a battered wooden box with a broken lock. I lifted the lid and saw big books bound in dingy brown leather. They reminded me of grandfather's books. Who had them now? I wondered. I was sure Uncle Cathal hadn't taken them to America, and Uncle Liam and Aunt Kattie hadn't had a single book in their luggage. Would Aunt Hannah have them? No! There wasn't space in her little house. I was sorry for those homeless books, for I felt sure they were gone from the old house on Fair Hill.

'Aren't there any story books?' asked Rosalie. 'They look horrid! Father! Let's have a bonfire and burn them all!'

I was horrified.

'You mustn't burn books, Rosalie! It's wicked!'

'Let's be wicked, just for once!' cried Rosalie, dancing about the attic. 'Let's have a bonfire on the hill!'

'Quiet, or yer mother will be after 'ee!' Mr. Martin warned her. 'She've come back. I heard the door bang!'

I lifted out one book. It was so heavy I dropped it, and

a huge spider darted across the floor. Rosalie screamed, and so did I, for though I liked watching spiders spin webs in a garden, I hated them indoors.

'You 'm scared that poor insect!' chuckled Mr. Martin. 'Here goes!'

He lifted one end of the box and tipped it, so that the books toppled out in a heap. One of the heavy volumes fell open and I saw that it was a book with lines of figures in it and half the pages empty.

'Here 's a lovely book!' I said. 'I can draw pictures and copy poetry in that.'

'Do a picture now,' said Rosalie.

I shook my head.

'I couldn't! Me pencil is in the bedroom. And I want to look at all these.'

Rosalie helped me by opening the books. Only the first had many blank pages. There were six bright clean books with '*Johnny Ludlow*, by Mrs. Henry Wood,' on the covers.

'Six books all about Johnny Ludlow!' said Rosalie. 'Who be Johnny Ludlow, father?'

'Never heard of the chap!' replied Mr. Martin. 'But here be that box of nails I lost. There be nothing like a rainy day for finding losings!'

A huge book with thick covers was the *Leisure Hour*. I didn't like the name so I put it on the pile. A dirty bundle of magazines tied with string was called the *Family Herald*. Right at the bottom, crumpled and without any cover at all, I picked up a whole volume of the *Strand Magazine*.

'Mrs. Martin don't hold with magazines,' said Mr. Martin, as Rosalie read out the names. He was sitting on a torn cushion, arranging the nails, and I stood turning over the pages of the *Strand Magazine*.

There were pictures, stories, poetry, and then I saw *The Magic City*!

'Rosalie!' I whispered. 'Here's a story about magic!'

The light was growing dim and I could scarcely make out the print. Besides, such a story must be read properly.

'Martin!' called Mrs. Martin from the foot of the stairs. 'Be 'ee going to keep them children up there all night?'

'Clear off!' said Mr. Martin. 'Find anything good, Patty?'

'I did, Mr. Martin. Can I come back another day?'

'Next wet day we'll all come,' promised Mr. Martin.

We drank weak hot cocoa by the fire. Mrs. Martin followed the directions on the tin for making one breakfast cup. She mixed it in a big enamel jug and filled the jug right up with hot water. I thought of my mother's lovely rich chocolate, foaming and creamy. But I knew *The Magic City* would make up for all the weak cocoa in the world.

'Mind 'ee blow out the candle the minit 'ee 're abed!' called Mrs. Martin, as we ran upstairs.

I had the *Strand Magazine* under my arm, for I was going to read in bed. Rosalie carried the candlestick.

'That's a terrible small candle!' I complained.

'You'm daft!' was Rosalie's reply. 'Just wait!'

The little attic was a clean, bright room with a sloping roof and a window jutting out from the middle. A seat with a cretonne curtain hanging from it went all along one side. Under this Rosalie kept her boots, books, treasures. She had cleared half for me and we each had a wardrobe made by a strip of wood nailed across a corner with a long curtain fastened to it. Behind, on the wall, were hooks for our coats and frocks. A chest of drawers painted light green stood beside the bed, and Rosalie put the candlestick on this along with my speckled shell. She groped under the seat and triumphantly brought out a cardboard box filled with pieces of candle. The rain was still falling. A bucket near the window caught a steady drip from the roof and an old umbrella with a broken stick was tied to the head of the bed to shelter us from occasional drops.

Rosalie lay down comfortably. I sat propped with a pillow and read *The Magic City*, by E. Nisbet, slowly. I was afraid of missing a word.

'Here's something!' said Rosalie, when I grew hoarse, and she poked out from under her pillow two apples, warm and shining.

'I wonder what E. Nisbet is like!' I murmured with my mouth full.

Rosalie didn't care. She wanted the story.

*The Magic City* was a long story—too long to read that first night. It was wonderful to me because it was in bits, mixed up with other stories—a chapter each month. I had never thought about who wrote the story books I read, but now I was making up a story and I determined to write out the whole history of Goldilocks and her white horse as I told it to Rosalie. She fell asleep, but I sat wondering about the people who wrote stories and drew pictures. I wanted to be one of them.

I went with Rosalie to the village school. There were flowers in jam-jars on each window sill, and leisurely bees buzzed in on their way to the orchards. At the end of the day the teacher gave out sweets to all who had been good at their lessons or hadn't been too bold or lazy. We had no home lessons, and after school we went with the other children to help the hop pickers. I watched the men chop the hop vine at the root and carry pole and vine together to the waiting pickers. I pulled a few of the crisp green hop flowers and dropped them into the canvas container as I followed Rosalie into the oast-house. There was a big fire at one side, and the air was heavy with the smell of drying hops. Some of the children stayed all night with the pickers, singing and drinking tea, but we had to return home at sundown.

We were going to school when we met a man pushing a handcart with a bucket of paste and a bundle of bills.

'Circus be coming!' sang Rosalie. 'Circus be coming!' 'I have my sixpence!' I boasted.

'Sixpence!' jeered Rosalie. 'Sixpence will get 'ee into the big tent. But there's the roundabout and the fat lady and side shows, ye'll have to pay extra for them.'

'I don't want to see the fat lady!' I protested. 'What is a roundabout, Rosalie?'

'Horses and boats go round and round and up and down. They're not real, but they're lovely!'

'You mean hobby-horses!' I told her scornfully.

'I don't! I mean roundabouts! And there's ostriches and camels!'

The circus opened on Saturday, and at breakfast Mr. Martin jumped up, seized a wooden box on the window sill, and lifted the lid.

'Guess I'd best go in with Luke. I'm all out of nails!' he said, looking very worried.

I opened my mouth to remind him of the box of nails in the attic when Rosalie gave me a kick under the table.

'Best take the gels in and get 'em good strong boots!' said Mrs. Martin. 'They'll be running round barefoot if you don't. Climbing walls, and skipping and kicking stones like two rough lads.'

'Wouldn't 'ee like to come in, missis?' asked Mr. Martin. 'The change would do 'ee a world of good!'

I thought mournfully that there wouldn't be much fun if Mrs. Martin came, but Rosalie looked quite content.

'I'm not a child or a flibbertigibbet!' declared Mrs. Martin. 'And ye can take in the list and tell the stores last bacon warn't fit to eat. 'Tis no use sending complaints by Juke.'

'I'll complain!' said Mr. Martin fiercely. 'I'll threaten to take away our custom!'

Rosalie and I were swinging on the gate when the carrier's cart came along the road.

'Hallo, Rosalie! Hallo, little gel from Lunnon!' called Luke Juke. 'Where's Martin?'

'Breaking sticks up along!' Rosalie told him.

We both stood out in the roadway. I ventured to pat the grey horse, who snorted and tossed his mane.

'Here's the parcels,' said the carrier. 'I'll drive straight on.'

'Wait!' cried Rosalie. 'Us be all going to the circus!'

'Circus!' exclaimed Luke Juke. 'What circus?'

'Don't 'ee be pretending, Luke Juke!' said Rosalie indignantly. 'Ye'll be at the circus 'long of us and well 'ee knows it!'

'Well, run up and tell Martin to hurry. I'm late!'

Mr. Martin was quite ready. But Mrs. Martin had so many messages and warnings to give him it was a wonder we were able to start. When we did get back to the road we saw the carrier helping old Mrs. Martin into the van, and there she sat perched on the seat beaming down at us.

'Granny! Ye've got yer best clothes on and it beant Sunday!' cried Rosalie. 'Ye'll catch it!'

'I saved me money!' declared old Mrs. Martin. 'And now I'm agoing to spend it!'

We scrambled up and sat on a bundle of hay in front of the old woman.

'Not missing mother, are 'ee, dear?' she asked, bending down.

I nodded.

'Indeed I am! When I remember, I do miss her!'

'Then write and tell her. She'm wondering—be my little gel safe and be she happy? Be them people good to she, and do they bring she up right?'

Mr. Martin drove and Luke Juke sat with his arms folded, his hat tilted over his eyes. Rosalie chattered, old

Mrs. Martin sang to herself, and I tried to see everything on the road.

'Father! Have 'ee money for the circus?' asked Rosalie, tugging his coat.

I wished I was rich. I had meant to save the whole of my sixpence for the circus, but the village shop sold wonderful allsorts—four ounces a penny—and we passed it on our way to school.

'Us always have managed. Us 'll manage now!' replied Mr. Martin.

The grey horse jogged steadily along the white road. We met three cows, who stood side by side and wouldn't move. Mr. Martin cracked the whip and they bundled against the side of the road, mooing indignantly. Rosalie and I laughed until the others laughed too.

'People shouldn't leave animals astraying on the roads!' grumbled Mr. Martin. 'Ye never know, there might be an accident!'

'Mother says wait till the engine cars come!' said Rosalie.

'They 'll never come to these parts!' declared Mr. Martin.

'Mother says they 'm acoming!' Rosalie told them, tossing her head.

'I won't have no motor van!' shouted Luke Juke suddenly. 'And I won't be druv into one!'

Rosalie looked up at him with a pout.

'I 'm only telling what mother says!' she complained.

'If 'ee 'd sit quiet and do a bit of looking like Patty here, us 'd all be happier!' said Mr. Martin.

'There 's nothing to look at!' muttered Rosalie.

She gave me a push.

'Tell more about Goldilocks!'

'To-night!' I promised.

'Granny!' said Rosalie. 'Patty 's making up a story about me. I 've long golden hair and a white horse, and I run away from school to join the circus.'

'Ye 'd soon come running home to mother, me lady!' chuckled the old woman. 'There 's Appledore, Patty, and there 's the circus!'

The road went under an avenue of trees with grass borders. The houses had long gardens and low red roofs. There were a great many small shops with big windows and wide doorways with steep stone steps leading up to them. The fruit shop had a basket of green apples and bundles of rhubarb on the steps. Next door was the butcher's, which had legs of mutton hanging like a necklace across the doorway. The chemist's big green bottle in the window reminded me of the shop by the bridge in Cork, only there should have been three bottles, red and blue and golden.

In a meadow between the houses and back from the road was a huge striped tent, with smaller tents scattered over the grass. In one corner several caravans were ranged in a hollow square. A woman sat at the back of one, peeling potatoes from a sack into a big tin basin. Two little boys were turning somersaults on the grass, following one another in a ring, faster and faster. A dozen horses were tethered to the fence, each with a nosebag; six were black and white, one was pure white with plaited mane and tail, the others were ordinary horses.

'Here we be!' said Mr. Martin, handing over the reins and whip to Luke Juke.

'Meet at three?' asked the carrier.

'Three it is!' agreed Mr. Martin. 'And 'ee won't forget the list at the stores, will 'ee?'

Rosalie was gazing at the big tent.

'Come along down!' said her father.

She didn't move. I squeezed past her and jumped. Mr. Martin lifted down the old lady.

'Get the basket, lad!' she told him. ''Tis under the seat.'

He tugged out a basket so big and heavy that he had to use both hands to bring it safely to the roadway.

'Now, Rosalie!' he coaxed, holding out his arms.

'She don't hear, bless her!' said the old lady. 'She's Goldilocks at the circus. Ask young Patty!'

Mr. Martin climbed back beside his daughter and swung her gently to the ground.

'I can't see down here!' cried Rosalie, stamping her foot

'Circus don't start till three,' her father told her. 'Luke 'll meet us here and us 'll all go in. Only first us must have money!'

He took her hand and pulled her into the boot shop. Rosalie looked over her shoulder until she was inside. At once she seemed to forget the circus.

'Father, do buy me ladies' shoes with high heels!'

'Ladies' shoes or circus, which?' demanded Mr. Martin, laughing.

''Tisn't fair!' grumbled Rosalie. 'Why shouldn't I have the shoes and the circus too?'

The shopman came towards us rubbing his hands. He wore a white apron and hadn't a hair on his head—not even eyebrows or eyelashes.

'Good day, Mr. Martin! Good day, Miss Rosalie! This will be the little girl from London. Good day to you, miss! What can we do for you, Mr. Martin?'

'I 'm not the little girl from London!' I muttered. But no one heard.

'The two little gels want strong boots, the missis says,' explained Mr. Martin. 'Now here 's fifteen shilling, and there 's the circus. What to do, Mr. Swales?'

Mr. Swales patted the smooth top of his head.

'Mm, mm! Mr. Martin. Mm, mm! fifteen shillings!'

Mr. Martin, holding out the money, looked at Mr. Swales anxiously.

'There 's two shilling to go in, Mr. Swales. There 's

the roundabout, threepence apiece. Lemonade and monkey nuts, can't be done under a shilling. Adds up, it does, Mr. Swales!'

'I've a cheap line here in boys' boots,' suggested Mr. Swales, putting his head on one side and looking earnestly at Rosalie. 'Numbers of young ladies are delighted with them.'

'I wouldn't wear boys' boots to save my life!' declared Rosalie. 'I want ladies' high heels.'

The two men looked at each other.

'Add it up, Mr. Martin,' said Mr. Swales. 'It can't be done!'

Mr. Martin couldn't add it up.

'I could do it on paper, with a pencil,' said Rosalie.

Mr. Swales added it up on a boot box.

'For all three,' he announced. 'Total five and six, and what about the old lady? Where's she got to?'

Old Mrs. Martin clambered up the steps.

'Nice son, 'ee are, Martin! Had to give the lad a sausage-roll to carry the basket over!'

'I clean forgot! Sorry, mother!' and Mr. Martin pulled forward a chair for her. She sat on the edge in just the way Rosalie sat.

'I've a present for 'ee, son! There!'

She held out half a crown.

'Just sold a beef pie to Mrs. Swales, round at the back door. Ye'll have it to dinner, Mr. Swales, and a nicer beef pie I never did make! Done it secret too!'

She clapped her hands and laughed. Mr. Swales nodded.

'Brings it down a bit, you've only three shillings to make up now, Mr. Martin.'

'I've me own money for the circus!' declared the old lady. 'Been saving, I have. Fat woman and all, I'm seeing!'

Mr. Swales searched under the counter.

'Here 's a nice line in girls' school boots,' he said. 'Marked seven and six. I 'll let you have them cheap— four and eleven. Good, smart stuff.'

We tried on the boots. They fitted perfectly.

'I want shoes!' grumbled Rosalie.

'Mother said boots!' Mr. Martin reminded her. 'And we 're safe for the circus!'

'Beant circus worth wearing boots for?' demanded the old lady. 'I want me dinner. That basket 's packed wi' good cooking!'

We carried the basket between us up to the high meadow, where we could look down on the circus field. Mr. Martin folded his overcoat to make a seat for the granny, and she opened the basket at once. There was a huge beef pie. When she cut it and I saw the thick crumbly crust and the rich jelly I felt starving. I was sorry for Mrs. Martin who wouldn't share it.

Mr. Martin cut the pie in five enormous pieces.

'There 's only four to eat!' said Rosalie greedily.

'Luke Juke promised he 'd be along,' explained old Mrs. Martin. 'I made him promise. There 'e be! Call him, son!'

Mr. Martin shouted and Luke Juke came running. We were already eating.

There was a baked egg custard in a dish—it was the dishes made the basket so heavy. A bottle of milk and a big bottle of elderberry wine were wrapped in hay. I had never tasted elderberry wine before and it was so good the bottle was finished quickly. The old lady gave Rosalie and me only half a cupful each.

'Milk for young 'uns,' she said. 'But us old 'uns want comfort.'

They began on the sausage-rolls, but I could eat no more. Rosalie was biting the end of her third roll when some men in shirt sleeves came out of the big tent.

'The circus!' she screamed, 'the circus!' and, flinging away her sausage-roll, jumped up and ran across the meadow.

Her father jumped up too.

'Let Rosalie be,' old Mrs. Martin advised him. 'She ain't got no money, so she can't get in. She'll be along back. Set 'ee down and finish dinner.'

I couldn't see where Rosalie had gone and I wished I had run after her. But we could hear a drum and a trumpet. The white horse and the piebald horses were led over to the big tent. A man in a long green coat and a white top hat stood on a platform near the entrance. He was shouting, but we couldn't make out a word he said.

'We'll be late!' I exclaimed, trying to see Rosalie.

The empty dishes and bottles were packed in the basket and Luke Juke was lifting it to his shoulder when she came running back.

'Do come!' she cried. 'The horses have gone in! Look! There's crowds pushing. We'll never get a seat!'

Luke Juke opened his hand and showed her five pink strips of paper—two small, three large.

'Five front seats!' he told her proudly.

Rosalie caught his hand and tried to grab the tickets.

'I'll go crazy if 'ee torment me so!' she said tearfully.

The trumpet sounded a long clear call. Now we were all running down to the road, and old Mrs. Martin was there as soon as any of us.

'I'll be along,' said Luke, racing away, the basket on his shoulder clattering as if the dishes were in pieces. Mr. Martin had the tickets and we squeezed in behind him. We were in the tent, we were running along between the seats, now we were on a bench, our feet resting on the sanded ring. The seats rose in steps until the back ones almost touched the canvas roof. From every row came voices: 'Hi, Nurse Martin! How be 'ee, Nurse Martin?

Be that the little gel from Lunnon? Rosalie—why beant 'ee in the circus? Bob Martin! Bob Martin! Does the missis know where 'ee are?'

Mr. Martin laughed, Rosalie scowled, and old Mrs. Martin blushed and began to sing to herself. A boy with a flat basket slung round his neck came along selling peppermint sticks, a girl followed him with little bags of monkey-nuts. Many people were eating bananas and when Luke Juke arrived he had his coat pockets bulging with oranges.

'Take a bite of peppermint, then suck yer orange,' Rosalie told me, and it did make a lovely taste.

'There was a circus once——' I began, when a queer-looking fellow in white clothes much too big for him came staggering into the ring. His face was painted white and his mouth was enormous. I didn't like him at all, neither did Rosalie, but every time he opened his mouth Mr. Martin and his mother and Luke Juke and every one else roared and shouted. I tried to laugh but Rosalie made a face.

'I hate clowns!' she muttered.

One of the piebald horses galloped round. His harness had dozens of little bells and they made a gay tune. The second time he came round a handsome young man wearing a gold tunic was standing on his back, arms folded. I was terrified lest he should fall, but when he came again there were two horses and the young man had a foot on each.

Would there be three next time? I wondered.

There were three horses. They trotted out one after the other, the young man riding the last. He jumped from horse to horse, then the three trotted side by side and he stood with a foot on each outside horse. I saw that the horses came through the archway where the band played. A red curtain with golden cords and tassels hung over it and was drawn back to let the horses pass through.

A man in a blue-and-gold uniform, carrying a very long

whip, marched through the archway and stopped in front of us. People stamped and clapped and shouted until he held up his hand. Then they became so silent we could hear unseen horses shaking their bridles and all kinds of noises coming from behind the velvet curtain.

'Lai-dees an' gennelmen!' shouted the man in uniform. 'I have the honour to announce Blanche—the youngest bare-back rider in the world—and her marveel-lous horse, White Wings!'

He stepped back, the band played, the curtain was drawn aside, and in pranced the white horse we had seen in the meadow. Now its mane hung almost to the ground and its tail was like a tossing plume. Standing on its back was a girl in a very short white frock with frilled skirts. Her golden hair was so long it flowed around her like a cloak, and Rosalie gave my arm such a pinch I pushed her off the seat.

'Now, now, lassies!' said Mr. Martin, pulling Rosalie up. 'Behave, do!'

'Isn't she lovely!' sighed Rosalie. 'If only my hair would grow!'

White Wings trotted round the ring while Blanche stretched out her hands and danced. She turned head over heels, her hair and skirts whirling so that she was like a white-and-gold wheel. She jumped to the ground and, when White Wings trotted by, jumped back again. Little boys turned somersaults before her, the clown leaped in the air and somersaulted backwards, then walked on his hands and clapped his heels together.

'That's a pretty little gel!' declared Mr. Martin. 'How would 'ee like to be a bare-back rider, Rosalie?'

'Oh, father, will you really let me?' screamed Rosalie, wild with excitement.

Mr. Martin made such a noise that Luke Juke thumped him on the back.

'Did the peppermint stick in yer throat?' he asked anxiously.

Mr. Martin shook his head.

''Tis our young Rosalie wants to be a bare-back rider!' he chuckled.

'Why shouldn't I!' cried Rosalie indignantly, as Blanche rode away kissing her hands.

The brown-and-white ponies pulled on a cage with a lion in it. There wasn't a sound as the man with the whip opened the door a little way, slipped in, and stood before the lion. He cracked the whip and the lion reared up and roared. He cracked it again and, turning round and round on his toes, drew a circle with the whip and the lion trotted round the circle. While we gasped at the man's courage he came out again and bowed and the people cheered.

The clown led in an elephant, so big that the tent shook as it marched round, and when it stood up on its hind legs and raised its trunk I thought the tent was sure to fall in on us.

When the show was over we had seen so much that I was falling asleep, but a big glass of lemonade roused me and I was quite ready for the roundabout. I rode an ostrich, and I could have ridden round and round all night. There was still the swings. The five of us went in one boat. I sat with Mr. Martin, Rosalie with Luke Juke, and old Mrs. Martin curled up at our feet. She said she felt safer there. Mr. Martin and Luke Juke pulled so hard on the ropes our boat flew higher than any other. But I didn't care for the fat lady and I was sorry for the monkeys who cuddled up against one another in a cage.

Now it was time to go home. Rosalie was cross because her father had teased her, he was worried because we shouldn't have gone to the circus, but old Mrs. Martin was happy. As we followed Luke Juke to the shed where he had left his cart she told us about other circuses she had been to.

'Why shouldn't I ride a horse in a circus?' demanded Rosalie.

'Why not?' asked the old lady. 'You 're young yet and mebbe I 'll live to see our Rosalie a lovely lady riding round and round.'

'Oh, granny!' cried Rosalie, and she was happy again.

We sat close together in the cart, for a cold wind was blowing. We could see the lamp in the kitchen of the farmhouse long before we reached it. As we climbed the path a lovely smell was blown by.

'Fried mushrooms!' cried Rosalie. 'I do love mushrooms!'

The kitchen door stood wide open. Mrs. Martin was standing at the stove and the fragrant steam of cooking mushrooms rose in a cloud from the big frying-pan.

'Come in, Martin!' she said over her shoulder. 'Ye 'll all need a hot supper after gadding at the circus. The gipsies told me where 'ee was when I bought the mushrooms. And now I want to know how ye managed with the money!'

## 28. CHRISTMAS STOCKING

I HAD grown fond of Goose Green. Clementine had thirteen little ones, though she killed the smallest by lying on it. They all laughed when I called them bonaveens; but even Rosalie was amazed when the big sow let me play with the little pigs and allowed me to ride on her bristly back.

Rosalie tried to stand up on Bonny, Luke Juke's grey horse. Sammy Pryde held the tail, I clung to Bonny's mane while Rosalie knelt, then slowly and ready to scream, she stood upright. Bonny gave a grumbling snort.

'Best get down, Rosalie,' urged Sammy. 'Bonny beant no circus pony!'

'I won't get down,' declared Rosalie. 'I be agoing to dance!'

She stood on one foot and waved the other. Bonny put down his head and threw me on my back. He lifted his hind leg and gave Sammy a quiet kick which landed him in the ditch. Luckily for Rosalie, she went flying into a heap of hay.

254

''Twas all your fault, Sammy Pryde!' she screamed. 'Tickled Bonny a purpose!'

She didn't forgive Sammy until he taught her to walk on a narrow plank laid on two barrels.

''Tis training for the circus!' she told her grandmother.

'Wish I was a young gel all over again,' chuckled old Mrs. Martin. 'The fun they do have!'

I didn't like milking, but Mrs. Martin said I was the cleanest little milker for my age in Goose Green, so pride made me go off with Mr. Martin to the sheds every day. When the plums were picked I filled more baskets than any one else. The old granny taught me to make pancakes and apple ginger, and at school I learned to recite *Robert of Sicily*. I learned it so well that Miss Florrie, the teacher, chose me as herald for the Christmas play, and I spoke the lines introducing the King and Queen of Fairyland. Rosalie was the Fairy Queen and Sammy Pryde the King, for he was the only boy, big enough, who could remember poetry. I had to blow a trumpet as each character came on, and it was Sammy who taught me. We practised in the barn, and Mrs. Martin was very cross with Miss Florrie for teaching us what she called rubbish and putting notions in our heads. But every one else in Goose Green was proud of the pretty young teacher, and every morning her desk looked like a flower shop. Rosalie and I brought her big plums and, when they were over, we coaxed brown eggs from Mr. Martin. Even Granny Martin was always making tarts for Miss Florrie and wishing she lodged at the farm.

We acted our play on Christmas Eve, and when it was over we were almost too excited to hang up our stockings.

'Let's hang 'em in the bedroom,' suggested Rosalie. 'We'll see what's in 'em without getting up.'

'Can't expect Santa Claus to climb the attic stairs in the dark,' objected Mr. Martin.

Rosalie giggled.

'Do 'ee lend him the lantern, father!'

I watched him hang our stockings, one at each end of the mantel. They were old stockings which Granny Martin had washed and darned. As they hung there, flat and wrinkled, I tried to remember what I had found in my stocking last Christmas, but it was too long ago. We stumbled with sleep as we groped our way to bed. As I turned my head on the pillow and blinked at the window, I saw a white butterfly drifting by in the moonlight. No! It was a snowflake!

'Wake up, Patty! 'Tis Christmas morning and the snow 's come. Wrap up and we 'll fetch the stockings.'

The candle on the chest of drawers was alight and Rosalie was bending over me, her hair tickling my face. We pulled on our knitted slippers, buttoned our coats round our necks without putting our arms in the sleeves, and crept down the dark stairs. Granny had been cooking all the day before and the house was filled with delicious odours. I thought if only a sledge would drive up the road through the snow with my mother and Patrick Henry in it I would be perfectly happy!

When would we be together again? I wondered, as I went slowly after Rosalie. Next Christmas?

The fire was glowing, though Mrs. Martin had damped it down, and by its light we could see our stockings, bulged and shapeless. Mine was the one nearest the window, but Rosalie went over to it before she looked at her own.

'Now where did father buy that? 'Twasn't in the village stores! That I do know for sure. Mebbe Appledore or Ashford.'

'Your father?' I said.

Rosalie put her face close to mine.

'Father, I said, baby! Do 'ee believe in Father Christmas? Do 'ee believe 'e comes down the chimbley? Take down your stocking and remember ye be nigh on twelve years old!'

I took down my stocking and stood in the dim warm kitchen, crying. Aunt Hannah had jeered at Santa Claus years before, but I hadn't believed her, though she had spoilt my Christmas. Now I did believe! Rosalie dropped her stocking on the floor.

'Patty! Don't take on so! I'm sorry. I didn't mean to hurt 'ee! Beant father as good as Santa Claus? He knows what us wants. Santa Claus is only a stranger from far away.'

I hugged the stocking. I wanted to see what was in it —now, at once!

'I've two red candles in mine!' said Rosalie. 'Come on up and I'll light the two on 'em. Beant crying no more, Patty?'

'No! No more! I really did know long ago!'

'We'll have fun!' whispered Rosalie over her shoulder as we climbed back up the ladder. 'Father does tricks at Christmas and to-morrow we all go to *East Lynne* in Cashman's barn. Mother says 'tis lovely! She's seen it twenty times!'

*East Lynne* was a lovely play, sad and thrilling. It was on the way home we had the snow fight. We were stretched on the hay at the back of Luke Juke's cart when Rosalie tugged my arm.

'Slip out after me, Patty. There's a snow fight on!'

The road was uphill and Bonny was going steadier. We could hear old Granny Martin telling how she had seen *East Lynne* more than fifty years ago. We scrambled over the back and dropped noiselessly on the packed snow.

'There be Sammy Pryde! We'll back him!' said Rosalie.

I was shivering with cold and excitement. Snowballs were flying through the air and one struck the back of my head, powdering me with hard bits of snow. I grabbed a handful, moulded it, and flung the ball away—anywhere! Children were running up and down the village street, laughing and screaming, but the real fight was in front of the inn. Dan Venny gave me a push and over I went, but the snow made falling easy. I gave Dan a handful in the face before Rosalie pulled me up and we ran laughing over to Sammy Pryde. Sammy was a good leader. His own younger brothers and sisters were there and most of the other children with him were young. Dan Venny's party were bigger, rougher lads and girls, who soon became spiteful. They squeezed their balls so hard that they were very painful and our smallest ones ran home crying.

''Tis too late for young 'uns to be out anyway!' declared Rosalie. 'Sammy! Send all the little kids to home!'

'Ye be right, Rosalie!' agreed Sammy.

He tossed another ball towards Dan. Back came a vicious shower and, as we ducked, a crash sounded and a splintered pane appeared in the big window of the inn. Out rushed Mr. Godfrey, the landlord, who was standing in his doorway with some friends.

'I warned 'ee not to put stones in the snowballs, Sammy Pryde!' shouted Dan, as we scattered.

Rosalie and I ran up the road, while the others disappeared down the back lanes.

'Don't 'ee say a word!' Rosalie warned me. 'We'll catch up! They'll never know aught!'

The snow had been pounded hard on the roadway by wheels and hoofs, and we slipped in our clumsy winter boots as we tried to catch up to the cart. Now I realized how the ground rose to the farm, for I was breathless, though Rosalie pulled me with her. I tugged myself free.

'Why shouldn't we peg snowballs?' I asked indignantly.

'Ask mother!' was Rosalie's reply as she pulled me on again.

Luke Juke had stopped at the turning before the gate and we came upon the cart suddenly. Four anxious faces looked down at us and we looked back in silence.

'Who gave 'ee leave, Rosalie Martin, to skip off and play snowballs wi' the village lads?' demanded Mrs. Martin.

'What's happened?' asked Luke. 'We heard a crash Any glass broken?'

'Mr. Godfrey's window,' Rosalie told him.

'Big 'un?'

'Big 'un!' answered Rosalie.

'That's a police job!' said Mr. Martin. 'Were you in it, Rosalie?'

'No, we wasn't!' cried Rosalie. 'And Sammy Pryde wasn't in it, neyther. 'Twas all Dan Venny. He's that spiteful!'

'Haven't I told 'ee never to go playing wi' them wild village lads?' said Mrs. Martin. 'I'll take a stick to Sammy Pryde for leading 'ee into mischief and I'll take a stick to 'ee minit us gets inside.'

Luke Juke slashed his whip in the air and Bonny lurched forward. We trotted behind. Rosalie was sniffing mournfully, but I saw the stars shining through the black branches of the trees and the snow glittered as if the world had been flooded with diamonds. We ran upstairs and were in bed before the others reached the kitchen. We lay listening to Mrs. Martin scolding and granny and Mr. Martin soothing her.

In the morning we heard that Sammy hadn't been home all night and Dan Venny had told Mr. Godfrey that 'twas Sammy whose snowball had smashed the window. No one believed Dan, but Sammy sent his mother a postcard from Dover telling her he had a job on a boat and would send her money every month.

'Just waiting for a chance to get away!' declared Mrs. Martin. 'What wi' lads running off to sea and girls wanting to go to circuses, I'm fair ashamed of Goose Green!'

Dan Venny came to the farm to clean the stables, but
though he was far quicker and cleverer than Sammy we
never liked him. Yet I stayed in the kitchen listening to
Dan as he talked with old Mrs. Martin. In the summer
the Vennys wandered about, buying old furniture and
clothes at farms and selling them in the towns. Dan could
tell of places so that they appeared real and he knew a great
deal about animals and wild herbs. I heard him saying his
grandmother came from Rye.

'That's a queer place, Rye!' said Dan. ''Twas once a
port, with the sea coming right up to the walls, but something happened and the sea went away. It sits there now
with the marshes all round, but they do say the sea's just
waiting its chance to come back and cover the houses and
the shops and the people and drown 'em all!'

'Sounds as though you'd like to see it done!' said the
old woman.

Dan laughed.

'Do you go to Rye?' I asked Luke Juke, for I was determined to see the strange little town.

'Nay, lass. 'Tis not my way,' the carrier told me. 'The
train goes to Rye. Nice liddle town, but strange and
queer like!'

I was saving to buy Rosalie a shell necklace for her
thirteenth birthday, and now I saved to go to Rye.

'I'm that hungered, I'm starving,' complained Rosalie
when I refused to spend any money on allsorts. 'I wish
granny would stop nursing! Mother don't hold wi'
eating!'

Mrs. Martin's cooking didn't encourage eating. Her
joints were hard outside, raw inside; her stews were watery.
She never made puddings or cakes and she scraped the
butter on slices of bread so thick we had to stretch our
mouths in biting them. But with Rye as well as the necklace to save for, I wouldn't spend a penny on sweets!

There were now no plums or apples, no mushrooms or blackberries, and though we picked bunches of primroses and cowslips for Miss Florrie, we couldn't eat flowers. At last I had the two and six for the necklace which was hanging in Miss Spragg's window. I was afraid someone else might see it, but I couldn't venture to buy it too soon, for it was impossible to hide anything from Rosalie. Her birthday was on Monday, and on Saturday, when I went down to the village with a message, I marched into the little sweet, tobacco, and toy shop.

'I gave the necklace a clean up, and here's a nice little cardboard box to pack un in like jewlery,' said Miss Spragg, without giving me a chance to tell her what I wanted.

'How did you know I meant to buy the necklace?' I asked. 'It's a surprise!'

''Tain't no surprise to me, child, nor to Rosalie neyther!' retorted Miss Spragg. 'I seen 'ee flattening yer nose 'gainst it every time 'ee passed, and us knows how 'ee 've been saving money!'

I had the box with the necklace in it under my pillow. But when I woke on Sunday morning Rosalie was sitting at the foot of the bed fully dressed and wearing the shell necklace.

'You are mean, Rosalie!' I cried. 'That necklace isn't yours until Monday!'

'Don't be horrid, Patty!' coaxed Rosalie. 'I want all Goose Green to see my present. Sunday's the day for dressing up and being looked at. 'Tis a lovely necklace and cost all of two and six. Hurry, Patty, or 'ee 'll be late for Luke Juke.'

The carrier always called for me on Sunday to take me to the Catholic church at Ashford. The cart was cleaned and two forms fitted in. There was never a seat to spare, though I was the only one to go to church. The other passengers were going visiting.

Rosalie was swinging on the gate when I returned.  She scarcely waited till I had jumped down.

'Patty!  Mother's letting me choose a treat for my thirteenth birthday.  Guess what I've chose!'

I couldn't guess.

'Us to go to Rye all by ourselves!   Us'll wear our Sunday frocks and take our dinner.   Father says there's the best cake shop in all England in Rye, and granny's given me two shillings for to buy our teas there and we'll eat the birthday cake she made to-day!'

'Rosalie, you are good!' I declared, for I knew it was to please me she had chosen the visit to Rye.   'And I'm glad you're wearing the necklace!'

The cake had white icing and 'Rosalie 13' in pink roses. Even Mrs. Martin was in a good temper and smiled at us.

''Tis to Rye Martin and me went for our honeymoon,' she told us.  'Wasted the whole day, we did!'

''Tis a pretty place,' said Mr. Martin.   'Why shouldn't us go along wi' the young 'uns, missis?'

'Have sense, lad, do!' was Mrs. Martin's answer.

## 29. LOST ON THE MARSHES

WE wore our new blue frocks on Sunday, and on Monday we put them on again. That made us feel it was a real holiday. Miss Florrie had agreed to let us stay away from school. Mr. Martin had asked her, for Mrs. Martin declared that if she liked to keep her daughter and little Patty at home no bit of a teaching girl was going to stop her. We had jam as well as a boiled egg for breakfast, Granny Martin gave us our lunches parcelled up, and off we went by the short cut to the station.

'Now mind 'ee come back by the five o'clock train!' Mrs. Martin warned us. 'There 'll be a clock somewheres, or ask in a shop. Don't 'ee talk to strangers and don't 'ee go down back streets. Take the road home from the station.'

There was a heavy mist over the fields, and we had reached a great beech-tree with twisted roots forcing themselves out of the ground when we heard frightening snorts and bellows right before us. We crouched behind one of the roots, too scared to run.

'You 've brought us wrong!' whispered Rosalie.

263

I shook my head. I knew the tree and there was the path going down out of sight.

Rosalie dropped her parcel and screamed. A herd of monsters plunged past us, charging into the mist. We stood up laughing, for now we could see the monsters were bullocks magnified by the mist and as frightened as we were. Rosalie wiped the mud from her lunch and on we went, just in time to buy our half return tickets and find two corner seats. It was so long since I had been in a train that I was as excited as Rosalie.

This journey reminded me of others when my mother and Patrick Henry were with me. But it was quite impossible to think with Rosalie giggling and chattering, not a bit more serious now she was thirteen than she had been yesterday when she was only twelve. We watched out of the window for Rye, and when we walked past the ancient gatehouse and sat by the wall eating our meat pie Rosalie liked it almost as much as I did. I recited *Robert of Sicily* and told her the story of the Snow Queen, only she was Gerda and Sammy Pryde was Kay.

We looked in all the shops and climbed wherever we could, though we took great care of our blue frocks and Sunday shoes. There were several teashops and, long before tea time, we tried to choose which cakes we should have and how many.

'Us won't have bread and butter,' said Rosalie. 'Us can have that any day at home. Let's share every cake, then we can have twice as many!'

At last we decided, and sat at a table in the window of the shop we thought best and cheapest. By the clock over the counter it was already a quarter to five.

'We'll have to eat very quickly,' I said.

''Tis my birthday,' declared Rosalie. 'Us'll go home later!'

I was content. We ate our cakes, drank a whole teapot-

ful of tea, emptied the sugar-basin and milk-jug, and talked
to the girl who served us.

'You should have caught your train,' she told us severely.
'The next is after eight and it 'll be dark long before you 're
home.   You 'll catch it!'

'Us 'll go by road, so the dark don't matter,' said Rosalie
serenely.   'And there 'll be no birthday for another whole
year!'

We lingered over tea, but we were longing for home
before eight o'clock.   We saw the mist growing heavier
over the marshes and I agreed that, though the road was so
much longer, we must take that way.

'Luke Juke might come along and gi' us a lift,' said
Rosalie.

We were both hopeful as we came out of the station and
went down the hill.   There was little mist here and the
rising moon promised us all the light we would need, but
when we came to the road leading to Goose Green we
went slower and slower.   The moon cut a narrow path
through the darkness thrown by the high hedges.   We did
not see bushes, but horrible creatures, stretching claws and
opening fearful mouths.   Every touch of wind made them
more frightening and we pressed as close to one another
as we could.

'If we wait,' I whispered, 'someone might come this
way.'

So we waited, shivering in our thin blue frocks.

'I 'm sleepy,' grumbled Rosalie, 'and I 'm starving!
There 's no filling in cakes.'

'Let 's shut our eyes and run!' I suggested.

'No!   We must take the short cut!' said Rosalie.

'We can't.   No one ever takes the short cut at night!'

Rosalie put on her obstinate look.   It made her very
like her mother.

'You 'm the best in all Goose Green for finding the way,

father says so. So does mother. And granny says you can find your way anywheres blindfold!'

I was flattered but I shook my head.

'Not across the marshes, Rosalie!'

I was a coward. I gave in, though I was as frightened of the marshes at night as of that dark, mysterious road.

'I do wish we'd come back by the proper train,' I sighed, as we climbed the stile.

Even the first field had a shimmer of mist hiding the grass and the footpath, but I went straight across to the muddy pool, where two stones swayed uneasily as we hopped over. Moonlight turned the path by the trees into a stream of light and we marched along quickly, keeping step and swinging our arms.

'Beant us sensible!' said Rosalie. 'No dark old lane for me! But 'tis terrible lonesome, Patty!'

The moonlight sent our shadows, long and slender, across the misty fields. They kept step with us, like two silent watchful strangers, and I was thankful when the path turned, even though we had to cross the river by a narrow plank bridge which was almost invisible.

'Keep behind me!' I told Rosalie. 'I must watch the path.'

There were no hedges or trees to guide us, only a faint track across the marsh. We walked in silence and I envied Rosalie, who had only to follow. Suddenly she gave me a poke which made me jump.

'Patty!' she cried. 'Us have come another way! There's the village!'

I knew the short cut should bring us to the back of the farm, nowhere near the village. But there were the lights, clustered and friendly.

'Rosalie!' I said. 'The village can't be there! I know it isn't! Goose Green is over that way!' and I pointed into the darkness.

Rosalie linked her arm in mine.

'Silly little gel!' she jeered. 'You'm brought us a quicker way and I be terrible glad!'

She pulled me towards the lights. I was puzzled; I knew that where the lights were showing there was no village.

'Sometimes there are lights on the bog that shouldn't be there, I remember! Maybe marshes are like bogs,' I whispered.

Rosalie laughed, then screamed. She had stepped up to her knees in water. Clinging to me, she stumbled back to solid ground.

'Are you hurt?' I asked.

She still clung to me.

'Patty! The lights are gone!'

I tried to be brave, so did Rosalie, but the mist was gathering about us in swirling waves. We were damp and cold, and all around sounded cough, cough, cough!

'All the tramps in England must be here,' muttered Rosalie, crying miserably.

I was too frightened to cry. We went slowly, step by step, feeling our way. I found a long stick and this helped, though I was so confused I couldn't tell in which direction the farm, or even the village, lay. We saw the lights again, shining through the mist. Even Rosalie no longer believed they came from the village, but they were so gay and comforting we tried to reach them, only to slip into a pool which soaked every bit of our clothes. We were so wretched that when we fell over a pile of sheep hurdles we clung to them, as if we were shipwrecked sailors who had discovered a raft.

'Where there's hurdles there's sheep, and where there's sheep there's shepherds!' said Rosalie. 'We're not so lost, Patty!'

'Maybe it's the shepherds we heard coughing,' I said. 'Rosalie, let's call out! They'll take us home!'

Rosalie sat on a hurdle laughing. She laughed until I laughed too.

'Patty! 'Tis the sheep coughing! Marsh sheep allers coughs!'

I wished the sheep would come closer and keep us warm, but though we 'baaed' until we were tired, hoping to be mistaken for lambs, none of the sheep was that foolish.

We ventured beyond the hurdles and found a hillock, dry and mossy. We lay down, holding each other, and I tried to tell Rosalie a bit of the circus story, but our own adventure was too uncomfortable for us to feel any interest in imaginary adventures. I had fallen asleep uneasily, with scraps of nightmares chasing through my mind, when a stamping and splashing woke me. Rosalie was awake too, and scrambling up we saw, in the dim light, a great horse trampling towards us!

'Horses don't hurt people!' I said, trembling.

'Wild 'uns do! Run!' cried Rosalie.

With a scream of rage, the horse rushed at us. I saw him fling his forelegs up as Rosalie dragged me with her past the hurdles, through pools and rushes which beat against us like whips. And those terrifying screams and dashes followed us until we collapsed on a plank bridge. I could hear a dog barking. Rosalie lay silent, shuddering and cold. If a horse would hurt us I no longer trusted dogs, so I lay silent too.

We must have slept, for the warmth of the sun made me stir. I thought I was in bed, a damp hard bed, but I wouldn't open my eyes to find out what had happened. Dogs were barking. Let them bark!

'Patty! Wake up!' called Rosalie. 'We're found!'

I opened my eyes. We were lying on the green slimy plank which led over a wide cutting separating the farm from the marsh. Mr. Martin with Pincher, Luke Juke with two big dogs, as well as Bobbit and Dan Venny were

running through the coarse grass, and Granny Martin was
trying to keep up with them.

'Didn't I say Pincher knowed where they was?' demanded
the old woman.

We were too stiff to walk. Mr. Martin carried Rosalie.
Luke Juke carried me. Our blue frocks were dyed red
from the marsh water, so was our skin. Hot water and
soap had no effect for days. There wasn't a sign of Mrs.
Martin, but granny gave us hot soup with squares of toast
in it as we lay in bed. I told her our adventure, which
now seemed thrilling. Rosalie looked proud and I felt
proud, but I made up my mind I wouldn't mention being
lost on the marshes when I wrote my Sunday letter. Then
I fell asleep and didn't wake again until the following
morning.

I heard Rosalie weeping. Were we still on the marsh?
No! Mrs. Martin was in our room scolding. I opened
one eye and shut it quickly. Mrs. Martin was white with
anger. She told Rosalie she was an ungrateful, disobedient
girl. If it wasn't for Mr. Martin she'd take a stick to her.
And Patty was quite as bad! She'd write and tell Mrs.
Lynch the kind of daughter she had! All that week I went
in terror of my mother's answer. I wanted her to be proud
of me and now she'd be ashamed. I was a disgrace!

The answer came and I was as surprised as Mrs. Martin!
My mother asked how she dared let her poor child wander
all night on the marshes. She wouldn't leave her Patricia
among the savages of Kent a day longer! I was to be sent
to London at once. She expected a telegram telling her
the time of the train. I was desolated to be leaving Goose
Green, but when I thought of my mother standing up for
me, I hugged myself.

## 30. SISTER FRANCIS

On the train up to London I sat silent in my corner. When I saw the dingy houses and streets I longed for Goose Green. I was forlorn without Rosalie, yet I was delighted to be on my way to my mother and Patrick Henry. They were on the platform and my mother grieved over me as if I had been dying.

'Those people!' she said fiercely. 'I'll tell Mr. Forbes what I think of his friends!'

'It was my fault!' I assured her. 'They were searching all night! If we'd taken the proper train we'd have been home in daylight.'

'Don't call that place home!' she exclaimed.

They took me to a restaurant and let me order my own dinner from the menu. I told them about Granny Martin's lovely cooking, the orchard, and the fun I had with Rosalie. All the time I spoke I was longing for Goose Green. I had promised to write Rosalie a letter every week. That was a comfort, so was the dinner, and to have those two listening to me.

I had new clothes and a little room all to myself looking

270

out on a square with trees so high I could watch the birds
going in and out of their nests.  I hadn't learnt much at
the village school and my mother was so ashamed of my
ignorance she sent me to a pleasant school at the other side
of the square where I had special lessons.

This was a part of London I hadn't known—quiet, with
lovely old houses and shops like those in a country town
My brother went to an office every day and my mother
made potato cakes and omelettes, and fried ham and eggs
All our meals were parties, and when Mr. and Mrs. Cadogar
and Mr. Forbes came to tea I wondered how I could have
stayed at Goose Green so long.  We had a maid-servant
a clean, hard-working girl, who quarrelled with my
mother because she wanted to do the cooking and wear
a cap.

'A nice little girl,' said my mother.  'And I like the
child.  But even to please her I won't live on raw meat
like a cannibal, and if she puts one of those things with
streamers on her head—out she goes!'

I had lessons with Miss Lydia in the Clock Tower room.
It stood up from the centre of the school and had big
windows on three sides.  The sun always shone on our
table.  There were never more than half a dozen girls
there.  Two were working for matric., two for a scholarship, two were backward, and there was me.

Miss Lydia sat in an arm-chair.  She was there when the
earliest came in, she was there when the last scholar went
away regretfully, looking back at Miss Lydia's big scared
eyes and her shrinking figure in its shabby grey dress.
Her voice was never much above a whisper, yet she made
history a thrilling story, geography as good as a holiday,
and even arithmetic, with her, was hardly a lesson.  As
for literature—we hated her to stop talking about books
and writers.

I made friends with May Marsh, who already played the

piano at concerts, but who was studying for a university scholarship.

'Miss Lydia has never had a failure!' May told me, as we dawdled across the square. 'She came here when she was the youngest in the school. She's won every prize, passed every exam., and, if she coaches you, you pass! Only the Head Mistress won't let her teach any girl who is rude or doesn't want to learn.'

'Then she's not frightened of the Head Mistress?' I asked.

'What makes you ask that?' May wanted to know.

'Because she is frightened, all the time. I told my mother about her. She says Mrs. Crabtree bullies her, and it's a shame!'

'Mrs. Crabtree doesn't bully her!' cried May indignantly. 'It's her family! How would you like it if you had a father who took all your money and made you serve in a dirty little shop and scrub the floor on Saturday afternoon? It's in that back street behind the library. I didn't know until I went in to buy a pencil, and Miss Lydia was on her knees with her hands in a pail of soapy water!'

'Does Miss Lydia's father make her do that?' I asked in horror.

'And clean your brother's boots and threaten to come round to school and make a scene if you grumble!' continued May, her voice growing hoarse and her face red.

'How do you know all that?' I asked suspiciously.

May might be sixteen and my friend, but I couldn't believe this of a teacher.

'My father was her aunt's doctor. It was the aunt sent Lydia to Clock House. It's true, Patricia, and it's horrible.'

'Can't the Head Mistress stand up for her?' I asked.

'Mrs. Crabtree tried to, but Miss Lydia's father threatens to come over and make a scene. If he did that, poor Miss Lydia would have to leave.'

We reached the gate of the square.

'Come in to tea and tell my mother all about it,' I coaxed.

'Won't your mother mind?'

'She loves visitors and she's making apple cake to-night!' I assured May, proud that my mother and brother were so much more interesting than other girls' families.

My mother liked May at once. She thought her pale face and gentle voice so refined. The apple cake was ready and Patrick Henry was home early for he was going off to Ostend in the morning. May told me afterwards she had never been to tea before where people called pie *cake*, and didn't bother about bread and butter. We all talked about Miss Lydia, and my mother was even more indignant than May.

'I'm going over to the school to-morrow!' she declared. 'I'll not allow this to go on. That poor girl!'

'What can you do?' objected my brother. 'I expect the Head Mistress would do anything she could.'

'Suppose this Miss Lydia was your own sister—would you sit there and say: "What can you do?"' demanded my mother.

I looked at her proudly and glanced sideways at May.

'Mrs. Lynch, come over and see my father!' she urged. Perhaps, between you, something could be done.'

'At once!' agreed my mother. 'You stop there!' she added to me over her shoulder.

She and May left their cups half filled with tea, their plates piled with steaming apple cake. My brother laughed.

'Lynch to the rescue!' he said. 'That's a grand motto, Tricia!'

'It sounds like a story!' I said enthusiastically. 'But what can they do?'

I was happy sitting there with Patrick Henry, even though we were talking about poor Miss Lydia's troubles.

'Find your Miss Lydia a school out of London where

her family can't reach her,' he said, putting his elbows on the table.

'No!' I cried. 'We can't spare her.'

But we had to. My mother and Dr. Marsh went over to the school. The Head Mistress didn't want to lose her treasure, but when I left Clock House at the close of the term, Miss Lydia was standing straight, forgetting to be scared, and I knew she had come to the end of her sorrows.

My mother still told me stories. But Miss Lydia had made me want to read books. I went into the library one half-holiday and demanded a story book. Instead I was given a form, and I had to wait a whole week tormented by the thought of all the books inside those red brick walls. Miss Lydia signed the form and gave me a list of books I should read. I was very fond of Miss Lydia, but when I saw the names were of histories and essays I decided to keep the list hidden.

At last I went up to the barrier in the library. I was the only one there, except the man behind the counter. Maybe the evening was too fine, or people were busy doing their home work, or just didn't want to read. The librarian had pale, primrose-coloured hair and very thick glasses; he was so neat and clean he was like a new book. I pushed my form towards him.

'What kind of a book would you like, Patricia Nora Lynch?' he asked.

'A story book!' I answered firmly. 'A very big one, with pictures.'

He opened the little door in the counter.

'Come in!' he said. 'It's against the rules, but you'll never love books unless you can take them down from the shelves yourself. One day all libraries will be really free.'

'Are these all your books?' I asked. 'Or are you paid to take care of them?'

The moment I asked I knew I shouldn't.

'Never mind,' I added quickly. 'You've a grand lot of books!'

'I am lucky enough to be paid to take care of them,' he told me. 'Would you like to be a librarian?'

I didn't answer—I was looking at the shelves stretching in rows on every side and rising to the ceiling.

'It'll take years and years to read all these books,' I said.

'You will never read them all!' he told me.

'Not if I live to be very old and read quickly?' I asked.

I walked beside him between those walls of books. Our feet made no sound on the thick matting and I was disappointed that the books looked almost as dingy as those in Mr. Martin's attic. The lights, the silence, the queer touch of the matting gave the place a feeling of mystery. The librarian stopped before a shelf of short, thick books.

'Ancient classics for English readers!' he read out.

'Are they story books?' I asked him doubtfully.

'Every book is a story!' he said. 'These are the foundation of all the stories in the world. If you read these and understand them, you will have something no money could buy. Will you take one?'

He asked so appealingly I couldn't refuse. I nodded. He pulled out the first book.

'You will thank me all your life,' he said solemnly.

'Please,' I asked, 'can I have a story book as well?'

'Is there any special story? What have you read?'

'I want *The Magic City*,' I told him. 'I did read it, but some of it wasn't there.'

He led me to another shelf, where the books looked as dingy as any of the others. But, when I opened them, I discovered not only *The Magic City* but *The Amulet*, *The Phoenix and the Carpet*, and, just above them, *Children of the New Forest*, and, below, *Kidnapped* and *Treasure Island*. I stood with my arms full, trying to choose.

'Only one story book?' I asked.

'Only one!' repeated the librarian.

I went out with *Greek Legends* under one arm and *The Magic City* under the other. I asked Miss Lydia had she read all the books in the library. She laughed, and the girls, who were grieving that after the holidays they would see her no more, looked up in amazement. She had never laughed before!

'It's good to read books,' she said, 'but it's better to write one.'

'Do you want to write a book, Miss Lydia?' asked May Marsh.

Our teacher shook her head and smiled at me. A queer thought went through my mind, so quickly I scarcely felt its passing. But Miss Lydia had made it impossible for me to be a teacher, a civil servant, or anything the school trained us for. I would write books and one day see them, with all the others, in the library.

Before the term was over I had read all the ancient classics in the library, *A Princess in Ancient Egypt*, *Marius the Epicurean*. I hated the burning of the Christians, but I walked to school dreaming of the white light of Greece. I discovered that the librarian was writing a history of books, from the days when they were written on tiles up to now. And then I said good-bye to the square, the Clock House, the librarian, and went to St. Joseph's.

I helped my mother and Patrick Henry pack, for I was better at packing than either of them. My mother bought me a travelling case with two locks and pockets inside in the lining. It was so light I could carry it myself, and Patrick Henry painted my initials in black on the green canvas cover. I no longer thought that boarding schools were prisons. May Marsh envied me and, when I wrote to Rosalie, telling her I was going to St. Joseph's Convent, I knew she, too, would envy me. I tried to write to

Goose Green every week, but no one answered those letters. I couldn't feel sure they reached the farm. And wasn't it strange to go to school in the holidays? No one else did that, I was sure.

'I wish you could come with us,' my mother told me. 'We're visiting Cousin Kate and she thinks it would be dull for you. We want Ulick and Patrick Henry to know one another. They're cousins, you see!'

'I'm a cousin too!' I thought indignantly. 'And how could I be dull with horses and trees!'

I didn't mind going off this time. I was wondering what the school would be like without the girls. Would the nuns be kind and friendly? Would there be a big garden, and a dog and maybe a cat?

We went in a new bright taxi-cab. There was scarcely time for my mother and Patrick Henry to catch their train, but they wanted to see me safely at the convent. My tin box was dumped on the pavement. My mother rang the bell. The gate was in a high wall and, after a few moments, a grille was pushed aside and a brown sharp face with pale unfriendly eyes looked out.

'This is my little girl, Patricia Nora Lynch,' my mother said rapidly. 'We have to catch a train. Will you take care of her?'

'Certainement, madame!' was the answer.

The grille closed. My mother went back to the taxi and the gates slowly opened with a great clanging and banging of bolts and bars. I looked back. The taxi had disappeared round the corner.

'Entrez!' ordered the lay sister who had opened the gate, and she dragged in the tin box.

I followed, my new suit-case in my hand. I was excited, but my knees trembled so that I could scarcely stand.

'Déposez le bagage!' said the sister.

I put down the case. She gave me a little push. The

convent rose on my right. I did not look at it. In front
were trees, and in their shadow a nun was digging, her
blue sleeves rolled to her elbows. Her veil fluttered in the
wind and the golden cross on her deep cream collar glittered.
As the gate clanged shut she looked up and leaned on her
spade, watching me, and when I came nearer her eyes
smiled. I stopped at the edge of the earth she had been
digging.

'I am Sister Francis,' she told me.

'I am Patricia Nora Lynch!'

Her face was brown but very thin, her golden brown
eyes were dancing. They changed every moment, they
laughed, they grew serious, sad, kind.

I put my hat and coat on a garden seat and helped her.
I filled a bucket with stones, carried plants, ran to the
lodge gate for water, then walked with Sister Francis along
a wide grass path between strips of vegetables. She walked
slowly, yet as if she were going to run. As I talked she
kept her head bent a little towards me, listening, but I
noticed her eyes straying up to the sky, or over to the
trees, and mine strayed with hers. She walked slower and
slower. At the end of the path she sank down upon a seat.

'I dig too much. I walk too much!' she said, in a
breathless whisper.

'Are you sick?' I asked fearfully.

'I have been very near the doors of death,' she told me.
'They opened a little way, then closed. I remained on
this side.'

'Were you frightened?'

Sister Francis looked at me. Her strange eyes were keen.
I thought of *An Cladamh Soluis*—the Sword of Light—that
was on the paper my brother used to buy at the Irish classes.

'When you came up to that high wall with the barred
door, and the bell clanged, you were frightened. Unknown
eyes looked through the grille. You heard bolts pulled

back and you stood there, alone and suffering. The door
opened and you came in to find a garden and a friend.'

She had answered my fears. I looked at her without
raising my head. Her thin face was severe. But I was so
happy, a bird seemed to be singing inside me. Still I
wondered—had she been frightened?

A bell rang.

'Time for your tea,' said Sister Francis.

I picked up my hat and coat.

'Don't mind Sister Damien,' she said. 'Like most good
cooks, she has a difficult temper and she detests opening
the door. She will be back at her own work after to-
morrow. Sister Clothilde will take care of you.'

Sister Clothilde was no taller than I was and very fat.
Her expression was so fierce I didn't dare say a word to her.
She led me down a flight of stone steps into a half-under-
ground refectory. Two narrow tables ran the entire length
and, at the far end, beside a window, a place was laid for me.

'You should wash your hands, but the dormitory is too
far,' she grumbled. 'Say your grace and I'll bring in your tea.'

'I did wash my hands and my face too, in the lodge,' I
told her. But she waddled off without listening.

The floor was stone and my feet made a hollow sound as
I went to the seat by the window. I pulled in my chair
and a big tabby cat climbed to the chair beside me. He
sat on his hind legs and rested his front paws on the table.
I stroked his head and he purred loudly, the full, deep
sound making me warmer. Our heads were close together
and I was talking to the cat for company, when Sister
Clothilde returned, carrying a tray. I was thankful to see
two beef sandwiches with plenty of meat, a plate of thin
bread and butter, a slice of cake, as well as a whole pot of tea.

'You make friends with Peter?' she asked, her sudden
smile making me wonder how I could have thought her
fierce. 'You like cats?'

'I do!' I agreed, nodding. 'This one's lovely!'

'You will not be lonely, look!'

Her podgy hand on my shoulder, she turned my head towards the distant door. In the dim light I saw a file of nuns pass by, noiseless in their indoor felt slippers, their hidden hands folded in the long sleeves of their blue robes, their heads bent so that they were shrouded in their veils Which one was my friend? I could not tell.

I was very hungry and I ate every bit of the food, except the fat and crusts. Peter climbed leisurely to the table and ate them from my plate in comfort, then he licked out the milk-jug. I was beginning to feel afraid of the uncurtained window. The sun had gone and the bushes, on a level with my head, were fading into the darkness when Sister Clothilde returned.

'I'll take you up to the study now,' she said. 'And you can have Peter for company. Reverend Mother will see you in the morning.'

I stooped to pick up the cat, but he stalked ahead. We went up a winding stone staircase; the steps were narrow and a few dim lights scarcely revealed the turnings.

'The dormitory is at the top,' Sister Clothilde told me 'Look! Up there! Here is the study!'

We entered a room all light and warmth. A log fire blazed on the hearth, a table with books and papers stood before it, and Sister Francis was sitting there in an arm-chair. I sat with Peter at her feet and told her all about myself.

'Do you remember all this or were you told it?' she asked.

I looked up and met her eyes, not dancing now, but quiet, intent. I wanted not just to please her, but to tell the truth.

'I don't know,' I said slowly. 'I think I must remember it, but I don't know.'

When my eyes began to close she stood up.

'The Sandman is coming,' she said, her eyes laughing.
'I 'll come to the dormitory with you.'

Without her I would have been terrified of that long
high room with its rows of little white beds. Along one
side were lockers, in the middle of the room were wash-
basins—a double row—and, almost out of sight it seemed
to me, were two bathrooms. Sister Francis walked up and
down telling her beads while I prepared for bed. She
combed out my hair and, while I said my prayers, stood
with her back to me looking out of one of the big, uncurtained windows. She was still there when I fell asleep.

I dreamed of a great, high, wind-swept cliff above a golden
beach, with coloured umbrellas stuck in the sand and people
bathing. I flew along the cliff, but, however I tried, I
could not fly down. I woke once to hear the waves and
saw the moonlight streaming across the foot of my bed.
When I was roused in the morning by the ringing of a bell,
I found out that it was the trees made the noise of waves
on a sandy beach.

After breakfast I went to Reverend Mother's room. She
was big, sensible, and friendly, but she asked so many
questions that in the end I could think of no answers at all.
She gave me two monstrous bonbons from a tall pink jar
with golden birds on it.

Every morning I went to Mass in the little chapel. I
helped Sister Francis gather the flowers and arrange them
on the altar. She taught me gardening, about flowers and
birds and the stars. The holidays stretched before me like
happiness without end. Only at night, when she had gone,
the empty dormitory was terrifying.

I asked her everything that came into my head. If she
knew she told me. Sometimes she said: 'Why do you ask
me that? Haven't you your catechism?' or: 'Think for
yourself! I can't do that for you!'

One day as we came in from the garden she took my

hand in hers, her thin, bony hand that was warm and strong.

'To-morrow the other girls will be here,' she told me. 'You will be alone no longer.'

'Will they like me?' I asked quickly.

'I don't know,' she said. 'Now don't bother so much about liking—liking food, liking people, being liked, always wanting to be happy. Are you able to give up everything you care for? That is what matters!'

'Are you angry?' I asked in dismay.

She laughed.

'Indeed no, Patricia. I am only trying to tell you that to-morrow everything will be different. There will be lessons. I will be one of your teachers. The holidays are over!'

## 31. THE SEWING CLASS

I was at breakfast with Peter, the cat, when the first of the girls arrived. She rushed in, tall, dark, pale with travelling, and gazed at the empty tables.

'First!' she said in disgust, and, sitting down, called Peter, without speaking to me at all. He deserted me at once and sat on her lap, rubbing his head against her chin and standing up with his paws on her shoulder. Peter had never done that with me! Sister Clothilde brought her in coffee and hot toast.

'This once!' she chuckled.

Even Sister Damien came in, and she and the strange girl chattered in French until my head ached. They were talking about me, for the stranger's eyes rested on me curiously and half smiling, but I stared mournfully out of the window, determined to make no new friends.

Louise L'Étranger was her name. I knew, because Sister Damien called her that every few minutes. I took another sideways look to make sure if I liked or disliked her, when suddenly the convent was filled with laughter, running footsteps, slamming doors, shouts of welcome. There were so many girls I couldn't distinguish them, and

283

when Peter leaped from Louise and rushed into the kitchen, I was spiteful enough to think he deserved to be upset. I squeezed against the wall and, because they were all so occupied with one another, escaped to the grounds unnoticed. I searched for Sister Francis. But, where she and I had worked, an old man, muttering to himself, hoed the ground between rows of artichokes.

By dinner time I learned that my seat at table was nearest the door, my seat in study was nearest the door. Luckily I kept the same bed in the dormitory, the one in the corner near the window.

The other girls called me 'the new one.' If I had been really new to the convent I would have liked their friendliness, their delight at seeing one another again, and pitied the homesickness which came upon them suddenly. But I was thinking of the days when I had been the most important person in St. Joseph's, with a refectory, a dormitory, a study, and Sister Francis all to myself. There was no more loneliness. I needn't tiptoe for fear of hearing my own footsteps, or glance back over my shoulder as I went up the winding stairs, or lie shivering in bed, telling myself stories to shut away the terror of the big room, with all the empty beds.

Sister Francis's arm-chair had been taken from the study, and the desks, which had been pushed against the wall, brought forward in a double semicircle. Mine was farthest from the fire and I felt this was most unjust, for the weather had suddenly turned very cold. But there was pleasure in having a desk of my own where I could keep my treasures as well as my books. I brought them all down from the trunk room and piled them on the desk before me.

'If that child hasn't brought a library of story books with her!' exclaimed Louise, the French girl. 'My father—the professor—says the love of fiction is at the root of all false knowledge!'

'There's a story in every book!' I declared, remembering my friend the librarian.

'A true story is not fiction!' retorted Louise.

'A story's a story!' I muttered crossly.

'Leave the child alone!' protested May, the eldest, whose desk was nearest the fire. 'Why shouldn't she have stories? She'll have lessons enough to plague her!'

'Where do you come from?' asked Louise. 'I'm homesick! I want to hear other people's troubles and experiences!'

We sat at our desks. Every one except myself had boxes of sweets, bags of fruit, and they passed these round. I began to tell all I could remember, but I stopped so often to eat a sweet or a pear or a banana that long before I had left Cork I was falling asleep.

'Bed!' said May. 'I'll bring you up some hot milk. You've earned it!'

I lay in bed listening to complaints. The beds were hard and there weren't enough blankets or hot water.

'It's like going to bed in the street!' exclaimed Louise.

A sandy-haired girl with freckles poked her head out of her night-gown as she was pulling it on.

'At the convent where I've been staying, every one had a cubicle with a wardrobe and a chest of drawers and an eiderdown for cold nights. This place has no style at all!'

Already I knew this was Mary-Jane, a girl from Ulster, whose stepmother would not allow her to come home. Every holiday the nuns sent her to a different convent unless one of the other pupils could be persuaded to invite her. Louise declared that Reverend Mother was always scheming to have Mary-Jane asked to parties where she might make friends.

'A word of praise from Reverend Mother,' said Louise, 'is always followed by: "You find Mary-Jane interesting,

my little one? Perhaps your parents would like her to
visit them? She is a moſt worthy girl!'''

Mary-Jane wasn't offended.

'Reverend Mother has given me wonderful holidays!'
she said. 'If she thinks I should go to France, I'll get
there!'

She shook her thin plait and scrambled into bed.

A bell ſtill wakened me. But now, every morning, the
older girls took turns at reciting a decade of the Rosary,
the others making the responses. My dreams were in my
mind as I dressed and I hated having to turn from them.
I never felt awake until after breakfaſt, and as I washed in
cold water, I thought only of drinking hot tea in the
refeƈtory. Firſt, however, came Mass in the chapel. It
was lovely with flowers, though now May and Nellie had
charge of the altar. The girls sang, Siſter Monica, the music
miſtress, played the tiny organ and sometimes made me
forget I was cold and sleepy.

I went on learning the piano, though it was ſtill the fiddle
I longed to play. But at St. Joseph's only the piano and
singing were taught. The music room was next to the
refeƈtory and my time for praƈtice was juſt after breakfaſt.
Louise praƈtised at the same time, but inſtead of playing
scales and exercises, we talked. I heard about her father,
the professor, of their house in Paris, the lovelieſt city in
the world, and how homesick she was.

'My father believes my Aunt Sophie to be the clevereſt
woman in the world and she thinks languages the only
subjeƈt worth learning. So I go to school in Germany to
learn German. Now I come to school in England to
learn English. But French is the only language worth
knowing!'

'I'm not good at languages,' I told Louise. 'I've been
learning Irish all my life and French since I went to St.
Winifred's, but I don't know much.'

'Say some Irish to me, Patricia! I did not know the Irish had a language!'

I said my prayers in Irish to her.

'But that is charming! You must learn all you can. It is chic to know something others do not understand. Misery! Now we must play scales!'

In the study I sat beside Mary-Jane. She was backward in everything but sewing.

'Every girl should know how to spell, do accounts, and write neatly,' she told me. 'You can't spell or add, and your writing is scribble. But sewing is the most important of all!'

'Will you listen to Mary-Jane laying down the law!' jeered Mary Ellen, admiring her own white hands and rubbing lemon juice into them from a bottle she kept in her desk.

'Tell me about your stepmother, Mary-Jane,' I coaxed.

'I saw a hole in your stocking this morning!' said Mary-Jane severely. 'A girl of twelve should be ashamed to have holes in her stockings. Tell me a story and I'll mend them for you.'

'I'll put on a clean pair to-morrow,' I promised. I was tired of whispering stories.

'Who darns your stockings when you're at home?'

'My mother, when the landlady doesn't like mending.' Every one in the study was interested.

'All girls learn sewing,' said May. 'And you'll have to.' I shook my head.

'You don't know my mother! She says any fool can sew and she's not paying good money for something I should know by instinct. I wish I could learn the fiddle instead.'

'Someone always reads when we do sewing. Why shouldn't Patricia read always?' demanded Mary-Jane, who hated reading.

'I have a better idea,' said Mary Ellen. 'Let her tell stories! She knows heaps and I hate listening to someone reading from a book about the saints!'

Louise objected. She didn't approve of stories.

'History is the only thing that matters!' she declared.

'You don't mind real old stories, do you, Louise?' I asked. 'I'll tell you Mrs. Hennessy's stories. They were so very old they must have been true!'

'Tell the stories I like and I'll do all your mending, every bit of it!' offered Mary-Jane.

'You're all talking nonsense!' declared Nellie. 'You might as well ask them to let me sing while we're sewing. The rule is we take turns at reading, and rules shouldn't be broken!'

The time for sewing came. Mary-Jane was embroidering an altar cloth, the others were making blouses—for the holidays, as in term we all wore blue uniforms with white collars. I decided to mend my stockings. I had four pairs rolled up, all washed, all with holes in heels and toes, one pair with the knees split.

'I haven't any wool or needles,' I told Mary-Jane.

'Sh!' said Mary-Jane. 'Stand up!'

The door had opened and Sister Francis was walking in. Now I noticed her arm-chair in its old place by the fire. Sister Clothilde followed, carrying a cushion, and Peter, the big cat, stalked beside her. When we sat down Mary-Jane remained standing. She was very flushed and she clutched the altar cloth in her fat, freckled little hands.

'Sister Francis!' she gulped. 'Need we have reading? Couldn't we have a story? Patricia knows all kinds of stories!'

Breathing hard, she flopped into her seat.

'Stories of saints, Patricia?' asked Sister Francis.

I shook my head.

'Not exactly, Sister Francis!'

'Stand up!' whispered Mary-Jane, giving me a poke.

We had to stand up when a nun spoke to us or we spoke to her, to open doors, to stand aside on corridor, and during the holidays I had been forgetting my convent manners.

'I must ask Reverend Mother,' said Sister Francis.

'I could tell the one you told me about St. Brendan! Wouldn't that do?' I asked.

'Why not?' agreed Sister Francis. 'Sit up on your desk, Patricia, and then we 'll all hear you.'

I sat sideways, my feet on the seat, and told the story of St. Brendan. Mary-Jane put away the altar cloth and mended my stockings. I watched her make a web like a spider's, and fill it in. Afterwards, when I thought of St. Brendan and his voyages I would always see Mary-Jane's clever, stumpy fingers, weaving a black web. Reverend Mother came in as I was describing St. Brendan's return to Kerry. Sister Francis explained. The girls' eyes were anxious.

'Sit down, my little ones,' said Reverend Mother. 'If Patricia knows any more stories about saints, why shouldn't she tell them? Her mother, no doubt, thinks sewing bad for her eyes.'

'I don't know any more stories about saints!' I declared.

I was standing on the seat of my desk, so that I looked down on them all, even Reverend Mother—a tall woman. Sister Francis glanced across at me. Her eyes were dancing.

'Patricia is very good at essay writing,' she said. 'If she has a gift—mightn't it be right to cultivate it? If the stories have a good moral—would that do?'

Reverend Mother beamed round at us all.

'Why not? You must consult Sister Francis about the stories, Patricia! When I have time I hope to hear you!'

I jumped down to open the door. She swept along the corridor, tall, straight, and I looked after her, feeling she had given me the biggest bonbon from her pink jar.

Every sewing lesson I told a story—*Robinson Crusoe, Hans Andersen, Sedan Chair, The Magic City*.   Sister Francis found a good moral in all of them—perseverance, courage, kindness, beauty.   When I finished all I knew, there were the books in the school library.   Some of the girls had books. I used them all, and when my audience found fault I altered the story.   Yet I learned to darn.   I became as proud of my darning as of my stories.

'You should have a doll,' Mary-Jane told me.   'Ask your mother to buy you one and I'll make its clothes. You can always give it away for a present.'

I no longer cared for dolls, I had never cared for any but Poosie, the rag one, and she was almost forgotten.   But Mary-Jane wanted to make the clothes, so I wrote to my mother, and Patrick Henry came to the convent with a grand doll in a box.   It had real hair and eyes which opened and shut.   To Mary-Jane's disgust it was already dressed in blue silk.   For all that she set to work on more doll's clothes.

Mary-Jane had a big cardboard box, filled with bits o silk and velvet.   She turned them over, and would hold up a scrap of pale pink or blue to her cheek.

'Does this colour suit me, Patricia?   Or this?' picking out a square of pale primrose velvet.

At last Reverend Mother coaxed an invitation for Mary-Jane from Louise for the next holiday.   She was measured for new clothes, and, one sewing afternoon, Reverend Mother arrived with a big cardboard box tied with striped green-and-white tape.

'Open it, Mary-Jane!' she commanded.

Red and confused, Mary-Jane struggled with the knots. We crowded round, thrilled and wondering.   At last she pulled off the lid, rustled among sheets of tissue-paper, and lifted out a white frock, all frills and daintiness.   She held it against her blue uniform and looked over it at Reverend Mother, blinking, almost terrified.

'For parties, my little one,' said Reverend Mother. 'Just the festive frock for an innocent young girl!'

She marched off, with half a dozen girls rushing to hold open the door.

'She really is a darling!' said May.

Mary-Jane stood stiffly, holding the frock.

'You try it on!' she pleaded, holding it out to Mary Ellen—our beauty.

'May I?' Mary Ellen asked Sister Francis.

Sister Francis looked serious, but she nodded, and Mary Ellen slipped the party dress over her uniform. She loosened her long golden plaits and held out her arms.

'It's beautiful!' whispered poor Mary-Jane, looking at the other girl's shining eyes, waving hair, and delicate complexion. Mary Ellen took off the dress.

'You'll have some grand parties in that frock, Mary-Jane!' she muttered.

Mary Ellen told me about her brother going in for literary competitions in a children's magazine.

'Why don't you try?' she suggested.

She had copies of the magazine in her desk, and there were prizes offered for the Best Life-Story of a Daffodil. I knew all about daffodils, and wrote about the big one I had planted in Miss Friend's front garden—the brown bulb, the soft earth, the roots going down into darkness, the slender green stem striving upward to the light. Sister Francis, now our English mistress, gave me four sheets of fine white paper, and asked Reverend Mother's permission for me. I copied the life-story in my best handwriting, and Mary Ellen sent it off.

I dreamed of the daffodil, I thought of it when I should have been learning dates or French verbs, and then I forgot all about it. Sister Francis was explaining the different kinds of verse when Reverend Mother came in with an envelope in her hand. All our letters were opened, but they were laid out on the table in the corridor every morning, so we looked with interest at this one.

'This has never happened before!' said Reverend Mother. 'I'm pleased, and I'm very proud of you, Patricia!'

She gave me the envelope. There were two slips of paper in it. One told me I had won the first prize for the Life-story of a Daffodil, which would be printed in the next issue. The other was a cheque for three guineas!

'I know you will keep that all your life!' said Reverend Mother.

She was wrong—my mother changed it at the bank on the first day of the holidays, and it paid all our fares to go down to Somerset. But before that happened, I said goodbye to Sister Francis. She was strong now and going back to her own convent. I walked down the grass paths under the trees with her for the last time.

'I may never see you again,' she said. 'Soon I am going on the foreign mission—to China, maybe. But I will never forget you and I will always pray for you!'

The girls were all my friends now, the corridors were no longer strange, and I was at home in study and dormitory, but without Sister Francis the convent was empty. Sometimes—turning a corner—I would almost catch a glimpse of her thin brown face, her dancing, fearless eyes, then know I had been dreaming!

## 32. MRS. CAPTAIN

WE lived in an old haunted house among the combes behind Minehead. My brother drove into the town every morning in Sam Prout's cart, which carried barrels of cider, and my mother walked to the cross-roads to meet him in the evening. Our landlady was a sea captain's widow, and the house was filled with treasures he had brought home from his voyages. Her youngest daughter, Miriam, lived with her, and the two of them cleaned and cooked all day long. We had clotted cream and strawberry jam for tea, tiny little straw cheeses, and cider whenever we needed a drink. There were cheese tarts and cornflour buns and a wonderful bread pudding that was first cousin to Christmas pudding, only lighter, and I liked it better; half-pay pudding, Mrs. Captain Cranley called it.

An old man did the garden and I helped him. He sang ballads about the sailor who went on board a strange ship at Blue Anchor and never came back no more; and the girl who watched the trees at the full moon and turned into one. He told me about the deserted mine up in the hills and the dead wood where every tree was dry and leafless, and not a bird sang there.

He looked after the hens too, and I helped him. One day we went into Minehead, and he brought back six young runner ducks in a basket. Patrick Henry met us in Minehead, and we had tea in an old house with the big front room turned into a teashop. We found Sam Prout and his cider cart at the station. Old Peter was there, sitting on a wall, with the basket of ducks on his knee. He let me hold them in the cart, and I listened to the queer singing noise they made. There was no moon, but the road glimmered faintly and the big horse trotted steadily. Lamps glowed in cottages and farmhouses, and old Peter sang one of his long ballads about a girl who ran away to sea, started as a cabin boy, and rose to be Lord High Admiral. My mother sat looking back at the lights of Minehead.

'Isn't the country terribly melancholy,' she said. 'Never a light on the roads, and those awful noises everywhere!'

Sam Prout and old Peter put their heads on one side to hear better.

'Waz it any special noize ye 'd be complainin' of, mizzuz?' asked Sam.

'How can you stand the darkness?' demanded my mother, instead of answering him.

'Uz get uzed to it, mizzuz,' he explained.

I listened to the horse's hoofs on the dry road. I loved the sound and the tiny squeaks of flying bats. The faint roar of the sea, the rustling of a rising wind in the trees, the grunts and sighs of animals made a kind of song. I heard the distant bark of a fox and I thought of the song Uncle Liam used to sing: 'A hungry fox went out one night.' My brother whistled a plaintive air, *The Snowy-breasted Pearl*, and I felt sad, but not unhappy.

I carried the candle as we went up to our bedroom. We

went up by one staircase and came down by the other. Mrs. Captain Cranley had been telling me how the place was a monastery before the Reformation, and one of the monks came back through all these years to visit his old home.

'She says the dogs howl and the doors slam when he comes,' I told my mother, as I sat up in bed, safe and snug. With her I had no fear of ghostly monks, or howling dogs, or even slamming doors.

'Now you tell me a story!' I added.

'Isn't it time you began to tell me stories?' she asked. 'I'll be jealous of those girls in the sewing class if you don't! Did I never tell you about the ghost your grandfather saw, when he was a young lad? 'Twas in our old place, not the Sundays Well house, the one before that— Cousin Kate is thinking of going back there, and it made me remember.'

'Tell me!' I urged.

'There's a big courtyard at the back, with stables and coach-houses and all kinds of sheds. One evening after sunset, he, that's your grandfather, was going up the stairs, when he looked out of the window. He saw a man in the old dress—knee-breeches and ruffles and buckled shoes—oh, very grand!—and he tiptoeing across the court-yard with a spade under his arm. There wasn't a soul about, but the man was looking over his shoulder afraid he'd be seen. He went into the coach-house, though the door was shut. He never opened it, he just went through.'

She turned to me, the brush in her hand, the candle-light throwing a golden tinge over her long dark hair.

'He saw it three times, Tricia! At last he told someone —Great-aunt Eliza, I expect—she was the one that had a poem in the *Nation*, you remember?'

'What happened?' I asked, as she sat there thinking.

'Oh—what happened? I was juśt remembering how poor Eliza became a cripple and sat there with her books looking out of the window. There was a man, a carpenter, terribly clever with his hands; but sure he had no learning —couldn't even read—he made a chair for her with wheels, so that she could go about and work it herself with a kind of handle to push backwards and forwards. She married him, and they went to live in a little house out beyond Mallow, above the Blackwater. He built it with his own two hands, and 'twas like a doll's house—everything lovely and polished. He made the furniture too, and she sewed cushions and curtains.'

'That was grand!' I whispered, for I wanted more.

'They had shelves of books and she 'd read to him in the long winter evenings. I used to run away to śtay with them. I had a great liking for Grand-aunt Eliza. Sometimes you remind me of her.'

My mother raised her eyes and looked at me. She laughed.

'If you 're not like a cock fairy, sitting up there in this queer, dark room! But I was telling you; Great-aunt Eliza told the carpenter about the man with the spade, and he went into the coach-house and searched. He found a big square śtone that fitted into a hole in the floor, and when he lifted it, there was a flight of śteps leading down into a cellar.'

'And the cellar! The cellar?'

'Of course they were all on to it then. They dug the whole floor of the cellar, and all they found were some old bones and ashes of burnt paper or cloth, maybe.'

'Is that all?' I asked.

'Isn't it enough?' asked my mother. 'Liśten now! You want a beginning and an end. Well, there never is, except in śtories. Now go to sleep and dream. Do all your dreams have a beginning and an end?'

I shook my head. She reached forward and blew out the candle.

'I meant to tell you, Tricia! Mrs. Cranley will keep you here for the rest of the holidays. We're going on!'

I didn't know the Cranleys properly until I was alone with them. Their day began early. I'd be far away in a dream, and the smell of hot buttered toast would bring me back to the big four-poster bed and Miriam Cranley standing at the table with a silver teapot in her hand. She pushed the table against the bed and propped me up with pillows. The tea was steaming and, though very strong, pale with cream. The Cranleys' cups were bigger than any other cups I had known, and very gay—crimson and gold. Their spoons were real silver—very small and thin. I liked Miriam in the morning, because she never talked much and moved softly. Her hair was so pale that for days I thought it grey. She didn't say 'Good morning!' but 'Had you a good dream?'

All my dreams at the haunted house were good, and though I didn't see the monk who so loved his old home he dared to come back, I dreamed of him.

I dressed in bits, putting on a stocking, then running to the window to see a flock of geese stepping down the road, the woodcutter trundling his barrow-load of branches, back again to wash in an enormous china bowl large enough for a bath, drying myself and watching a wagon of cider casks rumbling down to the cross-roads.

One morning an artist set up his easel on the other side of the road and painted a picture of the house with old Peter leaning over the gate and me peeping out from the window. Mrs. Captain gave the artist ten shillings for the picture, and hung it in the big room where she kept all the captain's curiosities.

We had our meals at a long table in the kitchen, where cream clotted slowly in a brown earthenware pan at the side of the range.  After dinner we had cups of tea and thin, crisp, sugar biscuits in the big room.  There were two arm-chairs, one on each side of the fire-place.  They were deep chairs, and so big that when I sat right back my legs stuck out straight.  A nodding mandarin in a yellow robe stood on the sideboard opposite the door.  When I came in, carrying the biscuits, he gave little jerky nods; when Miriam glided by, bringing cups and saucers, he quivered; for Mrs. Captain and the silver teapot he bowed gravely and steadily.

On the mantelpiece a galleon with three masts and a gilded figurehead of Our Lady was reflected in the black-and-gold framed mirror.  The round table, the sideboard, the corner cupboard with glass doors were crowded with little figures, shells with spikes, shells glittering like rainbows, or speckled shells six times as big as my one.  But the roar of the sea in them was no louder.  On the walls hung strips of black silk, embroidered with golden birds. In a carved red box Miriam kept a doll, dressed as a Chinese lady in silk clothes which could be taken off.  On wet days she gave me the doll to nurse, but I put it in one arm-chair, while I sat in the other, and we had adventures. When rain fell the big room was dim, and it was easy to imagine the galleon sailing through the walls away to the far countries the curios came from.

In the attic at the top of the back stairs I found a pile of paper printed only on one side.  Mrs. Captain let me take it to scribble on.  I wrote down the Captain's adventures as she told them to me, and the story of Rosalie running away from boarding school to join a circus.

I fell asleep in the arm-chair one day and dreamed I had lost the Chinese doll and the galleon, so I went upstairs to find them.  The balustrade was wide and carved, and leaning over I saw, instead of the dark hall, a wide river. This so startled me I woke up.  One very cold night in my sleep I went back to this dream, but when I looked over and saw the dark river, snow was falling into it. Snow was all round me; in my hair, my eyes, my mouth, and clogging my footsteps. I woke shivering in the dark, wishing Miriam would come in with the tea. The next time I went farther, and though snow was falling in this dream too, I could see more. There were dark houses on the far side of the roadway, for the stairs had turned into a road. Shuffling through the snow were figures wrapped in white fur, who never looked at me or spoke. I came to know that beginning and hurried, hoping to get a little farther. I had left St. Joseph's before I came to the bridge with high, carved sides, which shut out the snow and all sight of the river. Long after I crossed over, and came to where great white birds flew ceaselessly out of sight. In the darkness, so far away I had to screw up my eyes, was a white mansion with lighted windows.

Mrs. Captain had two other daughters: one a teacher in Minehead, and another who worked in a newspaper office. Both came over every Saturday for the week-end. All Saturday morning Miriam baked cakes and pasties, and we had coffee after dinner. When we sat in the big room Miriam played the harmonium and sang. Her voice had been trained and she had hoped to become a great opera singer. After five years' work and singing at one concert she came home again, to sing in the church choir and teach singing—when there were any pupils. The harmonium was squeaky, but Miriam's strong clear voice rose above it, and when I glanced out of the window I saw a crowd of people listening.

'You should have kept on, Miriam,' said Alice, the newspaper sister. 'It's a shame to bury yourself here!'

'I wasn't appreciated!' said Miriam crossly, looking down at her long fingers lying on the yellow keys.

'The neighbours like your singing,' Edith, the teacher, told her. 'Just look!'

'Country bumpkins!' muttered Miriam scornfully.

Her mother pulled me up from the footstool where I had been comfortably munching a plum tart.

'Here's a clever little girl who can write, Alice!' she said. 'She's filled pages and pages. I haven't had time to read them and I know she can't spell, but she'll learn! If someone don't take her in hand, in a few years she'll be like our poor Miriam. Tell her what to do, Alice!'

I felt hot and ashamed. I was terrified that Mrs. Captain would read out what I had written.

'What can I tell her?' demanded Alice. 'Go on writing and reading—that's all!'

'Sounds clever!' grumbled Mrs. Captain. 'They talked like that to Miriam. Go on singing, they said. If a girl can sing she wants people to hear her. If a girl can write she wants to see it in print. Now—Alice!'

Alice sat up straight and folded her arms.

'I'm like Miriam! I've been writing these ten years and I've had one short story in print. I've written a novel and every publisher in England has had a chance to read it, but it isn't published yet!'

I was thrilled.

'I'll go on writing!' I said. 'I can't stop! I like writing better than anything in the world—except reading!'

But Alice put two of my poems in her paper. I went into Minehead with Mrs. Captain on the cider wagon. She told Sam Prout I was going in to be paid for two poems which had been printed in the paper.

'And her only thirteen!' she said.

'I made up a zong once,' declared Sam Prout. 'I never thought to write it down, but 'twaz a right good zong!'

'Please sing it!' I asked. 'And I'll tell you my poems!'

He scratched his chin and closed his eyes.

'I can't remember a word, not a word. But once I made a zong!'

'You 're boasting, Sam Prout!' jeered Mrs. Captain. 'A man of your age!'

'Did you ever make a zong, you that 's zo clever?' he growled.

Mrs. Captain settled herself comfortably.

'I never did. But if I did make a song, Sam Prout, I 'd remember it. Be sure of that!'

Sam Prout was big, with round shoulders and thick straw-coloured hair which stuck out all round his hat. The two of them took so much room I had to sit on the edge of the seat, and only saved myself from tumbling on the road by clinging to the rope which kept the barrels in place. I was too delighted about my poems to mind where I sat, and when Mrs. Captain gave me a slow friendly smile I would have been willing to run behind all the way!

The newspaper office was in a narrow alley off the High Street. We crossed a paved courtyard and mounted a steep stairs which trembled with the thudding of printing presses. Mrs. Captain groaned as she climbed.

'Don't like stairs! Don't like smell! Printers' ink, Patty!'

We came into a long low room with trestle tables from end to end. Wearing a long overall, Alice was standing up, pasting printed slips on a big sheet of paper. As the door slammed behind us, she looked over.

'Why, mother!' she cried. 'You 've brought Patty!'

A thin grey man wearing big spectacles came out from another room. He was in his shirt sleeves and had a dab of ink at the side of his nose.

'Complaints and subscriptions downstairs!' he said, turning his back on us.

'Complaints your grandmother!' exclaimed Mrs. Captain. 'I 'm Alice's mother and this is Patricia Lynch.

She 's had two poems in your paper, and I 've brought her in to see an editor and get her money.'

The editor smiled at me and rattled some coins in his pocket.

'So you 're the poet?'

I nodded. He laughed.

'You won't always be so shy.'

He ranged four half-crowns on the table.

'What will you do with all that money?' he asked.

I had been thinking about that. At first I had decided to buy presents for my mother and Patrick Henry, but all the time I knew I would buy the bicycle standing at the back of the forge. The blacksmith had told me I could have it for ten shillings. It was small, but it had a free wheel and the tyres were sound.

'Buy a bicycle!' I told the editor.

'Wha-at?' he screamed.

'You can't get a bicycle for ten shillings,' Alice explained. 'Mine cost eight guineas.'

My shyness vanished. I grabbed the four half-crowns The bicycle might be sold to someone else.

'There 's one at the forge!' I said quickly. 'The blacksmith says I can have it for ten shillings!'

I ran out of the room down the stairs. I heard Mrs. Captain blundering after me and, remembering how kind she had been, I waited.

'Can you ride?' she gasped, clutching the big cameo brooch which fastened her long black coat.

I shook my head.

'You 'll manage,' she chuckled. 'You 'll manage!'

The forge was at the cross-roads and we hurried there As it came in sight I stopped.

'Suppose it 's gone?' I wondered.

'You 'll find another,' Mrs. Captain assured me.

I could hardly walk. I couldn't see properly.

'"Tis there!' said my friend. 'Run along now!'

The blacksmith wheeled out the bicycle.

'Tiz a bit zmall like,' he pointed out. 'A child's by rightz—a big child's, but there you be. Ztep up, mizzy! Can you ride?'

'Not yet!' I told him, and stepped up.

I sat on the seat and knew I would never be able to ride! It was too small and I was nervous. But I pulled out the four half-crowns and laid them on the blacksmith's grimy palm.

'I 'll give you a try,' he offered.

I clutched the handlebars and sat like a block of wood, while he trotted up and down with me.

'Now!' he said hopefully, letting go.

I clung to the bicycle with one hand and grabbed him desperately with the other.

'Sam Prout can take it up on the way back,' said Mrs. Captain. 'Come along, Patty. Edith is waiting for us and I 'm famished for tea.'

I walked silently beside her back to the town. How foolish I had been! Instead of being sensible and buying presents I had wasted four half-crowns. They seemed much more money than ten shillings. I 'd never be able to ride! Never! I was terrified of the bicycle!

A boy swept by, free-wheeling, his arms folded.

'Showing off!' I thought bitterly.

'You 'll be riding like that,' said Mrs. Captain. 'Alice can teach you. Write and tell your mother and I 'll do her up a jar of clotted cream.'

I learned to ride and, even on wet days, I no longer curled up in the arm-chair dreaming. I found the dead wood where all the trees were lifeless, and I came to the deserted mine. It had its own little railway, but the rails were rusty with neglect. I left my bicycle at the foot of the hill and scrambled where trucks had carried down the ore. At the top was a tiny chapel, with gaping holes for windows and doors and, where the altar had been, a sheep and her lamb were lying. They staggered to their feet and stood facing me, but I went softly away. I had been frightened too often to frighten anything else.

I rode through the tiny ports on the Somerset coast, and had begun to write a long poem about them and their ships, when the holidays were over and I went back to St. Joseph's.

## 33. AUNT HANNAH AND UNCLE MICHAEL

I SAT at my old desk, gazing at strange faces. Mary-Jane was teaching the smaller children and had her sandy pigtail screwed into a little bun, with big black hairpins bristling all round to make it look larger. Louise had gone home to France and May was a novice. I'd be too big for my bicycle when the next holidays came, for I was growing taller and taller. My uniform was too short, even though it had been let down so often it now had a false hem.

Reverend Mother came in when I was telling a story to the sewing class. She called me out to the corridor, and we walked up and down in silence. Suddenly she stopped.

'You mustn't tell any more stories, Patricia!' she said. 'You'll need all your time for study now. Your mother will expect you to pass your exams., my little one!'

I watched her as she went down the corridor, her shoes silent, her robe softly rustling.

'If I pass every exam. there is, me mother will only say: "Why wouldn't you pass? Wasn't your father a very clever man and your grandfather a great scholar?"'

I spoke out loud. Reverend Mother paused, then went on without turning.

After the comfort of Mrs. Captain's I found the crowded refectory and study very desolate. I sympathized with new girls who didn't like thick bread, fat meat, and plain cake, and were foolish enough to say so. The enforced silence of the study pleased me. Under my atlas I kept a story book and my own private exercise book, where I wrote poems and the stories I didn't tell any one. Most of the girls grumbled at the hard beds, but mine, in the corner, now we each had a curtained cubicle, was a refuge. The moment I put my head on the pillow and closed my eyes I was in another world, even without going to sleep. And the world was a different one every night!

We were all excited about the Christmas holidays, when my mother and Patrick Henry came to St. Joseph's. We sat in one of the reception-rooms, and though they both wore their winter coats, they shivered.

'This place is like an ice-house!' declared my mother. 'Why isn't there a fire?'

'We never have fires in the reception-rooms!' I told her. 'Never!'

'I pay enough money not to be frozen when I come to see you!' she said indignantly. 'It's bad manners to treat visitors this way! Still, if they keep you warm, it's all that matters.'

I thought of the cold dormitory and wondered what she would say to that.

'What's wrong with your hands?' she asked. 'My poor child! Did you burn them?'

'Oh, they're chilblains! We all have them on our hands and feet.'

She looked horrified.

'I'll be glad when we have a settled home. But we've been very unlucky lately.'

'Was it a gold-mine?' I asked.

'It was!' she sighed.

Patrick Henry walked over to the window and stood there tapping the glass with his fingers. My mother looked after him sympathetically.

'Patrick Henry! Show Tricia Hannah's letter!'

He felt in his pockets and shook his head.

'I gave it back to you.'

'What matter!' said my mother. 'Listen, Tricia! Hannah wants you to go to her for the Christmas holidays. Says she always had a grah for you, and Michael Keiran is for ever wanting you over!'

My mother and Patrick Henry were watching me.

'She's the only one left in Ireland,' went on my mother. 'I never thought she had such kindness.'

'You want me to go to her?' I asked incredulously.

'She is your aunt!' she exclaimed. 'And you always did like Michael!'

I sat dreaming. I might see Fair Hill again. Dinny was gone. They were all gone! But the old house was still there, and maybe I'd find a way to reach the Hennessys and the O'Callaghans.

'I'll go if you want me to,' I whispered, for my lips were trembling.

'You'll be on a ship!' my mother reminded me.

There were few passengers and I was the only young one, so they were very good to me. They gave me sweets, lent me books, and praised me for not being seasick. Even the captain talked to me, and at Southampton I went on shore with the first mate.

I was asleep when we came up the Lee. I woke to see a strip of wet pavement outside the porthole and sleet lashing along on the wind.

'This can't be Cork!' I told myself. 'It can't be!'

I drank three cups of hot coffee, but I couldn't eat. A

fat, friendly man, who had shown me American magazines with gorgeous coloured pictures, sat opposite.

'So we're both returned emigrants,' he said. 'Now, Pat, I know you're not going to your mother, or the aunt you like best. But you've come back to your own country, and that's taken me fifty years of hard work. Drink up the coffee and remember it's home, if you didn't know a soul!'

We went on deck together. He shook hands, wished me a happy Christmas, and went off on a side-car piled with his luggage and boxes of presents. I stood between my smart suit-case and my battered tin box, waiting for Aunt Hannah. She came at last, not as I had expected, looking like a tinker, but decently dressed in black, with a fur collar turned up round her hard, weather-beaten face. I heard her before she came along the gangway.

'Is there a young girl here by the name of Tricia Nora Lynch?'

''Pon me word, ye're small! Yet look at the long legs of ye, for all the world like a colt. I wonder the nuns wouldn't put a respectable length to yer frocks!' she complained. 'I thought ye'd be nearly grown by now. Ye must be a terrible torment to poor Nora, God help her!'

I laughed. Her grumbling voice, its sing-song accent, made me feel like old times.

'Ye never did have much talk, but ye've grown dumb!' exclaimed my aunt. 'Speak up, girl, and tell me how things are with the pair of them!'

'They're both very well, thank you!' I said.

'God be good to us!' cried Aunt Hannah. 'They've put an English tongue in yer head, that's sure! Mike will have a great laugh when he hears ye!'

Aunt Hannah never used an umbrella and I had no mackintosh, so we were well soaked as we went over

Patrick's bridge up to the station. I saw the giant bottles in the chemist's glowing with colour—red, green, gold. I looked along the quays, where I had wandered with Dinny and turned back. My aunt clutched me.

'Is it the box?' she cried. ''Twill be at the station. I fixed it. Stir yerself!'

'I'm going to Fair Hill, home!' I said.

'God give me patience!' exclaimed Aunt Hannah. 'Is it crazy y' are? Your home is with me! Fair Hill's nothing to ye or me either! The Lynches have gone from Fair Hill for ever! Come along now!'

My tears mingled with the sleet. Aunt Hannah had pity, for she took my case and, urging me on, spoke more kindly than I dreamed she could speak.

The train was crowded with country boys and girls going home for Christmas. Some had come from Dublin and one girl from London. She had travelled up through England, across the Irish Sea, and down south—a long way round, but it had taken her only two days to my more than three.

Our station was Dunmanway, and I stood on the wind-swept platform while Aunt Hannah went in search of Uncle Michael. The wind was bitter and I shivered. I took off my wet woollen gloves and dug my hands deep in my pockets, but my nose was so cold I could scarcely feel it, and my feet were like lumps of ice.

'Hi, Tricia! Tricia!'

Uncle Michael was striding across the lines, his old tweed coat flapping about his legs, a battered hat pulled over his eyes and the brim turned down all round.

''Pon me soul, Tricia! 'Tis good to see ye again after all these years!' he shouted, giving me a hug that warmed me. 'If ye haven't grown into a lovely little gerrul! We'll have great times, you an' me! Great times! Where's the tin box? The cart's over yonder, an' Hannah's with it. She's leppin' out of her skin wid delight to have ye!'

He took the tin box in both hands and staggered across the lines. I followed with my suit-case, and discovered Aunt Hannah leaning against the creel-sided cart, drawn by a small grey donkey. It looked a ghost of a donkey in the grey light, its head drooping, its long ears meekly folded. The moment my box and case were on the cart, Aunt Hannah gave the donkey a thump and we started across the station yard. Men and boys ran shouting in a confusion of carts and animals. My aunt marched steadily forward, and it wasn't she who gave way! We came out into the little town—its shops gay and frivolous for Christmas, and country people with bags and baskets still buying and selling.

'Did you get everything on the list, Mike?' demanded Aunt Hannah.

'I did indeed!' replied Uncle Michael cheerfully. 'An' I did better! I spent all the money I had in me pockets. I've oranges an' nuts an' apples an' a barm brack, a monstrous bag of sweets, an' the biggest red Christmas candle in the town! Tricia's goin' to have a rale hearty Christmas!'

My aunt stopped.

'Ye spent a whole pound?' she screamed.

People were staring and laughing. We were blocking the traffic of the main street. Uncle Mike grinned.

'Bedad, then, I spent every shilling of it!' he boasted. 'Biscuits an' sausages an' dear knows what! Anyway—Hannah, 'twas me own money!'

Aunt Hannah sighed, and we went on through the town. I saw Christmas trees and holly, glittering balls and strands of tinsel, and I listened to the soft sing-song voices I had not heard for so long.

'No need to walk, Tricia, when we've a carriage,' said Uncle Michael. 'Up wid ye now!'

He wedged me among sacks and boxes, while he and Aunt Hannah trudged on each side of the donkey. I fell asleep, not sound asleep, for I knew when we left the road and followed a rough mountainy track. I could have roused myself and looked round, but I didn't want to wake up and face this strange holiday. I could hear those two talking.

'Did ye bring in the turf?' asked my aunt.

'Surely!'

'An' the water?'

'Ah, Hannah! Isn't the barrel itself full to the brim wid the rain we're after havin'?'

'Ye tinker! Haven't I told ye time and time again, Mike Keiran, I'll not drink tea made on rain water? Ye can get down to the spring and bring up a bucket of clean, decent water, the moment we arrive! Stir yourself, Tricia!'

I sat up, blinked, saw the bog stretching to the mountains and the house where I was to spend Christmas. Slipping from the cart, I stared. The ramshackle hut I had visited with my mother a lifetime ago had grown as I had. It had been extended on each side and the walls leaned inward, the roof sagged. Even the windows were crooked, and though someone had begun to paint the door a bright blue, the work had been left half done. The turf pile was merely a heap of sods, exposed to wind and rain. There were rickety sheds at the back, and I felt that, but for the high fuchsia hedge, the whole place would have collapsed in the first storm. Ropes, with rocks hanging at the ends, were flung over the roof, and tree-trunks propped the end walls.

'When I have time to get round to it, I'll paint every bit of wall there is!' declared Uncle Michael, going up the path with a heavy sack on his back. 'I have a whole can of blue paint, an' I'm the man to use it!'

I was glad to go indoors. There was a smouldering fire on the hearth and unwashed dishes littered the table.

Uncle Michael carried my tin box through a door to the right, and I followed across a room crowded with boxes, piles of sacks, chopped logs, and all kinds of rubbish, in at a door so low he had to stoop. I stood watching as he set my box at the foot of a bed against the wall. There was a new, clean smell about the place which pleased me.

'D' ye like it, Tricia?' asked my uncle. 'I made it for ye, wid me own two hands, instead of clearing out the rubbish room.'

'You built it?' I asked in amazement.

'I did indeed. An' I made the bed an' the chest of drawers an' the chair. I'll make ye a table before I'm through!'

He went out in a hurry, banging his head against the top of the doorway. I looked around breathlessly. My own room! Everything made for me! No one had ever used them before! I ran to thank him and found my aunt sitting on a box, her skirt turned back, blowing the fire with a huge bellows.

'Please let me blow it!' I cried.

I knelt on the hearth and worked the bellows until a glorious turf fire was sending the kettle from singing to boiling.

'Tell me, Tricia,' said Aunt Hannah. 'What do they teach ye at that grand convent?'

'History, geography, maths, English, French, music, oh-everything!'

'And how to cook fine dinners, and how to sew like a lady?'

I shook my head.

'We don't learn cooking, and me mother wouldn't let me learn sewing!' I told her, sitting back on my heels.

'God forgive them!' cried my aunt indignantly. 'What's the use of a great lump of a girl that can neither cook nor sew?'

'But I can!' I declared, laughing up at her angry face.
'Old Mrs. Martin said I had the makings of a lovely cook!
So did Mrs. Captain; and Mary-Jane taught me to darn
and cut out. But I can't knit. I don't know why, but
I can't, or crochet!'

Aunt Hannah folded her arms.

'Ye say ye can cook! Let me tell ye, me lady, the
proof of the pudding 's in the eating!'

'I can make half-pay pudding!' I boasted. 'And I can
do chipped potatoes and scrambled eggs. And pancakes!'

Uncle Michael came in with a bucket of potatoes in time
to hear me.

'Sure the child 's light-headed wid the hunger an' the
tiredness,' he said wistfully.

I jumped up.

'Give me potatoes and eggs and I 'll show you!'

'There 's a pot of cold praties I had for the hins,' suggested Uncle Michael. 'But where 's the use of cold
praties?'

I had a grand time ordering Uncle Michael, while my
aunt sat, feet stretched to the blaze, and watched us. When
the potatoes, brown and sizzling, were piled with Uncle
Michael's sausages on one dish, and the eggs with chopped
onions mixed through them on another, we sat down to
my first meal at Aunt Hannah's. She had cut a pile of
thick slices of bread, and a lump of butter on a plate stood
in the middle of the table. We stretched out and hacked
bits from it.

'Me mother wouldn't like that at all!' I said severely.
'Even at school they butter the bread before it comes to
the table. Patrick Henry always likes his bread and butter
so thin it could be rolled.'

'Cock him up!' protested my aunt, her mouth full.

We sat on boxes before the fire.

'I haven't rightly got down to chairs,' said Uncle Michael,

'barring the one I made for yer own room, Tricia. 'Tis the least bit rocky. But I 'm larnin'.'

Aunt Hannah had her elbows on her knees. The floor was unswept and turf dust lay thick on shelves and dresser. The dirty crocks were still on the table and I was too weary to clear them away, but I was making up my mind to have Aunt Hannah's house as clean and tidy as a reception-room at St. Joseph's!

'How old are ye, Tricia?' asked my aunt suddenly. 'Ye must be a good hardy age.'

'Nearly fourteen!' I told her.

She shook her head.

'Nearly fourteen. Ye might as well say coming on to twenty. And when ye 've turned twenty, ye 'll wake up one morning and find ye 're forty and well on the way to old age. 'Tis time ye were settled!'

Uncle Michael pulled down his shirt sleeves and stared at her in amazement.

'What ails ye, Hannah? Ye 're turnin' the child into an old woman before she 's a young one! Fourteen! God help us! 'Tis no age at all!'

'If ye 'd get in the fowl for the night, ye 'd be some use in the world!' snapped my aunt. 'Tricia, pile a few sods on the hearth!'

I obeyed, and Uncle Michael, yawning and stretching, went out to the hens.

'Listen to me, Tricia,' said Aunt Hannah. 'Ye 're a girl without a father, and ye can see as well as I do how Nora is wrapped up in yer brother! Now we 've talked it over, Michael and me! Stay here, and the place is yours when we 've gone. 'Tis a hard, cruel world ye 're facing and I 'm offering ye a shelter to the end of yer days!'

'I 'll never leave my mother!' I exclaimed. 'And she is fond of me! They both are!'

'An' who says they 're not?' demanded Uncle Michael,

coming in with an armful of turf. 'Now, Hannah, ye did a kind act having Tricia here. Don't spoil it on the child!'

My aunt tossed her head and kicked a burning sod in on the hearth. Uncle Michael picked up a bit of the red-hot turf in his fingers to light his pipe.

'If I 'm not an unfortunate woman, pestered all me life with gommies!'

But she listened amiably while I told about the schools I had been to. She was quite interested in the Martins' farm.

'I 'd like that woman for a neighbour,' said Aunt Hannah. 'A decent, sensible woman!'

''Tis the old one an' her pancakes for my money!' declared Uncle Michael. 'Tricia! Did she larn ye to make pancakes?'

## 34. ON THE BOG

My bed was hard, but I slept so soundly I didn't wake until I heard Aunt Hannah scolding the donkey.

'Five good shillings ye cost me with the tinkers, ye ungrateful, obstinate animal, and now ye're as lazy as that Mike! Mike! Where are ye?'

I ran to the window of my room. It was the smallest window imaginable and it wasn't made to open. I could see the fuchsia hedge dripping, and more rain coming on the wind. Grey Lad was carrying two creels loaded with logs. My aunt was tugging at his halter, but the donkey's legs were spread out so that she could not budge him an inch.

'Wait, me lad, till I take a stick to ye!' said Aunt Hannah.

I could hear every word, for my uncle's building had left cracks and openings that let in noise and wind.

'Sure the animal needs breakfast before he'll work!' I heard Uncle Michael protesting. 'An' so does a man!'

I dressed so quickly I was out before Aunt Hannah came back with a broom to beat the donkey.

Grey Lad didn't wait to be beaten. He trotted up to the door and stood there, as meek and good a little donkey as could be. I carried in the logs one at a time, for they were heavy.

'Why wouldn't you put them in the shed?' I asked, for the room between the kitchen and my lean-to was so crowded there was just space to squeeze through.

'They 'll be handy so,' said my aunt. 'The less running backwards and forwards after dark the better. Ye 'll learn that, me lassieo! 'Tis a pity we couldn't have the turf inside!'

My aunt prepared breakfast. We had burnt porridge and stewed tea.

'Couldn't I make some toast?' I asked.

Aunt Hannah grinned. It was like being on Fair Hill again to watch her mocking, malicious face.

'Ye could, my proud madam, if we had bread and butter, but we haven't!'

'No bread and butter!' I cried. 'Aunt Hannah, you must have bread and butter!'

'Wrap yerself up, Tricia, an' we 'll go huntin',' called Uncle Michael. 'We 've no cow an' yer aunt doesn't bake, but come along wid me an' we 'll visit the neighbours.'

'All I ask,' said Aunt Hannah, 'is that ye 'll be back to cook the dinner.'

I wanted to stay and tidy up. I wanted to go with Uncle Michael. There was so much to be done I felt very important. The place wouldn't run away and I could tell by the look of Aunt Hannah she didn't intend to work.

'We 'll be back in heaps of time!' I declared.

Uncle Michael was a grand companion. He knew the short cuts across the bog, and where the pools were too wide for me to jump he took me by the wrists and swung me over. He told about the mountains we could see, their

strange stories and legends. Standing on a high turf bank
he showed me the smoke rising from distant chimneys.

'Yon 's the O'Hallorans'—they 're grand bacon curers!
I 'd love a ham from them for Christmas. That great
banner of smoke over beyond the trees—that 's the Dono-
vans', the best house for a dance an' a bit of a ceilidhe this
side the bog. The wispy flutter of smoke, the far side of
the beech wood—that 's the Widda Crosby's. 'Tis she
have the sweetest butter and the nuttiest bread ye ever put
yer teeth into. 'Tis there we 're bound for. A nice snug
little farm an' a dacent woman. We change eggs an'
praties for her bread an' butter an' milk.'

I liked the Crosbys before I saw one of them. The dog,
a big, massive, black-and-white creature, came slowly to
meet us, wagging his tail at Uncle Michael and looking at
me as if he knew I was a stranger.

'She 's a friend, Big Fella, like meself,' explained my
uncle, and the dog came to me.

The half-door was open and a very clean fat cat stretched
there, washing herself. There were white muslin curtains at
the windows, and empty flower-beds all round the house.
At the corners big bushes glowed with clusters of red berries.
Big Fella barked, and so many children came running to
the door I thought Mrs. Crosby must keep a school, but
they were all young Crosbys. They tugged us over to the
fire, and there was Mrs. Crosby baking bread in pot ovens.
She was so quick and pleasant she was like a bird. She
packed hot loaves of bread in the battered old basket Uncle
Michael had brought, and tied a lump of yellow butter in
clean butter muslin. She would not let us go straight back,
but made a pot of fresh tea, cut up a spiced loaf, and spread
the slices thick with butter. The children sat on their heels
in a half-circle before the fire and ate with us. They were
so friendly that before we went out of the door I knew
their names and how each child had its own task—to clean

the cow shed, milk the cow, bring in the milk, help in churning, mix batches of bread, and carry the loaves to regular customers.

Mrs. Crosby didn't keep hens, and she praised my aunt's eggs.

'She's the cleverist wid hins in these parts. I've never known her be widout eggs all through the winter. An' she's the only one can raise turkeys!' she told me. 'As for yer Uncle Mike, 'tis well known he's the quickest turf-cutter along the bog,' she added, smiling at my uncle.

'Sure, a man must do something to knock out a living!' said Uncle Michael, holding out his cup for more tea.

As we went back, he carrying the bread and butter, I with the can of milk, he sang ballads and told me stories of fairy rings and galloping horses. When we reached home, Aunt Hannah was cleaning out the hen-houses and she scolded us for being so long. I told her what Mrs. Crosby had said about her cleverness with hens. I could see she was pleased, though she pretended not to be. We had boiled bacon for dinner, and my aunt was scandalized when I wouldn't eat the fat.

''Pon me word—ye have grand notions!' she said indignantly. 'There's no better food in the world than fat bacon!'

'I was thinking why wouldn't I try for a ham from Jim O'Halloran!' suggested Uncle Michael. 'He hasn't an onion left an' they're scarce as diamonds. We've bushels of them!'

'Ye can try,' agreed my aunt.

I brought in turf and sticks, I carried water, I fed the hens and the pigs. Encouraged by my aunt and uncle I cooked all kinds of dishes. I had no failures. They ate everything, and when we went to midnight Mass on Christmas Eve, Aunt Hannah boasted of my talents to every one she met.

'Why wouldn't she be a good cook? Doesn't she come

from England?' one thin woman demanded. 'An' doesn't every one know the English is mad about atin'?'

Uncle Michael thought this funny. My aunt was furious. 'If I 'd told that old Mrs. Kerrigan Tricia wrote poems and had all the prizes in the convent she 'd have thought her the world's marvel! Because the girl can cook she makes nothing of it!'

'Why didn't you tell her I write poetry?' I asked resentfully.

The road to the chapel was as thronged as if we were on the way to ordinary Mass. Most of the people were driving or riding, but Grey Lad was having a holiday. The wind across the bog was bitter and the stars seemed so close and brilliant I kept tripping over the frozen ruts, for I had my head tilted back to look at them.

'I never seen the White Cow's Highway that grand!' declared Uncle Michael, waving his hand at the Milky Way.

'Tell me about the white cow!' I said.

He didn't hear me, for he had dropped back to talk to a card-playing friend. Nearly every night my uncle went off playing cards with neighbours across the bog, and Aunt Hannah sat by the fire reading novelettes. She had a sugar box full of them and read each one again and again. She wouldn't be bothered reading my books.

Coming back we could see tall Christmas candles glowing in the windows. When we reached home our big red candle was on the table, waiting for the youngest in the house to light it. I lit a spill at the fire, where the half-pay pudding I had made was bubbling in the iron saucepan, and we had tea and potato cake by the tall candle's soft light.

On St. Stephen's Day I looked up from the flour and eggs I was beating in a bowl.

'When will I be going back, Aunt Hannah?'

I was longing to tell my mother and Patrick Henry about

the room my uncle had built specially for me, though I
would be sorry to leave it.

'Ye 're not going back!' replied Aunt Hannah.

'Not going back to St. Joseph's!'

I laughed.

'She means it,' Uncle Michael told me.

I let the spoon splash in the batter.

'Am I going to another school?'

I was dismayed. I dreaded facing a crowd of strange
girls, and I had grown used to St. Joseph's. Aunt Hannah
was reading a novelette. She looked up from it impatiently.

'How d' ye think Nora can put money into gold-mines
and send ye to an expensive school as well? From now
on ye must earn yer keep. And did ye really imagine
your uncle built a room and made that furniture for a
holiday? Though sure he 's fool enough for anything!'

'But I like going to school!' I protested. 'Everybody
goes to school!'

'Everybody doesn't go to a grand boarding school!' and
my aunt returned to her reading.

'Nora will be sending ye again when she can raise the
money,' said Uncle Michael consolingly. 'An' ye do like
being here, don't ye, Tricia?'

I nodded and went on beating pancakes. I had made a
great pile of them when I heard the Wren boys coming up
the road singing:

> 'The wren, the wren, the king of all birds,
> On Saint Stephen's Day got cot in the furze.
> Although he is little, his family 's great,
> Now please, Mrs. Keiran, do give us a treat.'

They weren't all boys, for the Crosby children were
there. The boys wore their coats inside out over girls'
frocks, and the girls had boys' trousers, as they did at
Hallowe'en. They had a paper wren inside a wire cage,
with coloured paper twisted on the wires.

'Such rubbish!' grumbled Aunt Hannah.

But she made a fresh pot of tea and I handed round the pancakes. They sat on their heels in front of the fire, while Uncle Mike did tricks with cards. When the Wren children were gone he tried to teach me, but I was never any good at cards.

I came out one morning to see my aunt loading the cart with a sack of oats as well as a crate of hens.

'If I get the price for those birds I should get,' said Aunt Hannah, 'there 'll be money in the bank!'

'Ye 'd best leave it till tomorra,' Uncle Michael told her. 'There 's snow on the way!'

'Ye 've a head on ye, so has a pin!' jeered my aunt. 'I 'm to wait for the snow, so that I 'll not be able to stir a step. This is the last day of the season to sell old hens and I 'm off to sell them!'

'Ye 'll not get back!' Uncle Michael warned her.

The moment the donkey turned into the wide path leading to the road by the Rocky Valley, Uncle Michael slapped his hands.

'Listen, Tricia! I 've a message to do in Bantry. If I leg it off there now I might get a lift an' be back before herself. Ye won't be lonesome, an' ye won't inform on me?'

'I won't tell! But she 'll be mad if she finds out, Uncle Michael!'

'The back of me hand to her!' said Uncle Michael cheerfully, and off he went, hatless and coatless, only I ran after him.

'Put on your hat and coat, uncle! You 'll catch your death of cold!' I gasped.

'God bless ye, Tricia! Ye 're a dote! I 'll bring ye back a present, see if I don't!'

'A book, Uncle Michael!' I called. 'A story book!'

I was delighted to be left alone. I determined to have

the house like Mrs. Crosby's before my aunt came back. I swept the floor and brought in as much turf as I could pile neatly round the hearth. As I brought in the laſt sod, snow began to fall. By the time I had washed the crocks the room was so dark I had to light a candle. Then I began to scrub potatoes.

'I wonder when will they be back?' I said to myself.

There was nothing for dinner but the potatoes. As I heard them bubbling I remembered a heap of tins in the room off the kitchen and went to look for them. The candle caſt shadows which ran up the walls, darted into corners, and played hide and seek with one another. But I was determined not to be scared away. I found the tins, and when I saw crayfish, pineapple, salmon, condensed milk, and sardines, I forgot the shadows. I had a grand dinner of crayfish and potatoes, with *Robinson Crusoe* propped before me. I knew it so well I would have liked a new ſtory, but I didn't expeět Uncle Michael to bring me one. He was kind, but terribly forgetful.

I tidied the bedrooms and darned all the socks and ſtockings. Then I made a potato cake for my tea. The ticking of the clock was like a friendly voice. I found some blank paper and wrote a poem about a house in the snow. I tried to draw a piěture to go with it. But I was losing my drawing. Still I went to bed humming 'Oh, the days of the Kerry dancing.'

In the morning I was tired of the house. Besides, I wanted water for the kettle. After breakfaſt I would go across to the Crosbys. I went to open the door. Unluckily Uncle Michael had made it to open outward, and I could not force it againſt the snow. I was a prisoner! I had used all the fresh milk, I had no water, so I couldn't make tea or porridge or even boil potatoes, but I could roaſt them. Yeſterday I had been happy in my loneliness, now I was desperate. Snow was piled againſt the windows and I couldn't see out. Even if I broke one, the panes were too small for me, to scramble through. Suppose Uncle Michael and Aunt Hannah didn't come back for days! I sat by the fire wondering what I should do. I hated just waiting. And then I heard a shout.

'Are ye there, Tricia? Are ye there?'

'Where else would I be?' I called back indignantly.

Wasn't it just like Uncle Michael! I could hear him clearing the path. He kept on shouting and, at last, was able to drag back the door. I rushed out delighted, forgetting to be angry.

'Will ye ever forgive me, Tricia?' he said. 'I got to Bantry an' I couldn't get back. Are ye starved? Were ye terrified out of yer wits? Ye won't let on to Hannah, will ye now?'

He had brought me a bag of sweets, but no story book.

'Sure ye have heaps!' he said, when I reproached him.

We melted snow to make tea, and then, so that Aunt Hannah wouldn't have a word to say, cleared a path to the spring and another to the turf pile. As Uncle Michael finished, the wind changed, the sun came out, and snow fell in sheets from the roof. While we were eating our dinner, rain was beating against the windows, and Aunt Hannah arrived with Grey Lad in a downpour.

Every day the room Uncle Michael had built for me became more and more my home. The drawers in the chest which stuck and had to be thumped, the chair which rocked even when no one sat in it, though it wasn't meant to be a rocking-chair; the wooden bed, the mat of rushes; I put them into stories. I put them into poems, and when Aunt Hannah started a bonfire with my stories and poems, it didn't matter. While Uncle Michael found paper and pencils I could write more.

Wind blew always across that upland bog, and I watched clouds sailing like treasure ships over thousands of miles.

I tiptoed out at night, shivering, to watch the stars, and longed to know more about them. If I spoke of stars Aunt Hannah snapped: 'Sure, ye 're daft!' and my uncle shook his head. ''Tisn't good to live wid so much sky! Give me the kind roofs of Bantry!'

When spring came Uncle Michael was out on the bog at all hours. As soon as there was any dryness in the air he took his slane and started cutting turf. I stood the sods on end to dry, then, loading the cart, I led the donkey back. Grey Lad was the most sensible creature alive and knew I was fond of him. We were great friends, and when I talked to him he answered as if he really understood me.

When our own stack was built Uncle Michael cut turf for the Crosbys and other families beyond the bog, while Grey Lad and I took the loads. My face and arms and legs were brown, and I could run as fast as any of the boys and girls who came to work on the bog with their fathers and mothers. I sauntered with Grey Lad along the roads and lanes. Though all the people I met were kind, I made no real friends. They called me 'the young gerrul from England,' and that made me feel as strange as when Aunt Hannah said I was a changeling or that my mother had bought me from the tinkers. When I wanted to visit Mrs. Hennessy there was always a good reason to prevent me, until I gave up asking.

One morning Uncle Michael brought in a baby rabbit —a tiny grey creature I could hold in my hand.

'Mousie will be company for ye,' he said.

Mousie grew quickly, for I fed him on bread and milk, as well as the food he found for himself. I wouldn't have him shut up, though Aunt Hannah was always grumbling at his way of nibbling everything. If the door was closed he would thump against it with his hind legs, and he had a queer, excited squeak which brought me running. He hopped beside me to the spring and the turf pile, but he was nervous of the cock and, when I fed the hens, kept behind me. He trembled with pleasure when I drew his lovely ears through my fingers or stroked his soft grey fur.

The elderberry against the gate was in blossom, and at night the big clusters were like moons. I was lonely for my mother and Patrick Henry, and I was tired of life with Aunt Hannah. I had grown strong and worked very hard, but she grumbled unceasingly.

We were eating a stew I had made with all kinds of herbs flavouring it.

'Ye never made a better stew,' said my aunt.

I was smiling when, at the door, I heard Mousie thumping to be let in.

'Ye should kill that beast, Michael,' she said to my uncle. 'There's great eating on his bones. Let him grow old and he'll turn hard and tough!'

I pushed my chair away from me and sprang up.

'Kill Mousie!' I cried in horror.

She laughed.

'And eat him too, Tricia! Sure ye're not a child! Who keeps a rabbit for a pet? Are ye daft?'

'I'll not live here any longer!' I said. 'I'm going away and I'll never come back!'

I ran from the room. Mousie, wanting to go in, not out, squeaked, but followed. He hopped so quickly he caught me up and we walked along, he stopping to thump and squeak for his bread and milk, I coaxing him on. When he would come no farther I picked him up. He sat in my arms, his nose twitching impatiently.

'Mousie, you're really a wild rabbit,' I told him. 'But we're friends, so I'm taking you where there are hundreds of other rabbits and you'll have a chance. Keep away from snares and dogs and men, and you'll live a long time. I do hope you'll be happy!'

I brought him to the Rocky Valley and put him down. He thumped and squeaked, hopped a little way, came back, went on. I stood watching until he went out of sight. I sat on a rock, lonely but glad.

'I thought I'd find ye here,' said Uncle Michael's voice. 'No need to run away, Tricia. Yer mother's sent for ye!'

'I'm going to her?' I asked in wonder.

'They're going to Egypt. They're taking ye wid them, and they've sent ye a mint of money to jine 'em! I was afeard of this all along!'

'Egypt! Oh, Uncle Michael, I'd sooner go to Egypt than to heaven!'

'I'd feel a bit quare, meself, in either place,' said Uncle Michael. 'Ye brought Mousie here?'

I nodded.

'Good for ye, Tricia! Good for ye! 'Deed, but I'll miss ye! So will herself! I wish ye were our own little gerrul. So does she!'

I liked Uncle Michael. But if I had been his daughter I wouldn't be going to Egypt with my mother and Patrick Henry!

## 35. THE ROAD TO EGYPT

THIS time I bought my own ticket, took care of my own luggage, and talked to the stewardess about which was best, top bunk or bottom. I would have been terribly disappointed if she had put me in the bottom one. But there I was, sitting up in my bunk, looking out of the porthole, and wondering what marvels I would see on the road to Egypt.

We were passing Blackrock Castle before I remembered— I hadn't been near Fair Hill. I hadn't gone in search of Captain O'Connell. Now I would never see them again! And the Hennessys and O'Callaghans! I hadn't really forgotten. I had been afraid—afraid of Fair Hill without my own people. And where would I have looked for Captain O'Connell? Indeed I hadn't the money to go seeking friends.

I had the cabin to myself. The stewardess was too busy to come near me, after she discovered I knew how to make up my bunk in proper sea style and warned me against going on shore by myself.

'I 'm on my way to Egypt,' I told her proudly.

'An' I 'm on me way to Jerusalem!' she retorted.

When we reached Plymouth I waited until other passengers were going up the gangway. Then I followed. I explored the back ways of the town and came unexpectedly upon a tiny harbour, filled with gay rowing boats. I bought a bag of pears from a fruit stall and ate them while I watched. I wandered to the Barbican and, counting the money I had left, decided on coffee and a meat pie. I felt very grand to be giving my own order to a smart waitress. I tried to pretend I wasn't the least bit excited, but I longed to tell her: 'I 'm on my way to Egypt!' I bought a copy of *Chatterbox*, a bag of sweets, and another of plums. The cushioned saloon tempted me, for I was very tired, and I went slowly back. As I stepped off the gangway I encountered the stewardess.

'Didn't I tell ye not to be stravaging round Plymouth on yer lone?' she asked indignantly. 'I don't know what yer mother 's dreaming of! Where is she?'

'Waiting for me in London!' I told her triumphantly. 'We 're on our way to Egypt!'

I marched down to the saloon and read my magazine, eating a sweet and a plum alternately. Just as I began to feel lonely the other passengers came in.

'Here 's the little girl on her way to Egypt!' cried a jolly, grandly dressed woman, wearing so many rings her fingers stuck out. 'Have tea with us, dear, and tell us all about it!'

I enjoyed the fuss, and we were steaming up the Thames before I grew tired of it. As we joined the crowd of ships edging towards the sheds, I trembled. Would my mother know me after this long while? Would Patrick Henry look at me with the eyes of a stranger? I followed the man who had my tin box on his shoulder and my case in his hand. Keeping very close to him, I frantically searched the waiting throng. There they were, squeezing up to the gangway.  Their eyes lit!  They had seen me!  They knew me!

We were in a taxi-cab going to an hotel.

'Poor Tricia!  What has Hannah done to you?' cried my mother.  'Your little rough hands!  She made you work!'

'She was good to me!' I declared.  'And Uncle Michael was very good!'

I didn't say much and they never asked many questions. It was fine to sit back and listen.  After the first moments of delight I noticed how shabby they were and my mother's hair was turning grey.  Even my brother had lost his confident, determined manner.

'Are we really going to Egypt?' I asked, interrupting the talk of trains and fares.

They turned to me.

'We really are!' declared my mother.  'I haven't been satisfied with Mr. Blanchard always, but now he is treating us fairly.  We found the title-deeds of your father's land in Egypt.  And he's helping us to go there and claim it.'

'Title-deeds?'  I didn't know what they were.

'Papers!' explained Patrick Henry patiently.  'They prove our claim.'

'And to-morrow you shall have new clothes!  We'll all have new clothes!' said my mother.  'We need never worry about money again.'

'Is it a gold-mine?' I wanted to know.

'No!' said Patrick Henry shortly.  'We've finished with gold-mines.'

We had late dinner and I had a glass of wine—red, rich, sweet wine.  Once more I lay in bed, watching my mother brush her hair.

'Tell me a story,' I said sleepily.

She laughed.

'Oh, Tricia, you're too big to be told stories now.  You

shall have a nice costume to-morrow, not a schoolgirl's dress, but a young lady's!'

'Brown shoes and stockings?' I asked.

'Black are much more ladylike!' declared my mother.

I sat up.

'I hate black. Every girl at St. Joseph's hated black. I love brown shoes and stockings. I've always wanted them.'

'Then you shall have them!' promised my mother.

I had the brown shoes and stockings, a navy blue costume, a smart felt hat, and a big travelling coat with a fur collar. We went on a smoky little steamer to Ostend, and on to Bruges to see the college where Uncle Henry had been before he was drowned at sea. We were going to Verviers, where my mother had been at school with Cousin Kate, but in Bruges I fell ill.

As we drove from the boat along the cobbled streets, the crimson cloth thrown over the horse fluttered in the wind and made me dizzy. The bouncing of the carriage over the cobbles made my head ache, and when we reached the house I had to grip the banisters with both hands to walk safely upstairs. The old house we stayed in was where the two girls had slept for one night, all those years ago. My mother sat talking to me while bells, bells, bells rang over the roof-tops.

'It was grander then,' said my mother. 'These people weren't here at all and certainly there was no wine shop! Again and again I've planned to come back with Cousin Kate. But I'm glad for you to see where I was young.'

'Is this the way to Egypt?' I asked.

'Not exactly! But we took the chance to see these places we may never see again. We don't know what's before us in Egypt. Life's a queer business,' went on my mother. 'Still, I'm glad to have seen a bit of this world.'

The thin lace curtains blew inwards and I heard the ceaseless chimings and ringings as I fell asleep.

I woke frightened in that strange room. The big four-poster bed, the dark furniture, the lace curtains, were black and silver in the moonlight. I tried to turn my head, but it was too heavy.

'What ails you, Tricia?' asked my mother's voice.

I could not answer. She slipped to the floor and stood over me, her face white as her night-dress, her hair black as the shadows.

'Thirsty!' I murmured.

'Sure, you can't drink that brown water! And they don't know enough to make tea! Tricia, you haven't been drinking Bruges water, have you?'

She went away, but I was no longer afraid. I was too sick and weary. Shadows and voices, footsteps, bells ringing, curtains blowing, bells, bells, bells!

The sun wakened me. I was propped against pillows and my mother was packing. My brother stood with his back to the window, watching me gravely.

'You'll not mind us going, now you're better?' she asked. 'You shall see Verviers when we come back. Madame has promised she'll take care of you. She's been terribly kind while you were ill. And this little lad will be a friend to you.'

A boy stepped forward. He was about my own size, yet he wore socks, very short knickers, and a big ribbon bow. I thought his clothes ridiculous—his long thin legs, his snub nose—but his merry eyes were friendly.

'What's your name?' I whispered, for I couldn't speak any louder.

'Josef!' he answered, his hands behind his back.

'Petit Josef!' said my mother, smiling.

She kissed me. The room was empty. I sat up there, weak, sad, proud. I knew I would never see Egypt!

'The poor little one!' said a kind, rich voice.

A stout, dark woman, very handsome, put a spoon to my lips—hot, delicious soup! I drank and drank.

'Josef! The grapes!'

He held up a bunch of purple grapes, each one a globe of glistening beauty. He pulled off one and popped it in my mouth.

'Remember!' said Madame. 'Not one in your own mouth!'

Josef sat beside me—pop! pop! pop! He pulled the grapes and only the last one did he put in his own mouth.

He vanished and I was lonely, but he returned with an omelette and fed me with a fork. Then Madame came with a cup of coffee, which made me so strong I wanted to get up and run after my mother.

'Non! non!' declared a big man, stouter than Madame, not so handsome, much fiercer, only his eyes were like Josef's, so I knew he couldn't really be fierce. He was Monsieur Baerasael and Madame was Madame Baerasael. Once M'sieu, feeling very energetic, had started painting his name over the wine shop. He made the letters so large that he could fit only BAER on the front and the rest had to go along the side, for the shop was at the corner of the little *place*. Now the letters were so faded it did not matter what they were. A bench stood in front of the shop window. It was just big enough for M'sieu and his favourite dog—Mitzi, a dachshund. Mitzi liked being nursed, but she was so long that when M'sieu sat in the middle of the seat with her on his lap, Mitzi's head was at one end of the seat, her tail at the other, and she had to twist painfully to look up at M'sieu's face. So I asked why didn't he sit right at the end with Mitzi's head and make her really happy? M'sieu thought this over. Then he flung back his head.

'Non! non!' he shouted.

The other dogs sat on M'sieu's feet, except when they lay under the counter in the shop, or went hunting with him on the plain of Flanders.

The three Baerasaels were always learning languages, so they talked English to me, except when Madame remembered her promise to my mother. Then they insisted on my talking French and M'sieu tried to teach me Flemish.

The first time I came downstairs I came very quickly. I was wearing slippers with rope soles. The bare wooden steps were polished with the use of hundreds of years, and I slipped. Instead of gripping the banisters I let go, and down I came, sliding three flights of stairs and landing with a thump on the mat at the bottom.

'Elle est morte!' cried Madame.

Josef burst into tears and M'sieu picked me up. The boarders, Jan, the young man who served in the shop, and a Flemish woman who polished floors and washed vegetables, stood round, silent and horrified. M'sieu snapped his fingers. Jan rushed down the dark passage into the shop and returned on tiptoe, carrying a slender glass filled with wine, pale gold and still. I drank every drop, not because I needed it, but because I could have drained a whole bottle.

It was a pleasant world I slipped into. At first I sat on the bench outside and saw the country coach come along at the end of the *place*. People sat and stood inside. Underneath were slung bags, baskets, parcels. On top rode hens and rabbits in crates, and once a goat gazed solemnly at the cobbles of Bruges. The water-cart was very gay, with its racks of soda-water siphons in blue, pink, and white.

The biggest dog in Bruges belonged to the woman, Mathilde, who lived opposite. She grew vegetables in her garden and sold them in the market. The big fierce dog drew them there on a small cart. No matter how Mathilde

piled the cart, he pulled the load patiently. But when
Mathilde seated herself on top, he lay down and refused
to move. Every market day she tried to ride to market,
but never once was she successful.

Josef and I went shopping with Madame to the Grand'
Place, where the belfry soared above the statue of the
heroes. The shops there were very grand, but on market
days we had to squeeze between the vegetable and fruit
stalls and the piles of cheeses, from tiny ones I could hold
in one hand, to monsters like barrels. On Friday we went
past the belfry to the fish market, and Madame taught me
how to judge fish. If I pressed with my finger and the
slightest impression remained I must not buy. Colour, the
gills, the eyes, all had to be considered. And the price!
Not even my Aunt Hannah could beat down a price like
Madame! She would not linger. *Le déjeuner* must be prepared, *le dîner* planned. But she was kind and left Josef
and me to wander.

One day we had watched M'sieu set off on his hunting.
The hound-like animal, with the head of a collie, bounded
in front; the spaniel kept in step with his master; but poor
Mitzi, struggling along on her short legs, lagged far behind.
At every corner M'sieu waited, he patiently, the dogs
impatient, until Mitzi caught up and they went on again.
I was sympathetic to M'sieu's hunting, for he caught
nothing, but Josef was ashamed of him!

'We shall see where he goes!' said Josef to me.

We went into the belfry, paid our sous, and began to
climb. At the first window we looked out on the old, old
roofs, crooked and crowded. All the fairy tales I had read
stormed into my mind and I waited, my eyes wide open
so that I should miss nothing, for flying horses to rise from
the cobbles, knights in armour to prance on tall black steeds,
and princesses, with crowns and trains, to step forth from
the tall, narrow doorways.

'Montez!' ordered Josef, pulling me after him.

We came to the clock-room. Two little men, no bigger than we were, nodded and smiled in welcome. It was useless to speak, for the hour was striking and our ears were stunned with tumult. They wore leather aprons stained with oil, their hands and faces shone. One had a bald head and a long beard, the other's face was smooth, but his shaggy brown hair stood on end. They showed us the great key lying behind an iron grille and I wondered how they could wind the clock, for the key was six feet long!

The clock was still striking when Josef, always restless, urged me on, and we toiled to the gallery looking far out over the city to the great plain. We had hoped to see M'sieu and his dogs. The Grand' Place had dwindled to the size of a handkerchief. The houses, the stalls, the carts and horses, were no bigger than the toys I used to play with, the people were ants and beetles. Out on the plain a few dots moved, but M'sieu, so big and imposing, was not to be seen. A mist crept over the ground.

'Waterloo!' and Josef stabbed the air with his finger.

Waterloo was a date in the history books, a station in London. You couldn't see it from the belfry of Bruges!

'Le Grand Napoleon!' sighed Josef.

Napoleon was real! But not Waterloo!

Josef gave me a brooch with the head of Napoleon on it for my birthday, and I wore it at school, fastening the real lace collar which Madame and M'sieu presented to me. I went to school in Bruges at the convent near the college where Uncle Henry had been. Josef went to a school near by, and, carrying our books, we strolled through the Beguinage, watched the lace-makers, and listened to their complainings that young girls would not use their fingers and their eyes on the lovely pillow lace.

'My mother used to make lace!' I boasted. 'The most beautiful you ever saw!'

'And she did not instruct you, her daughter?' they asked.

My mother had left money with Madame, but now it was all gone. Madame assured me my home was with her. But school—for any one but boys and babies—was school of any use? She could teach me French, I could use a needle, and if I did the marketing I would have all the sums I needed. I was delighted to be finished with the dull school, where I was among the dunces because I was a foreigner. I couldn't even tell them stories, for my French wasn't good enough, and the only ones who really liked stories wanted them in Flemish.

My room was an attic under the roof, but it was a grand attic, with a real window and lovely furniture which had been ancient before I was born. There stood my speckled shell and my books were ranged on a carved bookshelf which made me proud of them. The old ones which had travelled so far with me were there and a few new ones. I had bought *The Life of Cardinal Richelieu* for three francs from a heap on a stall in the Grand' Place. It was so heavy my arm ached carrying it home. I fitted its dingy cover with a piece of flowered silk so that I wouldn't be shaming the Cardinal. When the processions went through the streets on holy days I imagined him sweeping along the Diver under the trees in his crimson robes, over the haunted bridge, and by the Black House where the Duke of Alva's ghost still appeared on Christmas night. Crowded on top of the others were my lesson books—Latin grammar, geometry, *Guide to Matriculation*, Gill's geography, history, algebra, elementary chemistry.

I had a solid little table against the window, where I could write stories when I had the time.

That was the difficulty—time! We rose early, we went to bed late, and all day we fought a leisurely battle with the hours and, like most of the bells and clocks in Bruges, we were always behind!

The boarders liked the clean, comfortable beds, the good food. One, Miss Carmichael, came for a week and stayed on and on. We all liked her. She was good-looking, pleasant, and was always willing to talk. She had the big room on the first floor over the shop, and Madame told me she had been to Egypt. I carried Miss Carmichael's *petit déjeuner* to her in the morning and stood by the window talking to her while she drank the hot foaming coffee and crunched the *crôissantes*, still hot as they came from the *pâtisserie* at the far corner. She was like my mother, I thought, for she had spread her treasures, so that the room was lovely. She had books and tiny statues, a crimson brocade covering for the bed, a silver-backed hairbrush, a green scent-spray, a travelling clock which chimed the hours, and a long black velvet cloak with a high fur collar.

'I have a spotted shell,' I told her. 'You can hear the sea in it.'

'What are you doing here?' asked Miss Carmichael. 'You don't belong to the Baerasaels!'

'We were on our way to Egypt,' I explained. 'Then I fell ill and stayed behind.'

Miss Carmichael finished her coffee.

'Where do you come from?'

'Cork—but that was a long time ago!'

Then I had to run. Madame was making a shrimp omelette and the shrimps had to be skinned. When I went to tell Miss Carmichael the omelette was coming to the table I found her tapping at a portable typewriter. She put on the cover and looked round.

'There's a shrimp omelette, and it's ready. Do you write books, Miss Carmichael?'

She laughed.

'No, articles! I travel and write. Now for the shrimp omelette.'

We had two new boarders that day—women teachers from Lancashire. They had ten days to see everything in Belgium and they allowed two for Bruges. Each had a list of places, with the time they could spare for each one. They had planned half an hour for *déjeuner*, but while they ate the omelette I was making a green sauce for the little carrots. Josef cleared away the first plates and stood watching while I stirred the sauce.

'A spoonful of cream, *ma petite*; of the vinegar one drop! one drop!' Madame instructed me.

I was very careful. If two drops fell together she would declare the sauce ruined.

'*Bon!*' she cried, and patted my shoulder. 'Now the fish! Run, Patrice, and discover what is tormenting the strange ladies!'

I ran into the *salon*. The teachers from Lancashire were beating their forks and spoons together, not in fun, but anger.

'We have been kept waiting five minutes!' the older one told me. 'What is happening?'

'A green sauce! It's gorgeous!' I bragged. 'Here it comes!'

They gobbled their food, leaving most of that delicious sauce on their plates. And they refused coffee! Miss Carmichael's eyes were laughing as she placidly watched them.

'Two days for Bruges!' exclaimed Madame indignantly. 'Do they know how many years we spent building our city?'

'They are good women!' declared M'sieu. 'They do not take coffee. Now I can have two cups or three!'

The nights grew cold, mist crept up from the canals, and there were no more boarders, only Miss Carmichael. Josef and I dawdled along the Diver and wondered when the canals would freeze.

'I shall teach you to skate!' he promised.

We were talking of Christmas as we crossed the Grand' Place. How we managed it I do not know, but we lost ourselves in the little dark streets. There were no lamps and the houses were closely shuttered. We stumbled over the cobbles, not knowing whether we should turn right or left and growing more bewildered at every turning.

'There's a light!' and I pointed. 'Let's knock!'

We were afraid of the houses in these dark streets. But we were desperate. Timidly we rapped. The door was flung open. A man in his shirt sleeves, a dark, hairy man, with gleaming eyes and teeth, stood there, holding a long, pointed knife. He ran his fingers along the blade. Clutching one another, we rushed away. A canal stopped us; we turned, splashed and floundered along the muddy bank, raced over the bridge, and, when we could run no more, emerged once more on the Grand' Place and bumped into Miss Carmichael. She caught us by the arms to prevent us falling.

'What's wrong?' she asked.

We panted as we told her. And she laughed.

'Only for the good God our throats would be slit and our bodies cast to the fishes in that vile canal!' declared Josef.

'I expect the poor man was carving his supper,' said Miss Carmichael. 'Come along now, we'll have chocolate and pastries!'

We were always ready for pastries, and the hot, whipped chocolate sent our terrors scampering.

'What are you going to do with yourself?' Miss Carmichael asked me.

Josef gave me a poke.

'Tell her about Egypt!'

'I've told her! I hope it won't be like the gold-mines!' I muttered.

'Gold-mines?'

I told Miss Carmichael how we were always trying to be rich. She asked question after question and I answered every one.

'Perhaps writing will be your gold-mine,' she said. 'You 've had a few little nuggets. You should learn short-hand and typewriting. With them and a good knowledge of English a girl can go through the world.'

I stopped eating pastries.

'You mean I 'll be a writer—like you?' I asked.

'It 's a good life!' said Miss Carmichael.

The canals began to freeze. The circus came to Bruges and camped about the statue of the heroes. I wrote a description of it in my neat, best writing and sent it to the continental *Daily Mail*. It was sent back with a letter which I showed Miss Carmichael. Her amused expression made me uncertain.

'He says: "Try again when you 're older," ' I pointed out.

She shook her head at me.

'The most encouraging letter isn't as good as the shortest acceptance, and you won't get that until you make them forget you are young.'

'I won't be young much longer,' I said cheerfully, and took the letter to show M'sieu, because Madame was too busy. He couldn't read English, so I told him what it said. He shook my hand and gave me a big glass of pink grenadine.

'One day I will tell them in the shop: "Here she lived when she was young and poor and unknown. But I— I knew!"'

At night when I went up to my room, I pulled back the curtains and sat in bed, propped with pillows, a thick red dressing-gown over my shoulders, and looked at the pointed roofs and glittering windows across the *place*. Beyond, the dark square belfry rose to the stars and I couldn't think of the sky without it.

One night I would decide to save the money Madame gave me and follow my mother to Egypt. The next I'd plan to return to Ireland—not to Aunt Hannah's, but to Mrs. Hennessy's. But I feared my old friends would have forgotten me. I longed to be older and wiser, clever enough to earn money and give my mother and brother everything they wanted. In my mind I built a house where we would live together without any more partings. It had to be near a city to please them. I wanted it to have a green door with windows on each side, a green tiled roof. It must be big enough for our friends—Mrs. Hennessy, the Cadogans, Francis Joseph, Uncle Mike, but not Aunt Hannah. I must have a big garden where I could grow all our vegetables, keep hens, a few ducks, geese; I didn't want turkeys, they were too bad-tempered; a pig maybe, a horse for Patrick Henry to ride, of course a donkey, and a grey stone wall all round, with a green gate and a flagged path leading up to the door. The windows should look out on the mountains and the sea with the ships steaming by. I knew now that neither of them really cared for money. They were like the adventurers in the stories who went seeking El Dorado. Would they, I wondered, be happy in that house of mine? But I went on building. I would fall asleep sitting up, and dream so hard I'd be confused when I woke and heard the bells.

The garden at the back was covered with glass, and now it was almost as warm as the house. The nightingale who lived there, in a wicker cage with an open door, told us the ice was coming by hunching its head down among its feathers. The night before Christmas Eve the canals were frozen hard. Miss Carmichael, M'sieu, Josef, Mathilde's son and daughter from across the *place*, and myself—we all skated from the Grand Basin down the canal to Sluis in Holland. I couldn't skate properly, but we crossed arms and it was like flying. The moon rose and M'sieu lit the Japanese lanterns we carried. In front other lanterns bobbed and flickered. We sang carols. M'sieu sang a Flemish song and I thought of Egypt. We had coffee and honey rusks at Sluis. Our candles had burned down, but, as we turned back, the ſtars blazed on our icy path.

I was sleepy when we tramped up to the darkened wine shop. Madame was awake, and the smell of hot coffee warmed us even in the dark passage. We ate *crôissantes* and little cheeses, and Madame thruſt a queer-looking letter under my chin.

'They have not forgotten! All is well!' she cried.

It was a letter from Egypt with money. A cotton faɛory had been built on my father's land and my mother had been awarded a grant. A great deal of this had to be given for unpaid taxes, so we would not be rich. She had waited to write until she had good news, but now I could go to college and become a teacher or a civil servant.

I read out the letter. My friends thumped the table. M'sieu rushed to the shop and came back with a bottle of wine.

'Grenadine!' cried Madame. 'Pour les enfants!'

'Non! non!' shouted M'sieu. 'Le vin!'

And he filled our glasses.

'Success!' he roared. 'Success!'

'Which will you be?' asked Miss Carmichael. 'A teacher or a civil servant?'

'I'll learn shorthand and typing and go through the world!' I declared.

And I drank my glass of wine.